S0-BHY-175

*The Evolution of Love*

ENDICOTT COLLEGE
Beverly, Mass. 01915

# THE
# EVOLUTION
# OF LOVE

SYDNEY L. W. MELLEN

W. H. Freeman and Company
Oxford and San Francisco

W. H. Freeman and Company Limited
20 Beaumont Street, Oxford, OX1 2NQ
660 Market Street, San Francisco, California 94104

**Library of Congress Cataloging Publication Data**

Mellen, Sydney L W   1907–
  The evolution of love.

  Bibliography: p.
  Includes index.
    1. Love—Psychological aspects.
  2. Love—Physiological aspects.   3. Behavior
evolution. I. Title.
BF575.L8M37      155.7      80–18028
ISBN 0–7167–1271–7
ISBN 0–7167–1272–5 (pbk.)

Copyright © 1981 W. H. Freeman & Co. Ltd.

No part of this book may be reproduced by any mechanical, photographic, or electronic process, or in the form of a phonographic recording, nor may it be stored in a retrieval system, transmitted, or otherwise copied for public or private use without the written permission of the publisher.

Filmset by Northumberland Press Ltd, Gateshead, England
Printed in the United States of America

# Contents

# *Foreword*

If it is accepted that the world we live in has been formed through a long process of change and development and that living species, our own included, have arisen through biological evolution, then it follows that human nature and the human condition can only be properly appreciated in the light of an understanding of the past.

Relative to the primate stock from which we have arisen, and indeed relative to the animal kingdom as a whole, the human species has developed many abilities to an extraordinary degree. Books about human evolution rightly emphasize such important achievements as toolmaking and technology, communication and language, cooperation and flexible social organization, conceptualization and insight. However, few have grappled with that central but scientifically elusive quality in human lives: the capacity for love in its various forms. In this book, Sydney Mellen has attempted to do just that, in a manner which is bold and thought-provoking.

Being an archeologist by trade, I was somewhat taken aback on being invited to write a foreword for a book on love. Why me? I wondered. However, on reading the text, I found that Mr. Mellen was offering an intriguing application of ideas and information drawn from the study of the evolution of human behavior – a field of science in which I participate. The application, while controversial, is clearly sensible and yet is of a kind which researchers in the field have not attempted. Secondly, on reading and reflection, I realized that the book covered a topic which, in spite of its interest, has no experts – except in so far as we are all experts. The material considered ranges from zoology, paleontology, and archeology, to genetics, ethnology, and psychology. Indeed, it extends into what can only be called common human experience. The interest of the book lies in bringing information from all these disciplines to bear on a topic which each by itself could only treat incompletely. The foreword an archeologist could write was as appropriate – or inappropriate – as any!

Mr. Mellen explains, 'From the viewpoint of this book, the really great expansion or enrichment of the reproductive impulses in humans is the evolution of a tendency in most men and women to love each other – more precisely, the tendency of one particular man and one particular woman to love each other for some extended period of time.' It is the evolutionary roots of this tendency and its modes of function and malfunction in modern life that are pursued in the book.

The subject of love is approached from two directions. The first part of the book compiles information about human evolution drawing on zoology, primate studies, paleontology, and archeology as a factual basis for an admittedly somewhat speculative scenario of early patterns of human life, including reconstructions of relations among members of these early, small-scale, hunting–gathering societies, especially relations between protomen and protowomen. These reconstructions provoke thought about the ways in which the distinctive circumstances of early Pleistocene life may have influenced the development of behavioral tendencies that persist today. The second part of the book treats information about living humans drawn from ethnographic, sociological, psychological, and medical literature. Successive chapters discuss love between parents and children, love between men and women, and homosexual love. Having attempted to delineate a normal range of patterns for each, the book seeks to work out evolutionary explanations for as many of the observed features as possible.

From a first-hand involvement in research on human evolution, I can commend the book for providing a very fair summary of what might be termed the narrative of human anatomical evolution. As the book extends from this into inferences regarding stages in the evolution of behavior, society, and culture, it becomes both controversial and interestingly original. The partly speculative portrayal of circumstance and response in early protohuman social life does seem to me to provide at least a plausible developmental background for many human qualities; but every expert and many an interested lay person is bound to disagree over the validity of aspects of Mellen's reconstructions. This brings out the need for much better, much more certain evidence regarding such critical aspects of early life. The book therefore provides valuable stimuli to thought by making clear the interest of knowing the extent to which the lives of our ancestors involved division of labor between women and men, such as is implied in the gathering–hunting–food-sharing model espoused by Mellen. My own research on the archeological evidence concerning the behavior of human ancestors who lived between one and two million years ago has led me to favor such an hypothesis, and I am much interested to see our results applied in this book.

I am less able to offer technical comments on the second half of the book. However, I have found it most interesting to contemplate a generalized portrait of the human experience of love, with evolutionary explanations suggested for a whole series of recurrent patterns, which I for one had not previously considered in a coherent way. Not least interesting for me in this second half of the book is its demonstration that, in spite of the scope and scale of anthropological, sociological, and psychological research, we really do not have very reliable information on the frequency, sequence, and developmental patterns of emotional ties between modern men and women, let alone their prehistoric forebears! This is an important challenge to see set forth.

In recent years, both biologists and sociologists have become involved in a raucous debate about the way in which the biological basis of animal and human social systems has evolved; and conversely about the degree to which some features of human social systems are, or are not, genetically determined. Central to this controversy is the puzzle of how evolution established altruistic tendencies such as are an integral part of human love and friendship. The term 'sociobiology' was adopted by E. O. Wilson to cover a body of theory concerning the evolution of social systems. Sydney Mellen has wisely avoided becoming embroiled in the polemics of the debate, but in my opinion he has done well to incorporate quietly mention of some potentially important evolutionary mechanisms which are also a part of sociobiological theory: in particular, kin selection, a process whereby natural selection favors mutations that increase the success rate and survival chances of near relatives rather than of the mutants themselves. There seems to me to be a strong possibility that this evolutionary pattern has indeed been very important in molding human family patterns, in mating arrangements, and in the capacity for love. In addition, one finds in this book certain new suggestions concerning the evolution of altruistic behavior in humans, suggestions which biologists should consider.

The book deals with another subject which has become highly contentious, namely the question of whether or not there are inborn differences in the behavioral tendencies of women and of men. The book presents evidence to the effect that there are significant differences which are intelligible in the light of the evolutionary past of our species. Many, myself included, will have reservations about some of the contrasts that are proposed. However, there can be no doubt of the importance of this question or about the care and sincerity with which Mellen advances his arguments. The book should contribute to rational discussion on these questions.

This book was written in the retirement years of a man who, after taking an anthropology degree, worked for most of his adult life in a diplomatic service. The book emerges to this reader as having been inspired by the strong, compassionate curiosity of its author regarding the evolutionary origins and present workings of human love. As he puts it at the beginning of Chapter 8, 'Scientific research has done wonders with the atom and the DNA molecule, and not badly with visual–spatial abilities in children, but it has not made much progress yet with love between men and women.' This curiosity moved Sydney Mellen to search out and compile as much relevant scientific information as he could, and to develop ideas about the connections between ancient prehistoric ways and familiar patterns in everyday life today. The information and ideas are set out with gentle humor in a humane and humanistic manner that can make the book a pleasure to read.

*Berkeley, January 1980*                              GLYNN LL. ISAAC

# *Acknowledgements*

Anyone who dares to pursue a subject through six or seven specialized disciplines incurs more debts than he or she can possibly acknowledge. In my own case I owe particular thanks to all of the 300-odd authors listed by name in the Bibliography, from Acsádi to Zihlman, or chronologically from the immortal Darwin to Dawkins.

But my greatest debt is to those who have generously given their time in an attempt to enlighten and guide me individually – most of all to Glynn Isaac, whose scientific rigor and breadth of vision and imagination have in addition been a particular inspiration to me; also to Alan Walker for his valuable instruction in Nairobi in 1973, to several other scientists associated with the Louis Leakey Memorial Institute, especially Meave Leakey, John Harris, and Peter Andrews, also to Yves Coppens at his *Musée de l'homme* in Paris, to Sydney Margolese of the endocrinological world in California, and to Robert May of Princeton. In addition I am indebted to more than a dozen other kind members of the fellowship of scholars who have responded to inquiries of mine, often sending me copies of papers not yet published. I must acknowledge also the help of several anonymous and long-suffering reviewers or referees who at various stages have read and criticized typescripts of this book, sometimes with approval and sometimes not. I am grateful to my son Nicholas Mellen for fighting his way through a very early draft and giving me his robust criticisms. Finally, I pay special tribute to Michael Rodgers, whose flair as an editor and whose resourcefulness and critical judgement have made an important contribution to the final product.

In a sense, all science is an attempt to simplify the world in order to make it comprehensible. Yet simplicity is no warrant of validity... Our strategy must be to try out simple hypotheses and theories first, but be ready for more complex ones if evidence indicates the need for them.

Theodosius Dobzhansky *Genetics of the Evolutionary Process*

# 1

## Genesis:
## The Mammalian Heritage

Our emotional tendencies, along with our bones and our brains, are partly the result of a very long process of evolution. They all become easier to understand, and easier to cope with, if we look at them in the perspective of that process.

In the infinite continuum of time and space there is of course no such thing as an absolute beginning or ending. But it can be said that events important in the evolution of human beings were already taking place about 65,000,000 years ago. That was the beginning of the Tertiary Period of geological time, during which the placental mammals, already long in existence, diversified and spread over all the continents and seas, succeeding the last of the dinosaurs. At the start of the Tertiary, it is thought, North America and Greenland still had some land connections with Europe, but South America and Africa had already been broken apart by colossal upheaving forces and were separated by possibly a third of the present distance.

It was in the placental mammals that the primordial substratum was laid down for our own emotional nature, as for our bones and our brains. The process was a groping one, taking its directions blindly in the course of millions of generations. Then, starting perhaps 35,000,000 years ago, the events leading to the formation of human beings accelerated considerably, with the proliferation of the Old World monkeys and the apes, and the development of the important additions to the mammalian substratum which we share with them. About 15,000,000 years ago there appeared a small ape-like form with teeth showing certain resemblances to human teeth. Finally, somewhat more than 3,000,000 years ago, creatures were in existence which stood and walked erect in the manner of the genus *Homo*. These last creatures cannot be called human, but they inaugurated the stage of evolution in which the distinctively human adaptations were developed and the beginnings of human culture were laid down. Thus our joys and sorrows, and also our immense potentialities, have their roots very deep in the past, first in biological evolution and more recently in cultural evolution as well.

This book is an attempt to explore the roots, concentrating on the distinctively human ones. In part it is merely an attempt to speculate about them, since the present state of scientific knowledge is still only fragmentary in certain important areas. The future is sure to bring corrections and many refinements.

There is no need, indeed there would be no excuse, for me to embark on a comprehensive review of the morphological and behavioral evolution of our species. Many others have already done that with admirable success.* This book will focus on a single thread of evolutionary development, or bundle of threads, and follow it from the remote mammalian past down to recent times, namely, the tendencies of individuals to form emotional attachments with others, to love others. The evolution of our species will be taken as a given fact, and the growing fund of knowledge about it will be drawn upon only to the extent necessary for a single purpose: to give substance to inferences and speculations about certain emotions that animate our lives – primarily the love between a woman and a man but various other kinds of affectional ties as well – why they exist, and why and how they have come to be what they are. Other emotions, such as fear or hate, will be mentioned in passing, but they present fewer problems of interpretation and are documented all too well.

This introductory chapter will touch very lightly on the beginnings of our evolutionary history, placed arbitrarily in that long period of the rapid spread of placental mammals, down to the time when that of the monkeys and apes got under way – very roughly, from about 65,000,000 BP (before the present) to about 35,000,000 BP.

---

* Readers wishing to consult the existing literature on this subject or others may find it helpful to make use of the Index, which supplies two sets of numbers, one referring to pages of the present text and the other referring to numbered items in the Bibliography. This system has been adopted because it obviates constant references or notes in the text.

We owe to our remote mammalian ancestors the basic scheme of our skeletal form and the rudiments of our central nervous system; those structures are present today in recognizable forms in all the living mammalian species. But we also owe to the early mammals their unique system of reproduction and nurture of the young. It is this last which is relevant here.

Most fish and reptiles lay very large numbers of eggs and only a tiny fraction of them survive. One of the mammalian experiments was to specialize in quality rather than quantity, to produce a much smaller number of young at each birth – usually only one at a time in the case of most large mammals, and after a long gestation – and then to expend a significant amount of energy and time nourishing and protecting the valuable young.

Birds, although in a line of descent which is believed to have been separate from that of mammals for about 250,000,000 years, since far back in the common reptilian past, have nevertheless arrived at a reproductive system which has some resemblance to that of mammals, in the sense of extended nourishment and protection of a small number of young. It is clearly a case of convergent evolution, in which two widely separated lines have responded in a similar way to comparable environmental pressures, and it suggests that the similar features have had great adaptive value in both cases.*

But one of the special features of the mammalian system, which is of primordial importance for us, is that in mammals the nourishment of the infant young came to be provided actually through and from the mother's body itself. What is more, if it was going to work, if the animals in which it occurred were to survive, it had to be accompanied by compelling behavioral tendencies in both mother and infant to seek intimate physical contact with each other. The ensuing pressure of natural selection must have been relentless and irresistible: the only animals that survived were those in which the reciprocal tendencies were present in both mother and infant with compelling force. And in the course of tens of millions of years such tendencies became securely implanted in all surviving species of mammals, though with varying degrees of elaboration and of freedom as to specific patterns of behavior.

*The word 'adaptive' is used in this book consistently in its evolutionary sense – advantageous for survival and reproduction in a given environment.

These ancient mammalian traits lie at the root of the profound and special emotional intimacy between the average human mother and her baby today – honored in folk wisdom as mother love. The traits have been developed to a very high point in primates, and above all in humans. They also are the basis for the particularly close psychological attachment which in most higher primates, including most of the apes and especially humans, persists between mother and child throughout the extended period of learning – a period which in protohumans became long enough to allow full scope for cultural evolution, an immensely important process which will be discussed in the next chapter.

There is no need to labor the proposition that an emotional attachment of a rudimentary character unites the mother and the young of large mammals. In many zoos one can observe the maternal tenderness of giraffes and hippos. In the wild a mother lion will defend her cubs with ferocity; and even in such fright-prone, flight-prone genera as gazelles many mothers are exceedingly brave in defense of their young. Nor are the aquatic mammals an exception: whalers quickly learned that it was profitable to wound a whale calf because the mother would be near and would come to its rescue, so that then both mother and calf could be killed. In mammals generally, different kinds of emotional states – anger or fear, for example, as well as a rudimentary form of mother–infant love – are the driving forces for many behaviors essential for survival.

In large mammals the young are often helpless for a significant fraction of their early lives, needing their mothers to provide both food and protection. There are notable exceptions however; in several species of antelope the young can stand and almost run promptly after their birth, but natural selection has favored this exceptional adaptation among such animals because they occupy an environmental niche where they are almost constantly exposed to the danger of large predators and their survival depends on flight.

The father, in nearly all nonhuman mammals, takes no particular notice of his children, which is hardly surprising since neither he nor they have any idea of a particular relationship between them. In some species of bears, adult males may even attack the infants, and accordingly the mothers keep their young under their sole protection throughout a season. On the other hand, among lions the adult males are sometimes notably patient and gentle with all cubs, suffering the latter to pester them, bite them, and pull their manes or their tails; they do not lose their temper, and if the nuisance becomes too irksome they simply get up and withdraw to a quieter place. Thus, while a potentiality may have existed for a long time, it is only in the higher primates (see Chapter 3) that one finds in adult males a role of responsible protection of the young in general, and only in humans that one finds real paternal love.

As for the relations between adult males and females, these also bear little resemblance, in most mammals, to the delights and torments which fill the best part of our lives. There are however some indications, to be pointed out later, that the tender protectiveness and dependency of the mother–infant relationship in mammals may provide some of the basic emotional raw material drawn upon in the evolution of love between men and women.

The mating drive in mammals is irresistibly compelling – otherwise none of us would be here – and it is sometimes violent; but in most species it is strictly periodic, restricted to the females' cyclical period of estrus within which ovulation occurs, and in many cases to a mating season. The actual copulating encounters are usually extremely brief, and if there are accompanying periods of courtship or consortship they very rarely extend beyond a single estrus or in some cases a mating season.

To be sure, the mating arrangements and activities of most orders of mammals are only imperfectly known. The grossly unnatural life in most zoos will fail to reveal normal mating behavior or may even pervert and distort it, while only a limited number of species, apart from primates, have so far been thoroughly studied in the wild. Yet it is already clear that the enduring pair attachments formed by many species of birds are rare among mammals. In some solitary species – including moles and hamsters, bears and tigers – the male and female tend to mate very briefly during estrus and then go their separate ways. Among some social carnivores – such as wolves – the top-ranking or alpha males mate with numerous females at different times, and in many cases beta and gamma males are allowed the same privilege, within limits. Some gregarious hoofed animals – notably waterbuck and some types of deer – form separate herds, with females and their young in one, and adult males in the other. At rutting time the male herd breaks up and each male stakes out the best territory he can get and waits for one or more females to enter it; many of the females visit several males in succession before the season ends and the sexes segregate again. Some other species of deer live in mixed herds all year round, and the mating pattern is promiscuity modified by the ranking hierarchy. A number of species – including sea-lions and wild stallions – establish harems which the commanding males rule forcibly.

In the view of an amused natural historian of the eighteenth century, 'We regard the love life and marriage of birds with pleasure, that of mammals with repugnance, and that of man with peculiar thoughts.' Yet it must be added that in many species of mammals behavior has been observed which, for short periods, looks like affection between mating pairs. In the East African game reserves, male–female pairs of several species, including lions, have been observed consorting alone together during an estrus period, showing what seems to be affectionate attachment. A pair of giraffes can sometimes be seen exchanging long caresses in a manner that implies much tenderness (the precise word is 'necking'). Bull elephants, although murderously aggressive in defending their territories during the rutting season, can be gentle and chivalrous as consorts.

While awaiting more complete and solid information, perhaps the provisional conclusion should be that our mammalian ancestors did not as a rule form male–female attachments of an emotional character, but that in some species a potentiality for such attachments existed, usually for brief periods of consortship, in ecological situations where it was advantageous. The extraordinary flowering of the mating impulses in men and women opened out at much later stages of evolution.

# 2

# *Nature–Nurture and so Forth*

The primary concern of this book is the evolution of the genetically-determined factors in human love; if there were no such factors there should be no such book. I must therefore not shirk a brief confrontation with the nature–nurture issue. Yet the old controversy over that subject, over whether human behavior and capabilities are genetically or environmentally determined, is one of the more useless of those that have bedeviled serious scholars, not to speak of political and social ideologists. Still today social and political differences can exacerbate the argument, because some hereditarians tend to see social inequities in the world as inevitable reflections of genetic differences, while some environmentalists fight the hereditarian thesis, or even try to suppress it altogether, because they regard it as a dangerous obstacle to social reform.

Despite all the emotional and doctrinal fervor which still inflames the argument, by now even the die-hards on both sides tend to concede that the dichotomy is not 100 percent complete. Typically, they maintain either that human behavior is essentially innate but in some minor degree modified by environmental influences, or else that it is in principle acquired in the course of development but in some minor degree limited by genetic capacities or innate hormonal factors.

That is at least movement in the right direction. Nearly all traits, behavioral as well as morphological or physiological, are the results of both genetic and experiential factors. An animal which is born with a genetic constitution calling for above-average size will fail to attain full growth if it is undernourished during critical stages of its development. In behavioral traits also, though these are more complex and more plastic, there is ample evidence that both sets of factors operate. The normal human child is born with a capacity to learn and use a language and will readily learn one through association with its parents and others, but outside influences can cause the child either to learn several languages or to fail to master a single one fully.

A celebrated chimpanzee named Washoe was taught by B. T. and R. A. Gardner, in an experiment requiring monumental patience on the part of both pupil and teachers, to use the American sign language for the deaf. After four years of training she could use correctly the signs for over 100 words, could understand many more, and could construct simple sentences that made sense grammatically. This was only the first of a long series of language experiments with chimpanzees; many others have since been undertaken by the Gardners and others and are continuing, nearly all of them with more or less positive results. But no amount of training has succeeded in teaching those animals to articulate audibly more than a couple of words, and the main point is that, as a genetically-determined behavioral trait, the sign-learning ability of deaf–mute human children is vastly greater.

It follows that the unique human capacity for a language of words has provided humans with vastly greater potentialities for learning than any other animals. As S. L. Washburn has pointed out, language gives the nature–nurture controversy a new dimension. With language, cultural evolution became a major factor in human affairs, operating concurrently with biological evolution and in close interaction with it, as outlined in a later section of this chapter. At the same time there is abundant evidence that innate factors still exert a vital influence on some kinds of human behavior, establishing capacities, tendencies, and predispositions, determining limits and probabilities.

Human beings communicate not only by language but also through gestures and facial expressions; these are mainly learned by observation and imitation. Yet there are certainly innate elements in these behaviors. Children in a tantrum will stamp their feet and clench their fists even if they have never seen their parents or others do this. The ethologist Irenäus Eibl–Eibesfeldt has studied and photographed children born blind or deaf or both, and established beyond reasonable doubt that they smile and laugh as other children do when they are happy, making the correct sounds, incidentally, and that they cry as others do; although there is a possibility of some unintentional conditioning of the handicapped children by the adults taking care of them, Eibl–Eibesfeldt carried out supplementary tests which indicated that in general their behaviors do not depend upon indirect learning of any kind.

## *Genotype and phenotype*

An intermingling and interaction of genetic and environmental influences is so universal in living organisms that geneticists find it essential to employ the concepts of genotype and phenotype, the genotype of an animal being the total genetic constitution implanted in the fertilized egg cell from which the animal grows, and the phenotype being the visible form and character of the animal as it develops later in exposure to the environment. (Environment is understood broadly, meaning for example the mother's uterus at first, and later the physical and social environment. The terms phenotype and genotype are used also to refer to a single trait and to the gene or genes underlying it.)

Applying these concepts to the domain of behavior can be helpful in decrotting – to borrow a pungent Gallicism – the nature–nurture controversy: an individual animal's total genotype is the entire array of its genes, probably numbering hundreds of thousands in humans and many other animals; while the animal's phenotype, behavioral as well as morphological and physiological, becomes manifest in observable traits as the environment exerts its important influence.

The marvelous biochemistry of the genes – each one a tiny segment of a microscopic chromosome, thus a uniquely coded length of the elaborate molecule DNA which replicates itself in the famous double helix – is by now fairly well understood, though there is still a great deal to learn about the detailed mechanisms through which the genes participate in establishing the phenotype, especially in human behavior.* It has been

---

* A gene at a particular locus of a particular chromosome can exist in any one of two or more possible variant forms. Each such form is technically known as an allele – 'one . . . the other' – of the gene. In this book the word 'gene' is used to mean sometimes a particular gene (for example a gene for eye color) and sometimes one of its allelic forms (for example a gene for blue eyes), depending on the context.

discovered that many thousands of the genes give rise biochemically to enzymes, each such gene a particular enzyme, and that the enzymes – complex molecules of protein – perform myriads of vital catalytic functions in the cells of the body. For example, some thousands of the enzymes cause ingested food to be converted into tissues and organic systems of all kinds, including the bones, the circulatory system, the hormonal system, and the nervous system, and impart at the same time certain unique characteristics to each of those different tissues and systems in each individual, while other thousands of enzymes condition the functioning of the tissues and systems thereafter. Elsewhere there is much clinical and experimental evidence to show that the individual human personality is basically determined by the totality of all such tissues, organic systems, and conditioning enzymes, subject always to the powerful influence of the environment and learning.

Although a great many of the details are still to be filled in, the end results are unmistakable: that the genes are the hereditary factors in human traits of all kinds, morphological, physiological, and behavioral, and that they combine with environmental factors in determining the ultimate phenotype of each individual.

Some human genes, such as those for eye color, are manifested equally in both sexes; others attain phenotypic expression only or mainly in one sex; and some find expression at a particular stage of life. A familiar example of both of the last two cases is that of the secondary sexual characters which develop in adolescence. Those striking changes and the related physiological events are accompanied by equally striking changes in psychosexual inclinations and needs. Later chapters will review some of the voluminous evidence that such inclinations and needs are also somewhat different in the two sexes.

Genes are transmitted from parents to children in ways which are rather well known in all their complexity; the chances are almost infinite that no two individuals, except for identical twins, will ever have exactly the same genotype.

Genes can be thought of as biochemically-coded instructions or information concerning the development and functioning of an organism. Someone has pointed out that all the information contained in a fertilized human egg cell could be placed on a surface much smaller than the head of an ordinary pin, and somebody else has patiently estimated that the information so miniaturized would fill more than 1000 instruction manuals of 500 pages each. How are such marvels possible? The answer, surely, is time, not millions of years but billions: perhaps a first-class university team could do even better than natural selection if it had as much time at its disposal for working on living matter.

## Disentangling genetic and environmental factors

It is more difficult to evaluate the relative proportions of the two sets of factors in the phenotypes of humans than it is in the simpler animal forms, and the task becomes especially intricate in the case of behavioral traits where experience or learning is important. In morphology and physiology, a few traits, such as blood type or eye color, are not directly affected by the environment, so far as we know, while at the other extreme the acquired immunity to certain childhood diseases seems to be almost wholly experiential, the only genetic element being the capacity to acquire immunity. In behavioral traits one confronts an array ranging from a baby's tendency to want its mother, all the way to an astrophysicist's predilections concerning the big bang. Over the intervening range, traits of all kinds are the resultants of varying proportions of genetic and environmental factors. To complicate matters, there are numerous genetic traits which consist of a marked sensitivity or susceptibility to certain types of environmental influences.

In order to analyze particular phenotypic traits of humans, to tease apart and to evaluate roughly the genetic and environmental components of each one, some important work has been done with pairs of twins. (Unfortunately there exist also some very bad reports of work with twins, but those are excluded from consideration here.) The technique is to make statistical comparisons between pairs of identical twins brought up separately, pairs of identical twins brought up together, and pairs of non-identical twins. Such comparisons can often indicate whether or not genetic factors are important in a particular trait.

Identical twins are known technically as monozygotic or MZ twins because they develop from a single zygote – that is, a single maternal egg cell fertilized by a single paternal sperm cell – which promptly divides into two new cells, each of which then proceeds to develop into a complete embryo. Both members of any MZ twin pair, subject to negligible qualifications, possess exactly the same genotype; they are always of the same sex and blood type, able to tolerate skin grafts from one to the other, and extremely alike in general appearance and in fingerprint patterns. Such differences as there are are due essentially to environmental factors. On the other hand, non-identical twins, technically known as dizygotic or DZ twins, develop from two separate zygotes – that is, two egg cells which happen to be fertilized simultaneously by two different sperm cells – and they are as like or unlike each other as any other sibling pair, brother or sister: differences between them can be either genetic or environmental, more often the former if they are brought up together.

Consequently, if data are compiled on a significant number of twin pairs chosen at random, in which at least one member possesses a certain trait – say color blindness, or susceptibility to bronchitis – important indications concerning the presence of genetic factors in the trait can be obtained by comparing the percentages of concordance or non-concordance in the MZ pairs as compared with the DZ pairs, with respect to the trait in question. In the example of color blindness, MZ twins have been found to be regularly concordant whether brought up together or separately, and DZ twins to be not more concordant than other sibling pairs. In the case of susceptibility to bronchitis on the other hand a significant degree of non-concordance has been recorded in pairs of MZ twins. Thus there is evidence that color blindness is largely determined genetically, but that susceptibility to bronchitis is essentially environmental.

It must quickly be added that the evidence obtained from twin studies is subject to some important limitations. The first is the fact that any twins brought up together are exposed to approximately the same environment, and that even when twins are brought up separately it often happens that the environments are similar in some respects – as, for example, when one twin is brought up by an aunt or a grandmother. Therefore one needs to be very careful about concluding that genetic factors are present, based on similarities between members of MZ twin pairs. A secondary limitation is that parents and others are likely to treat identical twins as a special kind of pair, exaggerating their inborn similarities; a playful geneticist has remarked that uncritical use of twin data can lead to a conclusion that clothes are a genetic trait. Finally, there is always a risk of biased or unrepresentative sampling.

Nevertheless, when twins studies are carried out with due care, and when it is recognized that conclusions drawn from them usually require independent confirmation, they can provide valuable information. For example, twin studies have yielded useful evidence of a high level of genetic control of a person's stature, and of moderate levels of genetic influence in weight and in susceptibility to numerous diseases including rheumatoid arthritis and tuberculosis. Twin studies permit a high presumption of a major genetic component in schizophrenia and manic depressive psychosis, while a few studies have yielded suggestive indications of a fairly important genetic component in a miscellany of personality traits including social inversion, aggressiveness, involuntary mannerisms, and alcoholism.

As for IQ scores and the ideological warfare over them, good twin studies have by now placed it beyond reasonable doubt that some substantial genetic component is involved in IQ differences between comparable individuals, though disagreements persist over just what proportion of total causation that component represents. Various students now favor proportions lying somewhere between extremes of 75 percent and 25 percent – a range that leaves plenty of room for further argument. When comparisons between different racial or cultural groups are made, they often reveal statistically significant differences but do not explain what those differences mean. One difficulty is that the groups compared usually differ not only in race or culture but also in health, nutrition, or economic level. Another difficulty is to decide what, exactly, IQ scores measure: many of the test problems now in use are easier for members of one culture to solve than for members of a different culture.

Consequently the polemics over racial differences in intelligence can best be left somewhat longer to people whose preference – determined no doubt by a combination of genetic and environmental factors – is to be convinced without complete information.

Twin studies also throw important light on the nature of homosexual love, as outlined in Chapter 11.

There are other valuable techniques for disentangling the genetic and environmental elements in human traits. For example, most useful comparisons can be made in families where children adopted as infants are brought up side by side with the foster parents' own biological children: quantitative studies of such cases have shown that in certain traits – and in IQ scores – there is significantly closer correlation among the biological children than there is between them and the adopted children. Sometimes adopted children can be studied in other combinations also, showing for example their correlations with their own parents as against their correlations with their adoptive parents, and the results of such comparisons are consistent with those of the first type, as regards various traits and IQ scores. At the same time, studies of adopted children yield convincing evidence that conditions of upbringing are also of great importance in the development of children's intelligence.

In addition, geneticists can sometimes learn a great deal by tracing the occurrence of a trait in records of a family tree if the trait is conspicuous enough to have been recorded. Thus ordinary color blindness, like hemophilia, has long been known to be an inherited trait arising from a recessive gene located on the X chromosome.*

One must remember, however, that in all such matters as these it is very rare to have absolute proof of anything. The mere absence of proof of a particular hypothesis cannot legitimately be used as an argument for an alternative hypothesis. (On the other hand, if it can be demonstrated that one hypothesis is

---

* One of the particular forms (alleles) of a gene is called recessive if it usually does not attain phenotypic expression when present in an individual in combination with a different form (allele) of the same gene, which latter form is then called dominant in relation to the first one.

highly improbable this may afford support for one or more alternative hypotheses.) What reasonable people must try to do is to consider all the evidence on a particular problem at a particular time, and then to judge as well as possible at that time the relative probableness of different hypotheses.

For clarity on the nature–nurture question it is desirable to make a sharp distinction between *behaviors* and *behavioral traits*: in adult humans the former usually reflect a predominant measure of learning or environmental influences, while the latter are sometimes heavily genetic. The loving attentions which a mother lavishes on her baby are behaviors, and in large part learned: she may know 'instinctively' how to hold the baby, but she has to learn to burp it on her shoulder after feeding. On the other hand the behavioral *trait* is the primordial mothering impulse which makes her want to learn. Falling in love is a behavior; the trait is the propensity for falling in love when the environment offers a suitable stimulus, indeed sometimes an unsuitable one. *Making* love is a behavior which most people are happy to learn with experience, attaining various degrees of proficiency (and chimpanzees reared alone in captivity are sometimes at a loss how to go about it), but a lonely man's sexual hunger and a woman's potential capacity for sexual response are traits very largely determined by inborn factors and hormonal state. These matters will be discussed in later chapters.

In music, obviously, the behavioral trait is not singing or playing the piano, but rather the ability to learn to do either, which some people possess in a high degree and others do not. Musicality is perhaps a good example of a behavioral trait which is likely to resist scientific analysis for a long time. How is one to account for the characteristically different patterns which distinguish the music of different composers? We know from the broad general kinship among the compositions of each musical culture, and particularly from each of the great trends in European music, that every composer is heavily influenced by the musical environment. But there remain the irreducible differences of pattern – between Bach and Telemann, between Haydn and Mozart, between Debussy and Ravel – and there remain the radically new and original styles of music which appear from time to time, for better or worse. It is as if composers

of genius heard not only the music of their immediate predecessors and certain contemporaries but also inaudible interior
patterns of sound peculiar to themselves alone. Essentially the
same phenomenon appears in the other arts as well, where every
painter, architect, or poet speaks partly in the idiom of his or her
time but also partly in a unique individual idiom. Are these
individual differences mainly inborn or mainly acquired, and
how did they all evolve?

In comparison with such subtle mysteries as these, the
emotional interactions of men and women seem relatively
massive and relatively accessible to study and analysis. Even
here one is working in a dim light, in the sense that existing
knowledge is incomplete or even fragmentary, but here, I dare
to hope, a little new light can be shed.

In short, this book starts from the premise that human
behavior is compounded of both genetic and environmental
elements, that sometimes it is possible to form a reasonable
judgement that one element or the other is predominant, and
that sometimes it is not. In searching out the evolutionary roots
of human love, or in speculating about them, the book will focus
less on behaviors than on behavioral traits – tendencies,
predispositions, susceptibilities, deficiencies, capabilities – since
it is in the latter that the genetic elements are apt to be
important.

At the risk of tedious repetition, it can be added that at the
human level the existence of a genetic basis underlying a
behavioral trait does *not* mean that a corresponding behavior, or
even the trait, is predetermined. Rather, it means that there are
certain probabilities and certain limits, which sometimes ought
to be explored or tested, concerning the modification of the
behavior or the trait by means of learning or environmental
influences.

## Biological evolution and cultural evolution

In a sense nature and nurture are the products of two great
evolutionary systems – biological evolution and cultural evolution respectively – which combine and interact in complex ways.
At the level of protohuman and human behavior, they have

been jointly and more or less coequally responsible for some extraordinary developments, including, I believe, the development of various kinds of love. Before proceeding to inferences and speculations on that subject it may be worth the effort to take a careful look at the two evolutionary systems in conjunction.

The basic processes of biological evolution, although of engrossing complexity, are by now widely agreed upon by scientists. The starting point is that in our protohuman and human past heritable mutations of genes took place occasionally in every breeding population, through errors of replication of DNA or through chromosomal aberrations occurring in or just before the fusion of egg cells and sperm cells. Any of those mutations which did not prove lethal gave rise to new additions to the population's gene pool; and from time to time some new genes were introduced from other pools. Thereafter, endless shufflings of genes took place within each breeding population, each father and each mother passing on half of his or her myriads of genes to each child. In this way there arose an infinity of variations in individual genotypes – and also, over longer periods of time, many random differentiations among small isolated breeding populations, sometimes referred to as genetic drift. Some individuals happened to have, in greater measure than others, genes conducive to various physical and behavioral traits which proved advantageous in changing environments. Under the slow but relentless pressures of natural selection, in generation after generation, those favorably endowed individuals survived longer and left more surviving descendants than those less favorably endowed. In this way the frequency of the genes underlying the advantageous traits increased in the gene pool, and in the course of the 3,000,000 years which this book will take as the human stage of evolution, say 150,000 generations, many advantageous physical and behavioral traits became widespread in the populations that survived. If a trait was exceptionally useful, or if the lack of it was especially disadvantageous, the more intense pressure of natural selection could double the rate of change.

Some very distinguished modern zoologists like to picture natural selection as taking place at the level of genes. They regard individual humans and other animals as vehicles whose degree of success in surviving and reproducing determines the success of the genes which they carry – more or less as a chicken could be seen by Samuel Butler as an egg's way of making another egg – but for the purposes of this book it will be simplest to regard natural selection as operating on individuals, while remembering that some of each individual's genes are carried also by his or her blood relatives – on average, half of the individual's genes by a brother or sister, a quarter by a niece or nephew, an eighth by a first cousin, and so on. The arithmetic means that biological evolution often takes place through natural selection operating on an individual's close relatives: this is an important process called kin selection, in which for example the survival of two brothers or sisters of an individual counts for just as much in evolutionary effects as the survival of that individual.

In any case, whether natural selection is viewed as taking place at the level of genes or at the level of individuals and their close relatives inclusively, it is important to recognize that, in biological evolution, the value of a particular trait to a breeding population or to a whole species is as a rule of considerably less significance. When a genetically-based physical or behavioral trait evolves in a species, it is usually not because the trait is advantageous to the species as a whole. There is now general agreement that the adaptive value which a genetically-based trait may have for a population or a species as a whole is usually not a major primary force in biological evolution; what *is* important is the value of the trait to individuals, that is, the individuals possessing it, together with their children and their close relatives who may carry the same gene.

The reasons for this are interesting and important but by no means self-evident. Until just a few years ago many biologists, as well as practically everybody else, had failed to grasp them. The essential point is that, in biological evolution, natural selection at the level of groups – that is, selection resulting from differences between groups – usually takes place far too slowly to be effective in comparison with selection at the level of individuals. As a rule selection is very slow at the individual level, but it is incomparably slower still at the group level. A new gene underlying a particular new trait is established in an individual immediately, but many generations are needed in order to get it established in a whole group; and, in the ultimate test, ill-adapted individuals in a state of nature are eliminated in a single generation, but many generations are likely to elapse before a whole group dies out as a result of such a trait. Natural selection at the level of groups can and certainly does supplement or reinforce selection at the individual level if they are both working in the same direction, favoring or opposing the same genetic trait (an important point which nowadays is sometimes overlooked), but it can never or almost never be effective in a direction contrary to that of selection at the level of individuals.

The standard illustration of this principle assumes a case where one of two possible alternative forms of a particular gene causes the carrier to behave in an altruistic way – that is, benefiting others but harming the behaver, in terms of survival and reproduction – while the other alternative form of the same gene causes selfish behavior. An individual carrying the gene for altruism tends to cause his or her group to prosper and to increase faster than other groups, but in the illustrative case the altruistic individual suffers or dies, and meanwhile selfish individuals are thriving and multiplying in the same group. Consequently the gene for altruism decreases in frequency before the group enjoys much benefit from it, and the gene for selfishness spreads like wildfire.

But once group-level selection has been rejected as an explanation for inborn altruistic tendencies another explanation is needed, because altruistic behavior unquestionably does occur, under genetic control, in various species of animals, ranging from certain remarkable social insects to human beings. And indeed a succession of brilliant zoologists, starting with W. D. Hamilton in the 1960s (who himself could pick up a hint dropped by J. B. S. Haldane a generation ago), have provided some very ingenious explanations. These are based on kin selection and on systems of reciprocal altruism, and it is shown mathematically that those two processes could produce, through well-known genetic mechanisms, a variety of observed behaviors which are called altruistic. It is necessary to add that in the case of human beings the processes of kin selection and reciprocal altruism can account for altruistic behavior only within defined limits, rather tricky limits when it is reciprocal altruism that is invoked. (I will have something new to contribute on this subject in the last chapter.)

A note can be added here about the evolution of the system of sexual reproduction itself, in which group-level selection may, very exceptionally, have played a major part. Without needing to grapple with the conflicting theories about how this wonderful invention may have first arisen in nature and started to evolve (the earliest forms of life on earth having been asexual, nonsexual, reproducing simply by fission or budding), one can see that reproduction by means of interaction between two organisms of different sex, once having arisen and become established, has been of vast importance in the evolution of life. The fundamental reason is that it vastly increased the number of heritable variations occurring among individual organisms, upon which natural selection could then operate in changing environments.

In the easy words of Stephen Jay Gould of Harvard University, 'Asexual reproduction makes identical copies of parental cells, unless a new mutation intervenes.' When, however, two separate organisms collaborate in a process of sexual reproduction, each parent contributes a set of genes in which many particular genes are different from the corresponding genes furnished by the other parent; and then the shuffling of genes can begin, through which each new organism acquires a unique new combination of heritable traits. As a matter of arithmetic, these new combinations arise not with the rarity of mutations but almost infinitely more often. (If the total number of effective genes which could differ between different individuals of a given species were only 10,000 – an absurdly small number for humans and many other animals today, though the situation was undoubtedly very different in the early days of life on earth – and if each of those 10,000 genes existed in only two possible alternative forms, the total number of unique gene-combinations and resulting variations that would be possible for each individual of the given species would be $2^{10,000}$, a number well on the way to infinity.) Consequently, the rate at which variations are submitted to natural selection is always vastly greater than the average mutation rate. In changing environments, and especially when there were catastrophic changes in environments, such variance must often have been crucial for the survival and reproduction of individual organisms.

It will not be overlooked that sexual reproduction entailed substantial costs. In a species reproducing sexually, it is only the individuals called females that produce the eggs or analogous structures which, when fertilized, can develop into new organisms, whereas in a typical asexual species every individual organism produces offspring. In sexual reproduction half of every participating individual's genes are lost too, and there are also other costs. Yet in the end all the costs together have been outweighed by the advantage of vastly increased capacity for evolution, based upon vastly increased variation among individuals.

Gould has illustrated these points with great felicity, observing that for at least two billion years, according to the fossil record, the only forms of life on earth were bacteria and blue-green algae. But when the evolution of cells somehow reached a point where efficient sexual reproduction became possible, and mobilized endless new combinations of existing genetic characteristics, the explosive opening out of biological evolution in the Cambrian Period soon followed, assisted no doubt by certain other factors, 'and, less than a billion years later, here we are – people, cockroaches, sea horses, petunias, and quahogs.'

All these essentials of biological evolution are by now pretty firmly grounded in fact and theory. But when once biological evolution had established a certain critical level of intelligence – as in some species of higher mammals, most notably higher primates – cultural evolution came into existence as a new evolutionary system. In this book the term 'cultural evolution' means the evolution of learned behaviors, a process which can take place either with or without the aid of genetically-transmitted tendencies.* More explicitly, cultural evolution means the establishment of particular learned behaviors with a marked frequency in social groups and of subsequent changes in

---

*Biology is the study of living things, and therefore must include cultural evolution. The term 'biological evolution' is used in this discussion in its familiar but more restricted sense of evolution involving genetic inheritance.

their nature or frequency. It consists of the processes through which learned behaviors are established in social groups and subsequently modified. In the human stage of evolution, during which language and unprecedented capacities for learning developed, cultural evolution, including nurture, opened up another vast new expansion of the evolutionary processes. Systematic study of this subject by evolutionists is as recent as it is important and fascinating; the analysis of cultural evolution as a process has come to have a prominent place in published scholarly studies only since 1977, and largely in reaction to the 'new synthesis' of sociobiology and its preoccupation with the genetic factors which it perceives in altruistic behavior in species ranging from ants to humans. Current definitions and theories of cultural evolution vary, and some of them still need to be tested factually and mathematically. Most of the notions proposed in the paragraphs following have appeared in recent literature, and some additional ones are offered; together they should be regarded as provisional.

Basically, cultural evolution proceeds extremely fast in some situations, and after a certain point it tends to accelerate. Cultural innovations – that is, departures from cultural tradition – can occur more frequently than genetic mutations, and they can be propagated or diffused laterally within a few generations or even a single generation, to many members of a social group regardless of genetic relationship, and sometimes to other groups with which there is contact or communication.

As a consequence of this possibility of far more rapid propagation, the evolution of learned behaviors follows entirely different rules. The most fundamental one is that, in strong contrast with biological evolution, it can and often does work very potently at the group level. When a particular cultural innovation happens to prove highly advantageous – for example, in protohuman times, making tools or hunting large animals, and in later times practicing agriculture or developing mechanical technologies – it quickly confers an enormous selective advantage on the members of a whole population and enables them to increase in numbers at a decisively higher rate than those of other populations. It sometimes enables one population to enlarge its area of habitation and to spread, peacefully or otherwise, into an area previously occupied only by a population with a weaker culture; ethnography and history provide many examples of this process.

Because of the speed of cultural evolution, it is probable that during the past 3,000,000 years it has initiated or promoted in humans a far greater number of new behavioral trends than biological evolution has, even though many behavioral tendencies which developed genetically because they were advantageous for protohumans have been retained (given the slow rate of change in biological evolution) until the present.

There is another fundamental difference: in biological evolution the only criteria of natural selection are those of survival and reproduction (by definition of natural selection), primarily at the individual level; but cultural evolution can, up to a point, operate on the basis of other criteria as well, including those of mere pleasure for individuals or of general welfare for entire groups. The swift spread of contraceptive practices in our time is the ultimate example of cultural evolution's emancipation from the simple criterion of reproductive success.

As an instance of group advantage, cultural evolution can produce altruistic behavior, as well as biological evolution and indeed better and more profusely. During the protohuman past, cultural evolution must have produced many kinds of altruistic behavior, involving some immediate cost to the behavers but some advantage to small or large groups. And I suggest that, in all cases where the group advantage was great enough so that the altruists themselves received in the end, on average, a net advantage of one kind or another, those behaviors would have spread, and the groups in which they became common would then have prospered and increased in numbers at higher rates than comparable groups. Such cases are clearly possible, because today varied human societies afford astounding examples of learned behaviors which are altruistic but not dependent on either kin selection or reciprocal altruism; some of them may, however, be associated with a hope for future rewards. It seems enough to mention certain familiar examples of extreme types: priestly or sacred orders in which devotees take vows of celibacy because of a religious faith or a desire to serve others; and soldiers in wartime, not only the extraordinary cases of modern kamikaze pilots or suicide squads but huge numbers of perfectly ordinary young men who risk their lives because they are taught to or because they have learned to love their countries or their causes. (To be sure, there are underlying genetic capacities or predispositions of some kind which make it possible for these improbable behaviors and others to occur, and in the last chapter a unifying explanation will be proposed.)

Moreover there is one vital feature of cultural evolution that is not seen anywhere else in nature: the emergence of foresight and conscious purpose. The next chapter will mention some young Japanese macaques kept under observation on a beach who learned by themselves in a rather short period of time to wash their sweet potatoes in a brook to get rid of the sand. When they did this they were acting with a rational purpose in mind; it was something essentially different from genetically-programmed patterns of animal behavior developed through the slow processes of natural selection. And when modern human societies equipped with industrial technology create for themselves new and artificial environments, there is, to quote Christopher Boehm of Northwestern University in a recent paper, 'a purposive and insightful interference into the very process of evolution ... conscious, intentional meddling.' Today many people are protesting that human manipulation of environments has produced some deadly unintended results; but what is more interesting is that, thanks partly to those people, humans are already taking steps to correct the errors. Thus we have nature's most marvelous paradox: blind and purposeless natural selection has in the end created capacities for seeing ahead and acting with rational purpose. Who can define the ultimate limits of those capacities?

Another characteristic of cultural evolution is observed by everybody and taken for granted. It might be called a snowballing effect: when once cultural evolution has started something new and succeeded in getting it established, there is very commonly a lengthy period of accretion. Individuals learn behaviors developed by their predecessors, and then add contributions of their own in the form of improvements, intensifications, or extensions. The phenomenon will be noted later in the slow irregular improvement in techniques for making stone implements during the protohuman past, and in the evolution of improved hunting techniques. In our own time it has occurred spectacularly in the development of organized warfare, organized industry and commerce, organized science, organized technology, even organized crime; also in modern music and painting; at the present moment signs of it are showing up all too glaringly in the rage of violence and terrorism. The common feature of headlong acceleration in the latest years must be due to great expansion in means of communication.

I note also that cultural evolution can within a period as short as a human lifetime take a new direction. For our world this affords hope as well as danger.

Finally, there is a great deal of complex interaction between the two systems of evolution. On the one hand biological evolution establishes the potentialities, probabilities, and limits for cultural evolution; for cultural evolution was brought into existence by biological evolution, and remains subject to it in the very long run. Yet cultural evolution can cause a rapid spread of genetic characteristics which have developed through biological evolution. B. J. Williams of the University of California at Los Angeles has published a calculation which illustrates this point well: assuming two breeding populations of humans which are of equal size at the start but which, because of cultural differences, have very different but realistic growth rates – namely zero and 1.5 percent per year – and assuming that some particular unimportant gene is present in the two populations with widely different but still realistic frequencies, the total frequency of that unimportant gene in the two populations added together can change by as much as 20 percent in a single generation, whereas on the other hand the amount of change which can take place in the frequencies of most genes in a human population as a result of natural selection operating at the level of individuals is very slight in a period of 30 or 40 generations. To this I would add that sometimes the distinctive genetic characteristics of a rapidly growing population may include significant frequencies of an underlying genetic propensity which facilitates the learning of precisely the behavior which is proving advantageous: in such cases the genetic propensity itself will become more widespread very rapidly. In addition the cultural evolution of a human population may produce changes in the population's environment, and if these are permanent they may in time have an effect on the biological evolution of the population; a culturally contrived nuclear holocaust would have unpredictable genetic effects.

At many points the two systems have worked together in parallel. Both have participated in the establishment and spread of most human behaviors, and it is now sometimes impossible, even with help from comparative primatology, twin studies, and other studies, to make a reasonable judgement as to which of them has been predominant.

There is one perverse test which I venture to propose for detecting the presence of an important biological contribution in human behavioral tendencies, including some which are very widespread or universal in humans but not necessarily found in other primates. If such a behavioral tendency seems likely to have been advantageous for the survival and reproduction of protohumans during a substantial part of the 3,000,000 years, and if it is still clearly advantageous – as in the case of a man's tendency to love his children – that tendency may have developed either through biological evolution or through cultural evolution, or through both together. But, given another well-known human behavioral tendency – for example, violent aggressiveness in males – if there seems to be reasonable ground for believing that it was advantageous in protohuman times but has not been advantageous in recent times for many generations (long enough so that if it depended only on cultural evolution it would have been lost in many parts of the world), then this other tendency is likely to be in some large part the result of biological evolution with its much slower rate of change. Many of the behavioral tendencies to be discussed in this book are of that kind – adaptive in the evolutionary past but today useless or absurd or downright dangerous. I admit that this odd test can hardly be thought conclusive by itself. In considering any particular behavioral tendency it will be advisable to canvass all of the available evidence or clues before attempting a judgement or a guess.

This book invites attention particularly to genetically-transmitted contributions to human evolution, but only for the special reason that in many of the physical and behavioral characteristics which are important in human experiences of love those contributions are invisible or not generally perceived; the great contributions of cultural evolution are in no danger of being forgotten. It seems safe to predict that the overlapping and interaction of the two systems of evolution will receive increased attention in many future studies, until the remaining nature–nurture questions are finally put to rest.

## Human consciousness and free will

Perhaps it would be well to disclose here the viewpoint of this book regarding two other time-honored controversies; they have sometimes perplexed and worried philosophers more than other people. The first is the question whether human consciousness is merely an epiphenomenon, an incidental froth on the surface of important physical phenomena – the latter being states of neural and biochemical activity in the brain and in other parts of the body – or whether on the other hand it is itself a valid reality, capable of exerting real force in the world. In my view human consciousness is both; it is an epiphenomenon and simultaneously a powerful creative force. When a fine tungsten filament is placed in an environment of inert gas and heated by an electric current to a certain critical temperature, its agitated molecules give off a bright luminous glow. The luminosity is indisputably an epiphenomenon, but it can help to make midsummer flowers bloom all winter and it has turned night into day for human civilizations. In a somewhat analogous way, conscious human feelings and ideas arise from material causes, but they are themselves at the same time illuminating forces, sometimes mighty causative forces; they have changed the face of the earth and are continuing to change it year by year.

Accordingly, when this book discusses the evolutionary background of human tendencies, it assumes that the biological causes which are suggested have operated and are operating on human behavior both directly and indirectly, in some cases without the aid of human consciousness and in some cases very much *with* such aid. When a mother caresses and comforts her baby her action can be independent of her conscious thought, but it can also be enormously intensified and improved by a love which she feels with vivid consciousness; both kinds of behavior have been promoted and developed by natural selection, and both have been reinforced by experience and learning.

The second question is that of free will, today not the classical question of free will versus divine predestination but the modern one of free will versus scientific determinism. Today many of us tend to believe that all events are causally determined, that nothing happens by pure chance. Admittedly, it is a safe bet that if someone tossed a coin several thousand times it would fall heads about half of the times and tails about half; and this is considered pure chance. But if there were absolute control of the tossing – with a coin of absolute symmetry, say, tossed in an absolute vacuum by a machine of absolute precision, and landing on an absolutely level surface – the coin could be made to fall heads every time. On the other hand our conscious minds tell us that we ourselves exercise free choices: we regularly have the experience of considering in advance two or more possible courses of action and of choosing one of them, often with great difficulty, but the exercise of our mind and our will; and we have learned that our choices can affect our own future and sometimes events in the world around us.

The viewpoint of this book is that every event which appears to be a chance event is indeed causally determined, but determined by such a vast number of antecedent and contributing causes of varying importance, starting at the beginning of time – the total number of causes might have to be written with a string of hundreds of zeros – that neither contemporary science nor any imaginable computerized science could ever identify and evaluate them all with sufficient precision to predict the event. The expression 'chance events' then remains a convenient and permissible approximation.

And seen from this same viewpoint the freedom of choice which we feel we possess is illusory in the last analysis, in the sense that our choices are really determined by a complex of antecedent causes (including our myriads of genes and our conditioning by myriads of exposures and experiences in life), but again the number of those causes is so vast (and our genes and our psychological conditioning so little known) that our claim to the exercise of free choice is a forgivable reductionism. Quite possibly the psychological process which we feel as the exercise of a free choice is actually a still more wonderful process, one in which our nervous system assembles all the pertinent information reaching it concerning the past, the present, and the future, together with all the emotional and other forces working within us, and then integrates all these elements in such a way that a course of action (or inaction) results, the integration taking place at electrochemical speed in the case of some automatic choices and slowly when the laborious exercise of conscious reasoning is employed. The difficulty often experienced in making a choice is possibly something that arises when the process of integration must include a reconciliation of two or more strong opposing forces. In any case, however, our choices are in themselves real and valid events, as all our states of consciousness are, and once they have taken place they become small or large causal particles in the infinite universe of causes. No matter how we may prefer to view them, our choices unquestionably can influence events.

The next four chapters will look into our primate heritage, into the fossilized remains of early hominids, and into the conditions of life for protohumans and humans during the past 3,000,000 years or so. In all these excursions the end purpose is to discover the biological origins and nature of human love in its diverse forms. Sometimes genetically-determined factors will be apparent, but generally speaking the evolutionary roots of human love are deeply buried and the surface signs of them are often not easy to recognize. It will therefore be left to later chapters to attempt more extended speculation about the biological factors underlying today's common experiences of love, and underlying also a curious assortment of associated phenomena. Throughout, an essential minimum of the factual information now available will be recited, in order to permit independent judgements, and the bibliographic references in the Index at the end of the book will indicate where additional information can be found.

# 3

# *The Primate Heritage*

The fossil evidence shows that primates had appeared in the world by 65,000,000 BP. Surprisingly, no traces of them as early as that have yet been found in Africa or South America, but they inhabited the northern hemisphere in regions that are now North America and Europe; the climates there were much warmer and wetter than today, largely tropical or subtropical. Those first primates were decidedly primitive – squirrel-sized or cat-sized prosimians, often arboreal but resembling rodents rather than monkeys in appearance.

Most of the early forms became extinct, but the survivors managed, over tens of millions of years, to multiply, to become larger, to spread, and to diversify. In response to varying environmental conditions, dozens of new species evolved. North America and Europe gradually drifted apart, and the northern temperatures slowly declined. According to one of the good modern hypotheses, the primates and some other mammals moved persistently southwards and crossed into Africa in the east and into South America in the west over intermittent land or island connections, sometimes drifting on floating vegetation.

By about 35,000,000 BP there were apparently very few primates left on the cooling northern continents, but divergent species had founded colonies in Africa and South America. In the course of succeeding geological epochs some of the thriving descendants of those colonies spread widely and diversified still further, some in the trees and some taking to the ground.

In Africa, at an early stage which is of special importance for human evolution, a bifurcation apparently took place between lines leading to modern monkeys and lines leading to modern apes: a fossil of about 30,000,000 BP discovered in the Fayum Depression of Egypt, at that time a tropical rain-forest, could well be ancestral to the chimpanzees and gorillas, and us. This was *Aegyptopithecus xeuxis*, a diminutive snouty little ape whose immediate descendants probably include some larger fossil apes of the genus *Dryopithecus*. Many dryopithecine specimens have been found in western Europe, eastern Africa, and elsewhere (including one given the name of Proconsul), with dates ranging from before 20,000,000 BP to something like 10,000,000 BP. The fossil record indicates that around 15,000,000 BP a new evolutionary line may have branched off in the direction of modern humans.

Meanwhile, as the landmasses continued shifting and changing, some primates are believed to have moved back northwards, in the Old World spreading across southern Eurasia. Notably, ancestors of the macaques, an outstandingly successful ground-living genus of monkeys akin to the baboons of Africa, spread across southern and temperate Eurasia from Spain to Japan, while certain species of *Dryopithecus* apes reached southeast Asia, where descendants of some of them now survive in the trees as gibbons and orang-utans. Certain prosimians, the lemurs, wandered or drifted to Madagascar where, isolated from certain dangerous predators, their descendants today constitute a majority of the prosimians still surviving.

Some of the structural and other adaptations which early primates developed for survival in arboreal environments have proved at least as valuable in the human line, indeed have turned out to be preadaptations for some of our highest achievements. Primates developed, during many millions of generations, notable strength and efficiency in their prehensile hands (and feet) for clambering and leaping about in trees. The hands served mainly to provide a sure grasp on branches – and for infants a grasp on the body hair of their mothers – but in the course of millions of years of evolution in the human line they later underwent enough refinement so that they could in due course fashion graceful stone tools and somewhat later assemble electronic equipment or perform brain surgery. Similarly the gradual migration of the eye sockets to the front of the head in primates provided full stereoscopic vision, useful for judging instantaneously the distance from one branch to another. This was accompanied by the neural development for distinguishing different wavelengths of light, or colors, a faculty lacked by most other mammals, which doubtless served originally for singling out and locating branches still more precisely and perhaps for identifying edible leaves and fruits. Together they opened up the vast realms of visual perception which we now have as our natural birthright.

Moreover, those complex early advances, and the still more complex neural apparatus for finely coordinated leaping and climbing activities, entailed a substantial development of the central nervous system. Even walking on two feet on a level surface is quite an art, and human babies are apt to spend several months learning it, but the art of moving about rapidly in trees as practiced by many monkeys and apes – climbing, balancing, running, swinging, springing, landing – involves a masterpiece of neuromuscular coordination and timing. It must have required an enlargement of the brain, accompanied by a relatively high intelligence. It may be that this was an important stage in the blind evolutionary advance, slow and staggering but at the same time staggering, in the general direction of the human mind.

As tree-living animals the primates could afford to do without a good deal of the acute sense of smell which many other mammals have. Their sense of hearing became sharp within a certain frequency-band of sound waves because it was advantageous to the members of a group to communicate with each other vocally in the foliage; thus many primates came to be the most vocally active of mammals.

One of the facts that stand out in this synopsis of primate history is that the evolutionary line which would ultimately give rise to the genus *Homo* must have branched off from the lines of New World monkeys something more than 35,000,000 years ago, from the lines of Old World monkeys about 30,000,000 years ago, and from the ape lines perhaps about 15,000,000 years ago. Since those times, the different lines have all been evolving in different directions. Consequently one should not be too glib about affinities between ourselves and other primates today, especially in behavior. Many similarities do exist, but they are not simply a matter of family resemblances; there must also have been potent ecological factors of one kind or another which long continued to operate in similar ways both in their lines and in ours.

The real value of facts about nonhuman primates of today is a little different: that they can sometimes cast light on the general characteristics of the apes and other higher primates at the time when the evolutionary line leading to humans branched off from them, perhaps 15,000,000 years ago; consequently they throw light on characteristics which our ancestors of that time are likely to have had. With that objective, the present chapter will summarize the principal findings of modern primatology which seem relevant. The summary will be confined to apes and Old World monkeys, and will be concerned with behavioral capacities and tendencies. The findings certainly vary in significance: at one extreme, behavioral traits which are found in a high proportion of primate species living today, including our own, despite major differences in environments, are very likely to have formed part of the genetic heritage of our first ancestors in the human line; at the other extreme, traits found in only a few species, and especially traits found in only a few individuals, are no more than suggestive, possibly indicating an ancient potentiality.

## Care and protection of the young

The higher primates of today are distinguished from the vast majority of other mammals by a progressive prolongation of the stages of individual growth and development. In most species of baboons and macaques the period from birth to the onset of adolescence lasts from three to five years, which is already long in comparison with most mammals, but in gibbons (very small apes), it is five to eight years, and in the chimpanzees it ranges from nine to ten years, while in our own case it ranges from eleven to fourteen years. After that there follows the rather turbulent period of adolescence, usually lasting four or five years in chimpanzees and six or more in humans.

This trend has been of great adaptive value to the higher primates. It is closely related with the trend towards increased intelligence, and the two trends in combination have made possible new levels of social learning and social organization – and thus cultural evolution, which at the human level at last opens out into a vast new expansion of the evolutionary processes.

At the same time, the progressive lengthening of the stages of individual development in primates had disadvantages: it placed the individual young in situations of great potential danger, since as infants and juveniles they were incapable of surviving alone. Nature's solution of the problem was this: in the long course of evolutionary time, natural selection operated powerfully to strengthen, elaborate, and prolong in higher primates the young-protecting tendencies which are basic in all species of mammals. In all of the score or more of higher primate species which have been well studied in their natural environments or in laboratories, there are conspicuous behavioral tendencies which result in exceptional care and protection of the dependent young.

One tends to think first of the behavior of the mothers. Among all the Old World monkeys which have been intensively studied, and all the apes, the mother normally spends a lot of her time in the early months licking, grooming, manipulating, and examining her infant, as well as nursing it and playing with it. As a rule she watches over it almost continuously during waking hours, pulling or calling it back to her if it starts to slip or crawl away; when she moves about in the trees or on the ground she keeps it attached to her front or her back, if necessary supporting its weight. The maternal impulses are so intense that in several species – chimpanzees, gorillas, grey langurs, and savanna and hamadryas baboons in the wild, and rhesus macaques and others in captivity – mothers have been observed in the pitiable act of carrying or clutching a dead infant, often for several days or even until the body has decomposed. Almost always, in the wild, the mother protects her infant from unwanted attentions or rough treatment by other members of the group, in one species not permitting any other animals to touch it, in other species allowing her infant to be groomed and examined only, in others entrusting it bodily to other adult females, and in still others extending this privilege in normal circumstances to subadult and juvenile females also.

As the months pass, and as the infant is able to move about a little by itself, this early maternal concentration is relaxed. In general, the mother still offers protection to the infant, holds it, and seems attached to it, but in most species she tends to punish it increasingly often and at times to reject it. When the baby teeth have emerged the infant begins to forage for itself in the wild, but the mother's milk still continues to provide nourishment for varying periods, up to a year or more in monkeys and two years in gorillas, while in chimpanzees milk is the principal food for at least two and a half years and complete weaning does not take place until after the age of four. Moreover a special attachment between mother and young continues in many species after weaning. In chimpanzees a close relationship usually continues until adolescence or even adulthood.

As might be expected, however, there is much variation among the individual members of all higher primate species. Jane van Lawick–Goodall has reported the case of an exceptional chimpanzee in the Gombe Stream Reserve in Tanzania: that mother took little interest in her juvenile young and repeatedly neglected them, and at least one of them soon died.

Anticipating here a discussion in Chapter 9 concerning genetic differences between the sexes in humans, it may be noted that juvenile and adolescent female chimpanzees often show an intense interest in their baby brothers or sisters. Van Lawick–Goodall has described the comical behavior of a small female who persistently tried to fondle her three-month-old brother, adopting a succession of different ruses to get possession of him despite their mother's protective opposition. Other more or less similar cases have been reported for other species. Juvenile male chimpanzees as a rule take a much more casual interest, or none at all, in their infant brothers and sisters. Those psychologists and others who maintain that 'gender roles' in growing human children are essentially learned, not inherited, are respectfully invited to consider the appearance of this difference at the chimpanzee level.

To a large extent the necessary care and protection of the young in higher primates is secured by the behavior of the infants and juveniles themselves, behavior which at the earliest ages must be the result of rigid genetic programming. Newborn monkeys show strong clinging, grasping, and nuzzling reflexes, which not only ensure their obtaining nourishment but also greatly increase their chances of survival when their mothers are leaping about in the trees or moving on the ground with a group;

newborn apes have similar reflexes but are more dependent on help from their mothers. During the months that follow, the infants make brief sorties from time to time to explore their surroundings, but they display a panicky need to return frequently to their mothers' bodies for safety or reassurance. In some famous laboratory experiments with rhesus macaques, H. F. Harlow and M. K. Harlow separated infants from their mothers for varying periods and caged them with inanimate surrogate mothers of two kinds, one a dummy covered with soft terry-cloth and the other a bare wire dummy. Each baby monkey promptly chose the terry-cloth mother and clung to it frequently; and if the bare wire dummy was equipped with milk bottles for nursing, the baby helped itself to the milk but returned immediately to the terry-cloth mother. In certain further experiments, painful but illuminating, some of the young monkeys were caged individually with only one of the dummy mothers and then confronted with novel situations such as an experimenter's threatening stare: in these cases the monkeys with terry-cloth mothers managed to get along, but those with only bare wire mothers showed symptoms of terror and withdrawal. To a baby rhesus monkey, it seemed, a mother is not just a source of milk but also softness and reassurance.

But the most important results of these experiments emerged when the rhesus infants grew up. They then proved to be socially handicapped, strikingly abnormal in behavior. They had difficulty in mating, and when some of the deprived females did finally produce young they treated them with hostility, hitting them away or grinding their faces into the floor. Other experiments in deprivation or isolation of young rhesus macaques and of young chimpanzees have produced generally similar results, the pitiable animals behaving more or less like autistic human children. Finally, it was found that the offspring of females who had become brutal mothers were in turn significantly more aggressive than normal young. No one should ask for a more convincing demonstration of the injury that deprivation can do to the young of higher primates. The parallel in human children will be reviewed in Chapter 7.

From among the free-ranging chimpanzees, van Lawick–Goodall has reported touching cases of animals who at the age of about three years lost their mothers. Two of these orphans were adopted by older sisters, but although they were no longer critically dependent on their mothers' milk and although their sisters lavished care and attention on them they both suffered traumatically. One of them became progressively lethargic, emaciated, and disordered in social responses, and two years later succumbed to an epidemic of polio and died. The other, whose sister was older and more capable than the first one, showed similar symptoms at the outset but later began to improve, and by the end of two years appeared to be more or less normal. A third case of an orphaned three-year-old appeared to end in early death: this one had no foster mother at all, and after two months of solitary depressive behavior was never seen again.

The meaning of all this is plain: infants and juveniles of the two species for which plentiful information is available have a compelling or even desperate need for a maternal attachment, and in all normal situations they would exert their utmost efforts to obtain it. Thus, inherited behavioral tendencies of the mothers on one side and of the young on the other complement each other in holding the two animals together, in close physical contact during infancy and in a continuing relationship long afterwards. And considering that a mother–child bond is well established in all other known species of primates, including the proudest one, there is no doubt that this was part of the genetic heritage of our very early ancestors.

Among nonhuman primates fatherhood is still unknown in almost all species, but the generalized benevolence of adult males towards infants and juveniles is carried several steps further than in other mammals. In addition to extending elementary tolerance or indulgence to young animals, adult males of nearly all higher primate species inhabiting open country will come to the defense of young animals who are threatened by a predator; different strategies are employed in different species or groups, but most commonly one or more adult males will put themselves between the young and a potential attacker, confronting and challenging the attacker for long enough to enable the females to take the young and flee to safety. This is clearly a genetically-determined behavior.

In addition, in some species adult males at times assume

certain parental functions in the care of the young, perforce viewing the young animals not as their own offspring but simply as young animals. In many species adult males show pronounced interest and curiosity concerning newborn infants, but beyond that point there is great variation. In several species adult males are apt to hold or carry infants who have reached the stage when their mothers are rejecting them because of a renewal of mating activity. In another species adult males have been observed starting to associate with particular infants just after the period of intensive maternal care is over. In still another a strong bond seems to exist between an adult male and infants from the beginning. In one droll New World species, the marmosets, an adult male commonly carries his twin infants most of the time, only turning them over to the mother for nursing. And in free-ranging chimpanzees and some other species it sometimes happens that when a young animal has been left without its mother's care, and no other female is on hand, a male animal of any age may step in and do his best to take care of it; in chimpanzees again, an adult male is apt to comfort a young animal in moments of distress, giving it a reassuring pat or helping it to its feet if it has fallen. On the other hand there are some species of Old World monkeys in which adult males seem to take no interest in the young, except for protecting them when they are threatened. All this variety suggests that, in monkeys and apes generally, evolution may have reached a point where young animals can sometimes benefit significantly from attention and care by an adult male, and where a potentiality exists, but where behavioral tendencies of that kind have not yet become established widely, except (in the case of open-country species) protection against predators.

There are also some adaptations, physical and behavioral, at the level of social groups, which have the pragmatic result of promoting care and protection for infants and juveniles; most of the behavioral ones are probably learned, but facilitated by learning-propensities transmitted genetically. In many species the infants of a helpless age have a distinctive body color which signals their presence to the adults and subadults – a light color in some species, a dark color in others (this system is paralleled in many other mammals and in birds). Similarly, the voices of baby monkeys and apes are usually quite distinctive, and they are often put to active and noisy use. In several species living in sizable groups, when a new infant is born there is a general tendency to cluster around and observe the proceedings, and females show a keen desire to inspect and touch the newborn. A female's prestige in the group rises when she has a baby. In several species infants form a focus of interest for both females and males. Sometimes a male who wishes to placate a stronger animal or to win favor with him will approach him carrying an infant. Certain species of monkeys which live on the ground in more or less open country, notably some baboons and macaques, have a tendency to adopt vaguely discernible troop formations when moving from place to place; such formations vary greatly, but sometimes the females and infants are in the center, not far from adult males, while young males may be on the periphery, often displaying a rather reckless bravado which could well have the effect of distracting a predator. All these examples are indications that the care and protection of the young is a significant element in the social life of many higher primate species, and may well have been so for many millions of years.

## Mating patterns

The mating behavior of apes and monkeys, in comparison with most other mammals, is directed a little more by the brain and a little less by the hormonal system. This is indicated in several ways. For one thing, the behavior of the apes and monkeys is more dependent on learning: rhesus macaques and chimpanzees, both male and female, have proved awkward or unsuccessful in mating if they have not had a chance as juveniles to observe and practice the appropriate behavior in a social setting; in several species of macaques and baboons the procedures of courtship or approach are quite variable, and may last half an hour; young males of savanna baboons apparently have to learn defer to their elders and betters. There are also three facts which suggest a greater input from the central nervous system: that the abnormal conditions and stresses of life in a zoo seem to cause greater disturbance of the estrous cycle and seasonality in apes and monkeys than in other mammals; that male hamadryas baboons, which maintain organized harems, show no inclination to mate with females not belonging to their harems; and that several species, particularly free-ranging chimpanzees, have been observed to avoid quite regularly matings between mothers and sons and between brothers and sisters. (Chapter 8 will discuss the biological basis of incest avoidance.)

In addition, in certain species there appears to be slightly less dependence on the estrous cycle. The females of higher primates have an ovulatory cycle of 25 to 35 days, including up to 10 days of estrus during which they are attractive and receptive to males and within which ovulation occurs and conception is possible. In chimpanzees and numerous species of macaques and baboons the estrus is signaled to males by colorful external markings, especially on the skin of the behind, while in some other species it seems to be signaled mainly by odors, as in mammals generally. (In experiments on a species of savanna baboons the signals have been induced by the injection of hormones.) The cycle is suspended during the period of nursing in most species of higher primates, during pregnancy in some species, and during a good part of the year in species that have a mating season. But the point here is that in a few species, most notably chimpanzees, copulation sometimes takes place, even in the wild where the cycle is undisturbed, when the female is not in estrus: this looks like an early step towards the human condition, in which signals of ovulation have disappeared and in which psychological factors are of much greater importance. (Incidentally, the apes and Old World monkeys share in varying slight degrees the human process of menstrual bleeding at the opposite point in the cycle.)

As for seasonality, most primate species observed in the wild show some signs of this widespread mammalian characteristic, but there is great variation, ranging from strict seasonality in some macaques, through savanna baboons, which have a seasonal peak but some births throughout the year, to chimpanzees, which are about as free of seasonal constraints as we are.

There is great variation among species in levels of sexual activity, even among the apes alone. Male chimpanzees in general seem almost indefatigable at the times when one or more females are in estrus, but gorillas and also gibbons are reported to be rather placid sexually. In addition, in free-ranging chimpanzees, extreme variations have been observed between different females during their periods of estrus.

Perhaps it deserves mention that although mating is manifestly a most important preoccupation in the lives of all nonhuman primates the culminating act itself is exceedingly brief. In chimpanzees again, it is reliably reported to last normally only 10 to 15 seconds and never more than half a minute, and once a male was observed to accomplish it without pausing to lay down a pair of bananas which he was holding. Here, it will be agreed, human evolution has made real progress.

But the copulatory activities of nonhuman primates are less interesting than the patterns of male–female relationships that are associated with them. Predictably, these are exceedingly varied among the higher primates, particularly in the chimpanzees. Nevertheless, in the score or so of ape and Old World monkey species which have been most thoroughly studied, certain predominant tendencies can be discerned.

The two theoretical extremes are monogamy on one hand, in the sense of a lasting and exclusive association between one particular male and one particular female, plus young; and complete promiscuity, in which any male mates freely with any female in estrus and vice versa. And both of them are rare. Monogamous patterns have not been found in the Old World except among the gibbons and the related siamangs or 'black gibbons,' living high up in forests of southeastern Asia and Indonesia, and among one or two groups of monkeys. On the other hand, pure promiscuity, so to speak, is now believed not to occur consistently in any Old World species, though the bonnet macaques of southern India come pretty close to it.

The behavior of a great majority of the species which have been adequately studied can be placed in three categories intermediate between the foregoing extremes: promiscuity modified by individual preferences; promiscuity modified by dominance ranking among males; and harems. The first category includes consortships, where mating pairs draw away from their groups and remain together for periods of hours or days; these are known to occur in some multi-male groups of rhesus macaques and savanna baboons, sometimes in the chimpanzees of Gombe Stream, and occasionally in bonnet macaques; they probably occur in numerous other species as well.

The second category appears to be very widespread, also occurring in species where animals of both sexes and all ages live in social units containing several adult males. In these cases there are normally no protracted associations between particular males and particular females, and the mating pattern is more or less promiscuous but in some cases restricted by the dominance ranking among the males. The curious complexities of dominance hierarchies will be dealt with in the next section, but the essential point here is that the males have some system of ranking among themselves, with differentiated rights of access to females. A few years ago, attention was heavily concentrated on this mating pattern among primates, partly because it appears in many species when they are in captivity, and perhaps partly because it is manifested in the wild by several common and easily observed species of savanna baboons. More recently, however, there has been due recognition that the pattern is by no means universal, and also that different patterns can appear in different groups within a given species, generally under the influence of local ecological conditions. Also, the pattern can work out unpredictably; for example, it sometimes happens that for special reasons low-ranking males manage to do considerably more copulating than the high-ranking ones. Nevertheless, after all corrections are made, the pattern is still a common one. It is found in the wild not only among the savanna baboons, but also, to a greater or lesser extent, in numerous other Old World forms, including some groups of the common hanuman langurs of India, the rhesus macaques spread widely over southeastern Asia, the Japanese macaques, some of the vervet monkeys of Africa, and sometimes the versatile chimpanzees. Recent studies indicate that it is important among gorillas.

The harem category, with social units consisting of one adult male and several females plus young, is also a large one. The best-known examples are the hamadryas baboons and the gelada baboons, ground-living species occupying different ecological niches in the general region of Ethiopia. One adult male establishes or joins – and dominates – a group of several adult females with their offspring, and such one-male units frequently remain united for many months or years. Typically, the hamadryas and gelada harems move about separately in the daytime for feeding but congregate at night with other one-male harem units and with numerous single males, forming large bands or herds. There is some rather intriguing evidence, in a study of interbreeding between hamadryas baboons and neighboring olive baboons, that the harem-forming behavior of the hamadryas males is at least in part genetically determined: neither the olive baboons nor the hybrid male offspring could learn such behavior, even though they readily learned to sleep on narrow ledges on cliff-faces as the hamadryas baboons do.

In addition there are a number of species which form isolated harems – isolated one-male groups, each with several females and young, while the lone males left over sometimes band together. This pattern is found in some very diverse species, for example (among Old World monkeys), in some of the hanuman langurs of India, in the patas monkeys of African savannas, and in some of the guenons, tree-dwellers of African rain forests, with ecological factors often a predominating influence.

Changing environmental conditions can cause a group to shift from one mating pattern to another. For example, if food becomes scarce a multi-male group with dominance ranking and the corresponding pattern of mating is apt to split up into several one-male units and disperse, whereupon the pattern normally becomes that of harems; a shift in the other direction can occur in appropriate circumstances. Also, adult males sometimes leave one group to form or join another. In real life all the patterns are dynamic and continuously developing.

Particular interest attaches to the mating patterns of the chimpanzees because of their close relationship to us. By good fortune they have been searchingly studied over an extended period, in or near their tropical African forests. Their social organization is very fluid, very variable, and affords examples of several different mating patterns. The commonest pattern is basically promiscuous or opportunistic: a female in estrus is accompanied by a retinue of males of varying ages and ranks, and they mate with her successively and frequently, without distinction (except for sons and brothers), though in a minority of cases there are distinct indications of individual preferences. One such preference reported recently by Caroline Tutin, from careful quantitative studies of a community of the Gombe Stream chimpanzees, was observed in 27 out of 30 cases where one of the adult males in the community had an equal choice between two estrous females: the 27 males elected to copulate with the older female. A striking case of the same preference had earlier been reported by van Lawick–Goodall – a case where high-ranking males monopolized one very old female, to the exclusion of young males. These two observations will be of special interest for a discussion in Chapter 10.

Tutin's studies also focused on two other mating patterns occurring in the same community of chimpanzees. In one which was occasionally observed, a male addressed persistent and possessive attentions to a particular female during several days of estrus, and by virtue of his position in the male rank-order prevented other males from copulating with her. The second pattern was that of consortships; although Tutin ascertained that this pattern entailed real risks and other costs to the consorting pair, she found that during a 16-month study period more than half of the males tried at least once to adopt it and that more than half of the females accepted it at least once; when a consortship was established, the pair went off together, away from the rest of the group, for periods varying widely but averaging about 10 days. During a consortship there was a lot of grooming, especially by the male. Tutin found that on the whole 'the females showed a preference for males who spent the most time with them, and showed the highest frequencies of the affiliative behaviors, grooming and food-sharing.' Although consortship accounted for only a tiny fraction of over a thousand copulations observed, because of their timing and duration the consortships accounted for at least half of the pregnancies that occurred.

Van Lawick–Goodall had earlier reported cases where females, especially young ones, repeatedly refused a particular male, while one apparently normal female had no success at all with the males. There was also one case where the same pair formed a consortship every time the female went into estrus.

Thus, although chimpanzees are basically inclined towards promiscuity, it is evident that they often have distinct or even strong preferences. Comparable expressions of individual preferences or attachments have been observed also in several species of baboons and macaques.

To boil all this down, it might be said that mating patterns among the apes and Old World monkeys are exceedingly varied, that monogamy is rare and absolute promiscuity still more so, and that the commonest patterns are promiscuity limited in differing ways by individual preferences, promiscuity modified by dominance ranking among the males, and harems, with shifts from one pattern to another taking place in the appropriate ecological situations. Both in harems of the best known types and in the rare monogamous pairings, the individual males and females may stay together, with young, for long periods. In addition, even in relatively promiscuous species including the chimpanzees, there are sometimes consortships lasting for several days and a variety of other signs of individual preferences on the part of particular males and females. The conclusion – necessarily a good deal more tentative than in the case of the mother–child bond – is that Old World monkeys and apes may long have had a genetic potential for forming individual preferences in mating, and perhaps for male–female bonding in environmental situations where it would be particularly advantageous; if so, such a potential may have been part of the heritage of our own very early ancestors.

## Dominance hierarchies

So far as is known at present, all species of apes and Old World monkeys which frequently form multi-male groups have a tendency to establish hierarchies or rank-orders among the adult males of such groups, especially marked when they live in open country. For students this is one of the more entertaining features of primate ethology, and for the primates concerned it is one of the major facts of life. Because of its relevance to certain human affairs, and because the subject is often misunderstood, it seems worthwhile to seek an accurate understanding of it.

In the present discussion the convenient traditional term of dominance is adopted, for want of a better term which is generally accepted, but it is emphasized that as used in this book the expression refers only to *a ranking system, primarily among males*, and in particular does not include a social pattern of male domination or supremacy over females, in cases where that may occur. (Inevitably some overlap exists, in that the dominance which a top-ranking male acquires over the other males in a group commonly carries with it leadership of the group as a whole, including females and juveniles; but this is something quite different from a claimed supremacy of every male over every female. In some species, rankings are observed among all animals of both sexes in a group, and in most but not all of these cases adult males outrank adult females.)

In many of the primate species separate hierarchies are also established among females, but in most of these cases the ranking of females is considerably less important in the relationships among them and with others in the groups. (One rather important aspect of it is that the male and female offspring of high-ranking females often start out in life with above-average rank.) Therefore the present discussion will be concerned mainly with dominance systems among males: why they are so widespread, what high rank consists of, and how it is acquired.

It is possible to visualize good reasons why tendencies to establish systems of male ranking should have come to be so very widespread among the higher primates. The primary reason is the classical one that in the beginning, almost certainly, adult males that succeeded in achieving high rank usually arrogated for themselves priority of access to food and priority of access to females in estrus, with the result that high-ranking males tended to live longer and to leave more offspring than the others – their genes thus tending to spread. Today those basic priorities are not always evident, and in many species complex ecological factors have been operating, so that varied patterns are found. The general rule, subject to exceptions, is that dominant males enjoy priority as regards both food and females.

A close link often exists between high rank and the performance of important social roles, including particularly that of defense against predators. It has been mentioned that the males of nearly all social primates living in open country play a special role in challenging and blocking predators, especially if an infant is threatened. And where a ranking system exists this role devolves most of all on the dominant males, as for example in troops of macaques and of savanna baboons. In addition, many cases have been observed where the dominant male in a primate group maintains internal order, stopping fights, calming down excitement, and on occasion punishing trouble-makers. Normally he also makes the decisions about movements of his group, choosing the direction to be taken for foraging or finding water, and directing the movement to sleeping-places. Social functions such as these – where the dominant animal simply asserts his own wishes, in effect – would have been of survival value to close relatives of a capable one, and they as well as he would have passed on some of the genes for dominance behavior.

There is a related fact which is almost always taken for granted but which is of such great importance that it needs to be stated explicitly: the evolution of systems of dominance among primate males has been accompanied by the development of an extremely widespread tendency of the males to compete with each other, to try to excel or to establish dominance over each other. In most species, particularly in chimpanzees, an animal's right to his position in the male hierarchy is likely to be tested many times, and he must be ready to defend it at any moment or else lose it; the ranking of males is continuously subject to challenge and change, and in many groups it does change rather often. The underlying competitive drive is almost universal, though it varies greatly in intensity, being mild in some animals and extremely powerful in a few. It has been both a result of the dominance systems and a dynamic force perpetuating and strengthening them.

The next point is that of the characteristics and behaviors which enable some males to establish dominance over other males in the same groups. It is established either initially or in the last resort through agonistic behavior, that is, aggression in the form of fighting or threat. In practice, threat is usually sufficient. Actual fighting is rather rare among nonhuman primates in their natural environments, and when it does occur it is apt to be only ritual or symbolic, rarely resulting in death or serious physical injury. If submission is not freely tendered, it can usually be secured through more or less portentous threats – the wide-mouthed 'yawn' of adult male baboons displaying their formidable canines, the charging displays and noisy commotion of chimpanzees, or the fearsome chest-beating of the ordinarily amiable male gorilla. Real combat remains imminent as the ultimate sanction.

Often, even threats are not necessary. A dominant male gorilla usually reminds a subordinate of his authority, which is absolute, by means of merely a glance or a light touch. In several species a dominant animal conveys to others its right to respect simply by its posture, its manner of approach – a relaxed self-confidence or consciousness of authority. (This factor may initially work to the advantage of a young male who has inherited above-average rank from his mother.) In contrast, subordinate animals often betray their insecurity by hesitation or tenseness. In one study of captive baboons it was suggested that the hierarchy is maintained, or expressed, chiefly by the behavior of subordinates.

Sheer size and physical strength are primary qualifications for leadership. But so are age and experience, presumably because of the associated knowledge of potential dangers or the whereabouts of resources: many touching cases of loyalty to old leaders have been reported, including one where an aging pig-tailed macaque was able to maintain his dominant status until a few days before his death even though he was suffering from badly infected wounds and had lost one eye and broken three of his four canines. Unquestionably, superior intelligence, resourcefulness, and cunning can be a decisive factor: van Lawick–Goodall has told how a young chimpanzee whom she named Mike romped rapidly up to the top rank in his group as a result of learning that he could greatly enhance the effect of his charging displays by using empty 4-gallon kerosene cans borrowed from the Gombe Stream Research Centre. Again and again he charged the other males, including the dominant chimpanzee Goliath, while hooting madly and banging two or three kerosene cans ahead of him, raising an appalling racket;

before long he vanquished Goliath in an epic contest of charging displays. Records of other primates show plainly that determination and persistence can also be important factors in an animal's rise to dominance. And it is clear that personality, or what might be called popularity or the ability to win friendly respect, can be almost as important as the ability to inspire fear; for several species there are occasional reports of lower-ranking animals tending to sit clustered around the alpha or top-ranking animal when they are all peacefully resting. Dominant male chimpanzees, gorillas, and some others are often particularly tactful and considerate of subordinates, giving them a reassuring pat or touch with the hand, or even a kiss on the neck, after administering a harsh scolding or punishment. And certainly success as a leader pays off in prolonged tenure – success, that is, in providing protection from predators, in keeping order within the group, and in deciding on the direction of movement for the group. Blind luck surely plays a significant part in all this, including a lucky accident in a contest between two animals. And sheer courage, even bluff, can sometimes be decisive: van Lawick–Goodall's Mike, soon after he had risen to alpha status, encountered occasional resentment on the part of some other males; after some preliminary rushes, an improvised team of five strong adult males, including the deposed Goliath, gave chase to Mike and drove him up a tree; but then Mike, to the amazement of the other five and the observers, suddenly turned and began to sway the branches violently and finally made a giant leap towards the five – who took fright and fled, leaving Mike with a spectacular victory. Although the five could have torn him to pieces, his astonishing courage and bluff enabled him to overcome them all. Last but not least, there are many accounts of long-term alliances formed between two or more adult males, enabling them together to establish dominance in their troop; sometimes such combinations seem to exercise a kind of collective leadership even though there is a bigger or stronger animal in the troop.

It has occasionally been observed that the prevailing character or tone of a primate group is influenced by the dominant animal's personality. For example, a certain exceptionally large troop of Japanese macaques had a number of leading males with an alpha named Jupiter at the top. Jupiter was violent to the point of cruelty, but when he weakened and died he was replaced by a gentle animal named Titan; thereafter the whole troop became more gregarious, with much closer spacing and more frequent contacts among the animals.

Another observation often made is that the tendency to establish hierarchies is stimulated or intensified by conditions of captivity or crowding. One may guess that the chain of causation is something like this: captivity or crowding causes stress, stress gives rise to aggression, and aggressive interactions lead to the establishment of hierarchies.

Finally, it appears that it is possible for a whole group to establish dominance over other groups. For example, on Cayo Santiago, a small island near Puerto Rico where C. R. Carpenter years ago established a colony of rhesus macaques in a more or less natural environment, there is now (with a little crowding) a dominant group which tends to occupy the better parts of the terrain at the expense of subordinate groups. Rhesus macaques in Aligarh, India, also show a pattern in which a dominant group forces subordinate groups to move out of favored areas.

In sum, dominance systems among the males in a group are very complex. They have proved to have selective value in a great many primate species, and they are associated with a variable but vital competitive tendency in primate males. Aggression is certainly a vital element, as the starting point or more often as the ultimate sanction, but many other faculties and behaviors can be involved in male dominance. Moreover a simple linear hierarchy like the classical pecking order of barnyard chickens is rare among primates; there is instead great variety among different species, among different groups within a species, and even, in the higher primates especially, among individual animals. It could be said that the status of any particular alpha animal depends on his possessing some combination of a majority of the following attributes: physical strength, fighting ability, aggressiveness, determination, experience, intelligence, personal appeal, success in protecting and leading his group, luck, courage, bluff, and a disposition to form alliances for mutual assistance.

If much of all this looks like a simplistic caricature of scenes in our own world, it must mean that behavioral tendencies which underlie systems of dominance among males were another element in the genetic heritage of the early hominids – almost as surely as mother–infant bonding – and that such tendencies have continued to be of high adaptive value during hominid and human evolution as well.

Among females of higher primates, rank–order hierarchies appear fairly freqently, and high rank undoubtedly carries with it biological advantages such as preferential access to food and superior protection for the privileged females and their offspring. Nevertheless, hierarchies among females occur less regularly than those among males, and they are usually less conspicuous in the life of social groups. This difference probably means that on the female side there are even greater reproductive advantages in strong maternal tendencies; in most primate species the females' behavioral tendencies are more developed in the direction of raising young than in the direction of fighting, whereas aggressiveness is one of the vital ingredients of dominance among males. Where some females have higher rank than others – perhaps a term other than dominance should be used for them, such as status, or the right to respect or attention – it often seems to be connected with reproductive success. This is the case among chimpanzees, for example, where a female's rank is high if she is especially prized by males and if she has borne several young; among chimpanzees a female's status, on both counts, tend to rise with age.

It has been observed that while some female primates seem to have enduring friendships with certain other females, such relationships are less common than among males and are usually not of a quasi-political nature, for mutual assistance and support. It has also been found that in those cases where a rank-order is established among the females it tends to be fairly lasting, whereas among males the dominance relationships change rather frequently and are continuously subject to challenge and change. This could be because a smaller proportion of the females have a strong competitive tendency or an urge to become dominant.

The existing evidence concerning dominance among females

is too meager to support confident inferences about the genetic endowment of the very early hominid females. One can speculate that certain differences between modern men and women in this respect may possibly have been present already at that early stage.

## *Intelligence*

Early hominids may not have been the only animals to use tools. Modern chimpanzees use stems of grass or stripped twigs to extract termites (a noted delicacy) from a termite mound, or crumpled leaves as sponges for scooping up water, and males wield broken-off branches of trees in charging displays. Both chimpanzees and gorillas sometimes throw small objects with rudimentary aim.

Experiments with a very large troop of free-ranging Japanese macaques have yielded some highly suggestive information about learning-processes in a group of higher primates. For these animals, research workers made a practice of throwing supplies of sweet potatoes on a beach. The macaques came to relish the potatoes but always took pains to wipe the sand off before eating them. One day a particular monkey discovered that the sand could more easily be cleaned off by washing the potatoes in a brook, and quickly adopted this procedure. An interesting detail is that the clever monkey was a young one, a female. Other young monkeys of both sexes soon learned the trick, and then a few of the mothers. Gradually, over several years, the trick spread through most of the young animals in the troop and a minority of the adult females. The adult males, who were accustomed to eating separately, did not learn the trick. Meanwhile the experimenters had begun throwing wheat on the sand as well, and the same young female tried casting handfuls of wheat and sand on the water, with still more successful results. Again the trick spread to the young and some of the mothers, but not to the adult males. It is clear that these animals, especially the young female, could make creative use of their intelligence, and also that those most ready to experiment with a new behavior were the young. Incidentally, in time the young monkeys came to prefer using the sea instead of the brook for this purpose; they then learned to play in the sea in hot weather; some of them learned to swim, and the sea became a new food source.

Reverting to the laborious Washoe experiments mentioned in the preceding chapter, it is known that apes and monkeys manage a good deal of communication with each other, both vocally, with various calls which have been described as screams, barks, grunts, pant-hoots, and howls, and also with a repertoire of distinct facial expressions and a great many bodily postures and actions. The great social pastime of grooming – picking about intently in the body hair of another for insects or particles of dirt – may be considered a form of communication, conveying reassurance, solicitude, affection, or reconciliation. Nevertheless, the inability of all the non-human primates to reach the critical threshold of a language of words has been decisive in barring them from great cultural advances.

## Emotion

Preceding pages have described the close emotional bonding between primate females and their young, and the bonding that occurs in some species for long or short periods between adult males and females. Here it can be added that a juvenile primate is closely associated not only with its mother but also with its siblings, and in large groups with cousins and others of about the same age. They spend a great deal of time together, playing endlessly. In chimpanzees and other species where a close personal relationship between the mother and her offspring continues until late in life, sibling associations are also apt to be strong. There are reports of young chimpanzee brothers who pass through stages of indifference or rivalry with each other but afterwards become close companions and allies. In one case at Gombe Stream a full-grown male stayed close to an older brother badly crippled by polio, and even waited and watched for the latter's return for months after he had been mercifully removed and shot. Lasting associations occur also between pairs of unrelated adult males; in some cases they spend hours in each other's company, grooming, feeding, moving together from place to place, helping each other when need arises.

Relationships of these kinds look very much like brotherly affection between friends.

All this raises fundamental questions about the place of emotion in evolution. In the 1960s David A. Hamburg complained, in an essay which has not received half the attention it deserves, that 'basic reference works on evolution rarely mention emotion, and similar works on emotion rarely mention evolution.' To a lamentable extent this is still true, though interchanges are gradually taking place between the disciplines of biology and psychology, and one can hope that someday a free and open flow will be achieved. I wish it were within my power to help in that endeavor. I would greatly like to find out, for example, whether it would be proper to view emotion as one of several grand modes of generating and directing activity in living organisms, developed by natural selection since the beginning of life on earth. Are tropisms such a mode, at a very primitive level of organization, causing some unicellular organisms to move towards the light, for example, and causing plants to grow towards the light? Are instincts or genetically-fixed programs of behavior another such mode, developed in more elaborate forms of life such as reptiles or insects and serving to generate and control their various kinds of activity? Are the pain-and-pleasure mechanisms of a simple nervous system still another? And, finally, are inherited emotional tendencies essentially a comparable mode, developed in mammals along with their increasingly flexible behavior and their unique reproductive system? Most mammals have ample capacities for both anger and fear, and natural selection has produced in all mammalian species some degree of emotional attachment between females and their infants because it has helped to ensure the continuous bodily interaction between them which has always been necessary for the survival of the infants. Was the limbic system in the brain developed in mammals because the emotional mode proved especially adaptive for them? The limbic system, only rudimentary at the reptilian level, became prominent in mammals, and it is known to play an important part today in emotional processes; in the course of evolution it has increased in size in the larger-brained species, including higher primates, and in the human brain it has even kept pace in rate of growth with our vaunted neo-cortex, the seat of cognitive intelligence. Such questions as these, and others more nuanced, probably cannot be answered except through man-and-woman-years of work – analysis, experimentation, and testing. In the meantime we must do what we can with what information we have. As Hamburg and others have pointed out, human emotional states – not only anger, fear, joy, and other momentary flashes of feeling, but also continuing experiences such as affection and love – are actually three things at the same time: they are powerful motivating forces for behavior that has proved important over long periods for survival or reproduction; they are physiological states giving rise to the motivating forces; and they are accompanying states of consciousness experienced subjectively.

We tend to concentrate on the third and subjective aspect of emotions because it is all that most of us know about with certainty. Yet the other two aspects are just as real if not more so. Natural selection has produced in mammals an emotional need to perform in certain situations certain volitional actions which for long periods of time have been important for survival or reproduction. Those actions are then easy to learn and hard to forget; the desire to perform them can be intense; and the blockage or deprivation of them leads to tension, stress, and either coping behavior or depression, in humans sometimes physical illness. This is the motivational aspect of emotion. And the underlying physiological causes consist of changes in levels of circulating hormones, activation of parts of the central nervous system, and many related bodily events, chemical, mechanical, and electrical.

Affectional states, then, consist of all three of these aspects. Further, there is no valid reason for fearing to attribute all three of them in some degree to some nonhuman mammals. The right way to avoid the anthropomorphic fallacy, I suggest, is to bear in mind that no other animals possess either the vivid, enduring, fully-integrated memory which the human brain can provide or the human capacities for understanding and conceptualization: the result is that humans normally surpass the other animals by an immense distance in the number and variety of stimuli – including the written word, and in special cases a musical score or even a mathematical equation – which can give rise to emotional states. But the subjective experience of direct emotional arousal, particularly certain kinds of love, some primates and other higher mammals almost certainly share with us in some measure. Anyone who has owned and loved an intelligent dog must be aware of the capacity that some animals have for love.

It is rather interesting that recognizable signs of the emotional state of love are seen especially in species of mammals possessing relatively high intelligence. One reason for this may be that such animals are similar enough to us so that we can recognize something of ourselves in them. But there is another reason as well, an objective one of greater weight: the more intelligent an animal is, the longer is its period of infantile dependency and the less is it controlled by inherited programs of action; the greater an animal's capacity for learning, the more variable its behavior. Rabbits, for example, reproduce by carrying out the appropriate behavior in relatively stereotyped patterns but with great diligence, and can survive despite the loss of many of the proliferating young; but for rhesus monkeys and still more for chimpanzees the tolerances are narrower: fewer offspring are produced by each female, the period of infantile dependency and learning is much longer, and the range of potential choices of behavior on the part of both mother and young is much wider. Consequently different grades of emotional development have been necessary. Natural selection has doubtless implanted some ephemeral mother–infant love in rabbits, but animals as intelligent as rhesus monkeys and especially chimpanzees could not have survived and raised their young without the aid of stronger, deeper, and much longer-lasting attachments.

In short, natural selection established in successful mammalian species a substantial genetic capacity for emotion, including at least a rudimentary capacity for love, and in many of the most intelligent species that capacity has been greatly increased because it happened to produce behaviors which for long periods were highly important for survival or reproduction in those species. On the evidence of living higher primates, including ourselves, it is clear that the genetic heritage of early hominids included a rich store of emotional capacity. That capacity was certainly put to use in their time for mother–infant bonding, and it is quite possible that it already provided a potentiality for other affectional ties also.

# 4

# *Hominid Fossils*

In recent years the rush of new discoveries and new ideas in the study of human origins has been pretty fast for non-specialists. Many valiant generalists and many specialists working in other fields have been left well behind. For their benefit, this chapter will attempt a synthetic review of the current state of knowledge and opinions concerning the most important fossils and associated stone artifacts, based on material published up to the end of 1979. As important new discoveries are being made every year and definitive studies are still awaited concerning many specimens already discovered, this review will be confined to broad outlines which for the most part should not rapidly become out-of-date; readers will be spared many details, especially doubtful ones.

Nevertheless some readers may well ask what all this has to do with love, unless one happens to love fossils. In response, I plead that in order to understand the evolution of human love it is highly advisable to adopt the inductive method of working, to start by obtaining as reliable and complete a view as possible of all the available evidence about what actually happened in our evolutionary past, and only then to attempt inferences and speculation about our adaptations. The contrasting method of 'straightforward deduction from evolutionary theory' has, in very capable hands, achieved some brilliant results, but also a few distorted or deficient notions about human behavior, while at the same time the methods of guesswork and breezy generalization adopted in a succession of popular books during the 1960s and 1970s have produced excellent entertainment but some very unreliable information.

So Chapters 5 and 6 of this book will probe the archeological record for as many clues as possible concerning the actual conditions of life of our protohuman ancestors, and will then try to spell out in practical terms some of the ways in which those conditions may have guided our ancestors' evolution, including especially the evolution of love. The present chapter aims to supply the essential evidence now available about who and what our early ancestors probably were, where they may have come from, and how long it took for them to evolve into what we are. A secondary aim is to indicate the nature of the evidence on which current hypotheses about such matters are based.

## Early hominids

Sometime after 20,000,000–15,000,000 BP, when the *Dryopithecus* apes mentioned in Chapter 3 were thriving in Eurasia and Africa, that evolutionary line branched out in several directions. One new line, called the hominid line, was to lead ultimately to modern humans; another line was to lead to modern chimpanzees and gorillas, our closest surviving relatives.

Those early events are still largely hidden in the shadows, but the fossil record includes some two dozen jaw fragments and teeth which are of particular interest for our hominid line. These are the remains of *Ramapithecus*, a genus of small ape-like creatures, dating from about 15,000,000 BP to about 8,000,000 BP. The major specimens have been found on the Indian subcontinent and in Kenya, but similar specimens have been reported from Hungary, Turkey, and Greece.

Some eminent authorities regard *Ramapithecus* as the first of the hominids (meaning fossil species closer to humans than to the apes, and all their descendants including ourselves), while many other authorities now prefer to consider *Ramapithecus* as no more than an advanced small ape. For the purposes of this book it does not greatly matter, because in either case it was a form bearing resemblances both to the early dryopithecine apes and to some indisputably hominid forms which existed after 4,000,000 BP; it could have been an ancestor, and if not an ancestor it could have been an ancestor's cousin. It had comparatively large cheek teeth, of a shape and composition indicative of hard grinding, and somewhat reduced canines. Associated remains of flora and fauna indicate in some cases a

forest environment and in others a borderland combining forest
and open country.

At one time some fanciful speculations were inspired by its
relatively small canines: that in order to survive without the
usual primate apparatus of powerful canines *Ramapithecus* must
have had other means of defending itself and procuring its food,
that therefore it must have used weapons and tools of some kind,
presumably clubs and stones, that therefore it must have been
proficient at standing and walking on two legs and must have
been intelligent. More recently, however, the speculation has
become more disciplined, taking due account of the fact that
*Ramapithecus* appears to have been superseded considerably
more than 5,000,000 years before the earliest manufactured
stone tools known in the archeological record. A rather appealing hypothesis is that of seed-eating, proposed in 1970 by
Clifford Jolly: that the tooth pattern of *Ramapithecus* – enlarged
and strengthened cheek teeth, together with reduced canines
permitting the lower jaw to move freely from side to side in an
efficient grinding motion – indicates successful entrance into an
ecological niche new for primates, a niche where *Ramapithecus*
(along with many birds and some rodents) exploited a concentrated, high-energy food in the form of seeds, in other words
grain. Even Jolly's model has been challenged by other experts,
who argue that the available evidence is insufficient; they point
out, for example, that baboons with very large canines can chew
with a rotary grinding motion of the lower jaw. Nevertheless it is
still tempting to speculate that the cereal-eating habits of the
hominid lineage down to our own time may have started with
*Ramapithecus*. And there are several enticing secondary aspects
of the theory, for example that dependence on the picking and
eating of seeds would have given selective value to quick precise fingers and an agile tongue, attributes for which nobler
uses have been found in human evolution.

If it should be correct that *Ramapithecus* opened up a new
ecological niche by feeding on seeds, that innovation would fit in
nicely with the known fact that hominids of a later time lived in
savanna environments – tropical or subtropical grasslands with
scattered trees and patches of woodland. (Chapters 5 and 6 will
review the challenges and opportunities of savanna life and the

great stimulus which they provided for human evolution, including the evolution of love.) At the same time, *Ramapithecus* would surely not have been confined to a diet of seeds but would have eaten also, at least seasonally, other coarse plant foods requiring heavy mastication, plus insects and, on an opportunistic scale, the meat of small vertebrates.

One of the characteristics usually identified with hominid status is that of upright posture and gait. This was certainly of enormous value to our early ancestors because it permitted development of the hands for functions much more useful than walking and running, not only for making and using tools and weapons but also for carrying things. (Upright posture has also had some disadvantages which still afflict us, such as an increased burden on the heart and circulatory system for pumping blood to the brain vertically instead of horizontally, and new stresses and strains on the vertebral column.) Yet up to now there is no real evidence that *Ramapithecus* was bipedal. It is quite possible that, like the grass-eating gelada baboons of today, it originally sat upright on a padded behind while feeding, and hunched itself forward in the same position. It may even have passed several million years of unhurried evolution in that style, perhaps standing up and walking bipedally with increasing frequency.

In any case the unquestionably hominid forms which followed, after a gap of several million years in the fossil record, were completely erect and bipedal. These were members of the genus given the ill-chosen name of *Australopithecus*, a combination of Latin and Greek for 'southern ape'; they will be reported in a later section.

It should be mentioned that in recent years scholarly attention has been drawn to work in advanced molecular biology which places at around 5,000,000 BP the date when the evolutionary line leading to humans branched off from the lines leading to modern apes. The objective of that work is to establish something like a 'molecular clock' by measuring in various ways, including that of immunological reactions, the genetic distance between molecules of protein which have evolved in the blood of humans and those which have evolved in the blood of apes; then calculations are made of the lapse of time required for such degrees of genetic change, and a very early base date in the fossil record is taken as a starting point. That intriguing work, however, has been and still is controversial; an opposing viewpoint is that 'one cannot even give good confidence limits to the presumed clock's accuracy.' Meanwhile there has been a daring suggestion that both hominids *and* chimpanzees and gorillas might be descended from *Ramapithecus* or a closely related form, which would make a 5,000,000 BP separation date perfectly possible. For final answers more time and study will be necessary, as well as more fossils.

## The nature of the evidence

Here it may be useful to pause and consider the bases for the judgements proposed in this chapter. The period of particular interest is from about 5,000,000 BP to about 500,000 BP – the Pliocene Epoch of geological time and the beginning and middle of the Pleistocene Epoch. (Pliocene and Pleistocene are Hellenic ways of saying 'more recent' and 'most recent.') There is now, after several changes of scholarly fashion, a rather general consensus among scientists that it is best to draw the dividing line between the two epochs at about 1,800,000 BP, while the Middle Pleistocene is now defined as starting about 700,000 BP; the end of the Pleistocene and the beginning of the Holocene Epoch – 'completely recent' – are still placed at about 10,000 BP. This is the scheme adopted here.

For the Plio-Pleistocene period, up to about 500,000 BP, most of our important and reliably dated information about early hominids comes from eastern Africa. In that part of the world it was a period of volcanic turbulence, in which the earth's crust was fractured in lines running from the Zambesi River northwards to Lebanon, leaving rift valleys, bodies of water, and mountain ranges which can still be seen. The volcanic activity created, incidentally, conditions unusually favorable for the fossilization of bones and for the dating of them today.

There are three regions in eastern Africa where major programs of modern paleoanthropological exploration have been carried out. The one first developed was Olduvai Gorge in Tanzania, southeast of Lake Victoria, that great treasury made famous by the discoveries of the late Louis S. B. Leakey and of his wife Mary D. Leakey, from the 1930s to the 1970s, with the collaboration of other scientists and many helpers. The Gorge, which is now dry and roughly 60 meters deep, was formed in the last part of the Pleistocene Epoch by earth movements and by the action of streams cutting down through earlier and earlier layers of Pleistocene savannas. In the clearly stratified walls of the Gorge, remains have been found of protohuman or human presence and activities dating from about 1,850,000 BP to about 30,000 BP.

Starting in 1967 and 1968, important new programs of exploration were undertaken in two other areas of eastern Africa, one in the remote valleys of the Omo and Awash rivers of Ethiopia, and the other in what is now a windswept wasteland in Kenya known as Koobi Fora, lying just to the east of Lake Turkana (formerly Lake Rudolf). In these areas, also admirably stratified, in which large organized teams of paleoanthropologists, geologists, chemists, zoologists, botanists, and others have been working, there are traces of protohumans and humans since before 3,000,000 BP in one case and since about 2,000,000 BP in the other.

All of these eastern African regions afford good possibilities for assigning absolute dates for hominid fossils and artifacts, so it is no longer necessary, as it has been in many other parts of the world, to depend mainly on uncertain faunal and climatic correlations for estimating dates. There are now half a dozen elaborate techniques, using very advanced laboratory equipment, by which absolute dates can in some situations be established for Plio-Pleistocene horizons. Nearly all of these dating techniques have been or are being applied in eastern Africa, but the two which have been most extensively used there are those of potassium–argon radiometry and of paleomagnetism.

In the first technique, use is made of the fact that certain volcanic substances contain small amounts of the unstable potassium isotope potassium[40] which through continuous radioactive decay is transformed into the gaseous isotope argon[40] at rates known to require 1.3 billion years for reaching the halfway point. When the two isotopes are present today in a given sample, extremely precise measurement of the proportion between them permits dating of the sample within a reasonable margin of error, up to dates of about 300,000 BP and perhaps later. Leakage or contamination can occur but there are procedures which can often provide detection and correction. And all of the eastern African regions mentioned contain at different levels of their strata certain distinctive and recognizable marker horizons – usually tuffs, which are compacted layers of fine volcanic ash – which recur discontinuously in a given locality. By applying the potassium–argon technique to samples taken from those marker horizons, it is often possible to establish maximum and minimum ages for fossils found buried at intervening levels and sometimes for surface finds. Usually several different samples from each marker horizon are analyzed, to minimize the chances of error. Several other radiometric techniques can also be used in some cases for dating early hominid remains, though not the well known carbon[14] technique, which is of no use for dates earlier than 100,000 BP.

Each of the radiometric techniques has its own limitations and disadvantages, so that things are often not simple and clear. Despite all precautions and corrections, errors and misinterpretations are possible. Differences of opinion sometimes arise among experts. To resolve such differences it is desirable to have recourse to one or more additional techniques, and paleomagnetism has been especially helpful for this purpose. It makes use of the strange fact that the polarity of the earth's magnetism, north and south, happens to reverse itself repeatedly in the course of geological times, say five or ten times in a million years. Since about 5,000,000 BP the earth's magnetic polarity has alternated between the present 'normal' direction and the opposite 'reversed' direction at intervals ranging from 50,000 years to 600,000 years; it is thought that each transition may have lasted several thousand years and may have consisted of a gradual diminution of magnetic intensity and a gradual building up in the opposite direction. There is at present no definite evidence of direct or indirect effects on climate or on living organisms, though it is supposed that changes in the intensity of the earth's magnetic field may entail fluctuations in cosmic radiation reaching the earth's surface, which in turn could affect mutation rates. The record of these curious and irregular alternations is found in rocks and sediments which were originally laid down at high temperatures at different times in the past; they were polarized magnetically in the directions then prevailing throughout the world, and after cooling have retained permanent traces of their original polarity. These traces can often be identified through laboratory treatment and analysis. And when today geologists are called upon to confirm or correct the date of a particular horizon at a particular locality, they slice or chisel out in that locality a series of oriented samples representing segments of a vertical column dozens or hundreds of meters tall, in which various marker horizons and other horizons are clearly observable and labeled; then in laboratory analyses they search out the succession of normal and reversed polarities recorded in the samples. Finally, by matching up the locality's vertical column with a standard geomagnetic polarity time-scale which has been reliably established for the world as a whole, they try to determine beginning and ending dates for each paleomagnetic segment of the locality's column.

Here again results are often not straightforward, for the paleomagnetic record in a particular locality can be confused or distorted by subsequent disturbances of the stratification, and also by a variety of geochemical events. Yet paleomagnetism can often provide a valuable check on the potassium–argon or other dates which are obtained independently for various marker horizons. Finally, in particularly difficult cases recourse can be had to faunal correlations.

## *The principal australopithecine fossils*

To return to the fossil hominids, a great many specimens of the australopithecines have been found in southern and eastern Africa. The reliably identified fossils consist of a dozen or two partial or nearly complete skulls, several dozen jaw fragments large enough to be informative, scores of other bones, and hundreds of teeth, and even one partially complete skeleton, all dated from before 3,000,000 BP to around 1,000,000 BP. (There is also one partial lower jaw from Lothagam in Kenya, reliably dated at around 5,000,000 BP, which may perhaps belong to an early *Australopithecus*.)

The australopithecines have occasioned in their turn some confusion as well as enlightenment in the study of human origins; at one time they were fancifully characterized as killer-apes ancestral to humans. Some of the confusion has arisen from the fact that the fossil record includes at least two widely different types of australopithecines, one large and robust (which some authorities subdivide into two species), and the other much smaller – 'gracile' or slight. Although the robust and gracile types are enough alike so that certain specialists could see them as male and female members of a single dimorphic species (i.e. occurring in sexually differentiated forms), somewhat on the pattern of the modern gorilla where the adult male is nearly twice as big as the female, yet the differences are generally regarded as fundamental enough to require assignment to different species. One of the differences considered significant is that the robust species had large and heavily worn cheek teeth but proportionately very small front teeth, a condition which has been widely interpreted as indicating the crushing and grinding of tough plant foods (though other explanations are also possible), while in the gracile species the canines and incisors were proportionately larger than in the robust species, even absolutely larger, a pattern which has been attributed to a diet including a fair proportion of meat; at any rate the robust and the gracile types appear to have had somewhat different eating habits.

Broadly speaking, the robust australopithecines were large hominids for that time, perhaps standing $4\frac{1}{2}$ to $5\frac{1}{2}$ feet tall and weighing 100 to 200 pounds, with a cranial capacity averaging 500 cubic centimeters or a little more, as compared with about 350 or 400 cc in modern chimpanzees. They were prognathous – their heavy mouths protuding forward – but less so than the apes. Some of them, presumably males, had a sharp sagittal crest of upright bone running back over the top of their lowbrowed skull as gorillas have, an anchor for powerful muscles operating the lower jaw. Fossilized specimens spanning nearly a million years reveal little or no evolutionary change. They may have made stone tools, but there is nothing to indicate

ENDICOTT COLLEGE
Beverly, Mass. 01915

that they hunted large animals. It seems clear from the fossil record that these ill-favored hominids died out sometime around 1,000,000 BP, leaving no descendants.

The gracile type on the other hand, comprising many specimens assigned to the species *Australopithecus africanus*, was only 3½ to 4½ feet tall, perhaps weighing only 45 to 70 pounds, and had a head which was more rounded and only slightly smaller, with various cranial capacities averaging something like 450 cc; it was also rather prognathous but had no sagittal crest. Certain well-known authorities have advanced the opinion that this australopithecine type became extinct also, and that the human line of descent is a separate one, but most others hold to the hypothesis, which is compatible with the published evidence available in 1979, that a gracile *Australopithecus* was the progenitor of the earliest forms assigned to the genus *Homo*. According to this hypothesis, while gracile australopithecines have not been found after about 1,000,000 BP, the reason is that they were simply replaced little by little by their own descendants; there are in fact good indications of progressive changes in the human direction, as noted below. All authorities could agree that the specimens assigned to gracile forms of *Australopithecus* belong either in the line of descent to modern humans or very close to it.

Five sites in South Africa have yielded excellent fossils of *Australopithecus*, of both gracile and robust types (at different localities, be it noted), but the determination of absolute dates for them by chronometric techniques has not been possible and is not expected to be possible in the future.

At Olduvai Gorge a representative skull of the robust type, found and reconstructed by Dr Mary Leakey, has been reliably dated at about 1,700,000 BP, and numerous fragmentary remains of the robust species and perhaps the gracile species have also been found at Olduvai.

In the Omo valley in southern Ethiopia, just to the north of Kenya's Lake Turkana, conditions are ideal for chronometric dating, but the river-delta conditions have not favored the preservation of hominid bones. The australopithecine specimens found consist mainly of a jaw fragment from a robust species, dated at about 2,400,000 BP, and many teeth of both robust and gracile species, dated between about 3,000,000 and after 2,000,000 BP.

In the Awash valley of eastern Ethiopia, in the Afar triangle, a great deal of valuable material is now being unearthed, but only a portion of it has so far been reported in detail. The most interesting find reported fully consists of a large portion of a single gracile skeleton, at first regarded as a specimen of *Australopithecus africanus*, but recently assigned by certain of its discoverers to a proposed ancestral species to which they give the name *Australopithecus afarensis*. This latter proposal has found acceptance with several eminent authorities, though the differences between the two species are only slight. The *afarensis* skeleton is that of a young adult female, who has been christened Lucy for sex appeal. Although she is given an inferred date of close to 3,000,000 BP, her pelvis shows that she had a fully erect posture; she probably walked as well as we do. Some fragments of the robust species have also reported from the Afar triangle.

In the Koobi Fora region of Kenya, expeditions led jointly by Richard Leakey and Glynn Isaac have found one admirably preserved skull of a robust *Australopithecus* and numerous skull fragments and other bones of additional australopithecines, as well as very important *Homo* material.

What emerges from this, and from additional information not summarized, is that from before 3,000,000 BP (before 5,000,000 BP if the Lothagam jaw is included) to about 1,000,000 BP, australopithecine forms existed in widely-separated parts of eastern and southern Africa. There is no persuasive evidence that they existed anywhere else; one or two authorities have suggested possibilities of their presence in Java and China at relatively late dates, along with much more advanced forms, but the evidence is disputed convincingly. There is another fact which seems to emerge also, though much less definitely: both in South Africa (where faunal correlations do at least permit saying that one site is older than another) and also in Ethiopia, gracile australopithecines appear in the fossil record earlier than the robust species. If future evidence bears out this difference in antiquity, it may mean that the gracile type was ancestral to the robust type.

## *The genus* Homo

Starting from the hypothesis that some gracile *Australopithecus* was ancestral in any case to modern humans, the story becomes more interesting as one proceeds to the stage of early forms of the genus *Homo*. The most important of these is the widely known species *Homo erectus*, but most authorities now recognize a transitional earlier species named *Homo habilis* (for 'handy,' because of an imputed tool-making skill). In the past few years new light and new shadows have been cast on these matters by some surprising new fossil discoveries. They will be noted below, following discussion of *Homo erectus* and *Homo habilis*. Both of the latter will be referred to in this book as 'protohuman,' the term 'human' being reserved for our own species, *Homo sapiens*.

Nearly all paleoanthropologists are now in agreement that members of the species *Homo erectus* were our ancestors. They were intermediate in form between the gracile australo-pithecines and modern humans, and a little closer to modern humans. They were of moderate stature, possibly averaging 5 to $5\frac{1}{2}$ feet and weighing some 120 pounds. Having a large cranial capacity – ranging from 750 to 1250 cc, entering the range of modern humans, and averaging about 1000 cc – they were decidedly intelligent beings. Yet they carried also a number of early features; notably, their jaws were heavy and somewhat prognathous, their skulls were thick and characterized by massive brow ridges and low receding foreheads.

Fossilized specimens of *Homo erectus* are fairly abundant. In Africa, half a dozen reasonably complete crania and several identifiable fragments, plus other bones and many teeth, have been found at Olduvai Gorge, at Koobi Fora, in the Omo valley, at Lake Ndutu not far from Olduvai, and perhaps at a South African site (Swartkrans). The earliest definite *Homo erectus* skulls now known, 1975 and 1976 discoveries at Koobi Fora, have undisputed chronometric dates of between 1,600,000 and 1,300,000 BP. (At the same locality and within the same reliable time range, an *Australopithecus* of classic robust type has also been found, the two together forming a laughable contrast, final proof that the two species were contemporaries in a single region and that the robust *Australopithecus* could not have been simply the male of an ancestral form, as some had thought.)

In addition, *Homo erectus* fossils have been found in eastern Asia, in Europe, and in North Africa. A series of good skulls have been found in Java, the first one having been discovered in 1890 and named *Pithecanthropus erectus*. Many more have been found at Choukoutien in northern China not far from Peking, which were long known as *Sinanthropus* or as Peking Man. Most authorities assign to *Homo erectus* certain jaws or cranial and jaw fragments found at Mauer near Heidelberg in Germany, at Ternifine in Algeria, and at Vértesszöllös in Hungary; some others consider these specimens too modern for *Homo erectus* and assign them to *Homo sapiens*. Despite a dearth of chronometric evidence, nearly all of the fossils assigned to *Homo erectus* in Asia, Europe, and North Africa are generally considered to be datable after about 700,000 BP, most of them between 500,000 and 300,000 BP. It is probably significant that intensive explorations in all of those regions have not brought to light any *Homo erectus* fossils with reliable earlier dates. The provisional implication is that the species arose and developed first in eastern Africa. A chronometric date of around 1,900,000 BP has been asserted for certain Javan skulls, but the evidence is not satisfying; in the opinion of F. Clark Howell of Berkeley, 'the precise temporal relationships and ages of these important hominid specimens are still largely unknown.'

Most authorities now recognize *Homo habilis* as a species intermediate between the gracile australopithecines and *Homo erectus*. The type specimen of *Homo habilis* is a reconstructed cranium from Olduvai Gorge with a potassium–argon date of about 1,700,000 BP. The most important of several morphological differences between *Australopithecus africanus* and the postulated *Homo habilis* is that of estimated cranial capacity – often dependent on a good deal of reconstruction. The following figures give a rough idea of what is involved:

|  | *Ordinary range of cranial capacities (cc)* |
|---|---|
| Modern chimpanzees | 350–400 |
| *Australopithecus africanus* | 430–480 |
| *Homo habilis* | 600–800 |
| *Homo erectus* | 750–1250 |
| Modern humans | 1000–2000 |

Among those workers who recognize *Homo habilis* as a species, there are differences in the assignment of particular specimens. In particular, of all the plausible *Homo habilis* specimens – 35 in total, nearly all from eastern Africa and dated between a little before 2,000,000 BP and about 1,000,000 BP – there are two or three early ones which certain workers prefer to regard as gracile australopithecines, and at the other end of the series there are two or three which other workers prefer to assign to *Homo erectus*. In other words both of the demarcation lines are hazy. What can be seen rather clearly is that starting a little before 2,000,000 BP, and continuing for half a million years or so, a very rapid evolutionary progression was taking place in certain populations in Africa, proceeding from a small-brained but upright bipedal form such as *Australopithecus africanus* or *Australopithecus afarensis* at the beginning of the period and leading to *Homo erectus* forms at the end. There appear to be persuasive reasons for assigning some of the intermediate forms to a pre-*erectus* species of *Homo*, *Homo habilis*.

During the same period some cultural events of great importance were taking place, namely the inauguration and development of what can for the first time be called a stone-working industry, in the sense of stone tools made in recognizable patterns. At Olduvai Gorge a simple industry known as the Oldowan has been found at sites with a potassium–argon date of around 1,800,000 BP. It is characterized mainly by rude choppers and other core tools (sometimes called pebble tools), commonly made of cobblestones about 6–12 cm long, rolled and smoothed by water action, on each of which at one end a few thick flakes have been knocked off on two sides to form a rugged chopping edge, while the other end is left untouched as a rounded butt which fits comfortably in the palm of the hand. Many of the flakes struck off are sharp enough to have served as cutting tools, or as instruments for fashioning simple tools and weapons of wood or bone. Starting a few hundred thousand years later, the Olduvai horizons yield a slightly more elaborated industry, the Developed Oldowan, which persists there until about 500,000 BP and even later elsewhere. This consists of a continuation of the early choppers, supplemented by the addition of a few new elements and an increase in others that were rare in the

Oldowan. Notably, these are protobifaces, or cobblestones worked on their two sides somewhat more extensively than the early choppers were, and various small tools developed from the struck-off flakes, plus spheroids and sub-spheroids. Paleoanthropologists who support the *Homo habilis* thesis attribute to that species both the Oldowan industry and the launching of the Developed Oldowan, connecting those cultural advances with the increased brain size estimated for the *Homo habilis* specimens. (Certain other paleoanthropologists attribute the early Oldowan tools to one or more australopithecines.)

Stone tools more or less closely related to the Oldowan have been found in South Africa, elsewhere in Africa, and beyond, with differences due partly to the use of different stone. In particular, very similar choppers, somewhat smaller on average, and many sharp flakes, have been found at Koobi Fora amid concentrations of clutter made by protohumans, embedded in a tuff of volcanic ash now dated chronometrically at around 1,800,000 BP (The KBS Tuff mentioned on page 72. In the Omo valley, in a horizon with a potassium–argon and paleomagnetic date of almost exactly 2,000,000 BP, significant numbers of implements of a different type have been found; these consist predominantly of very small angular fragments or flakes, all of quartz, definite evidence of a tool-making industry.

Starting in eastern Africa at about the same time as the Developed Oldowan or a little later, say between 1,400,000 and 1,300,000 BP, there appears rather suddenly an early form of the great Acheulean industry, generally believed to have been developed by *Homo erectus*. The Early Acheulean of eastern Africa is characterized by the first true bifaces, including rough hand-axes and cleavers. It seems to have evolved slowly into the classic Acheulean industry which flourished in Africa and western Europe after about 700,000 BP, reaching its most finished form between 400,000 and 100,000 BP. The classic Acheulean, first recognized in 1854 at the site of St. Acheul in northern France, is distinguished especially by fine symmetrical hand-axes, that is, large bifacial tools completely worked over on their two surfaces, in a form gently rounded at one end and converging towards a point at the other end. These tools testify that our *Homo erectus* ancestors possessed not only enough technical skill to skim off small shallow flakes with great precision from both surfaces of a prepared core but also, frequently, and increasingly with the passage of time, an astonishing insistence that the tool be graceful as well as efficient. Bravo *Homo erectus*!

At least a few tools of a hand-axe type can be found at nearly all sites, but a characteristic Acheulean complex of hand-axes and other tools has not been found in Java or China, or for that matter in central and eastern Europe. The stone tools found at the sites explored in those areas are in general more akin to the Oldowan types. This can be interpreted in different ways, and it may be largely a reflection of the purposes for which the tools were used in different times and places. It is possible also that *Homo erectus* groups, having originated in eastern Africa, moved slowly northwards and eastwards before the Early Acheulean industry had become well established throughout the original area.

I return now to the surprising new fossil discoveries of the past few years, which again were made in eastern Africa. The first was the early but in some respects modern-looking skull found at Koobi Fora in 1972 by a team directed by Richard Leakey. This skull, reconstructed from fragments, was found to have a surprisingly large cranial capacity, about 800 cc, later revised to 775 cc and finally to 770 cc. It also exhibits several other modern features, including principally the absence of the massive brow ridges typical of *Homo erectus*. It was therefore attributed to the genus *Homo*, but the species designation was wisely left open; the skull is well known by its Kenya National Museum catalogue number, KNM–ER 1470.

Several years of expert study and debate were required for dating the 1470 skull. For several technical reasons the task was exceptionally difficult. The skull was found partially exposed on the surface at a level about 35 meters lower than a volcanic tuff which has become widely known as the KBS Tuff, which stands for Kay Behrensmeyer Site, in homage to the young geologist who discovered the tuff and first recognized its importance. The KBS Tuff was originally given a radiometric date of 2,610,000 BP plus or minus 260,000 years, and that was soon provisionally confirmed by paleomagnetic studies; but such an astonishing antiquity for the 1470 skull was challenged on grounds of faunal correlations. Subsequently, several further radiometric studies were made, using different advanced techniques, and the paleomagnetic evidence and the faunal evidence were examined anew. The final result of all this work and debate is that the date of the KBS Tuff has now been placed at close to 1,900,000 BP. On this basis the 1470 skull is dated at 1,900,000 or 2,000,000 BP.

Meanwhile the continuing rush of new material from Koobi Fora has included several similar specimens, notably a fragmented immature skull with a cranial capacity as great as the 1470 skull or greater, and a partial cranium which is smaller but very similar in form, both of them also from below the KBS Tuff. There is now a tendency among specialists to regard all these specimens, and numerous others of somewhat later dates from Koobi Fora, as members of the *Homo habilis* species, within the range of individual variation of that species.

Probably the most remarkable of all the newly reported discoveries are those made between 1974 and 1977 by Mary Leakey and half a dozen assisting scientists and many helpers, in the Laetolil Beds in Tanzania, a little to the south of Olduvai Gorge. No artifacts were found – and if there had been any they could hardly have escaped the searching eyes of Dr. Leakey and her associates – but in 1974 and 1975 some remains of about a dozen hominids of a single type were found, consisting of jaws, jaw fragments, and isolated teeth, all from a bed bracketed between a pair of marker tuffs with potassium–argon dates of 3,590,000 and 3,770,000 BP. The best preserved of those specimens are two lower jaws, one adult and one juvenile, both of them with most of the teeth still in place. In general conformation and proportions, these show resemblances to jaws of much later date assigned to the genus *Homo*, but they also have several primitive features consistent with their extreme antiquity. The discoverers, at the conclusion of their technical report on the details, suggested that the specimens should be placed among the earliest firmly dated specimens of the genus *Homo*. Some other experts prefer to regard them as belonging rather to a gracile australopithecine. The final judgement of the scientific community will depend on further close study and debate.

In 1976 and 1977 Dr. Leakey and her associates made a still more exciting discovery in the Laetolil Beds, again with a potassium–argon date of between 3,600,000 and 3,800,000 BP: hardened footprints of hominids and many other animals. These footprints were apparently preserved by an extraordinary combination of events – a fall of fine volcanic ash on a flat plain at the beginning of a rainy season, followed soon by showers of rain forming a kind of muddy plaster which the animals traversed, a rapid hardening of the plaster by the interaction of moisture and sodium carbonate and calcium carbonate, followed by sunlight, a prompt deposition of a protective covering of new volcanic ash and windblown dust, and finally, ever afterwards, a slow accumulation and partial erosion of overlying strata. The footprints record the tracks of more than 20 species of animals, from hares to hyenas to elephants. The hominid tracks as reported when this book went to press had been traced over a distance of some 20 meters, and further reports are awaited.

Two conclusions of great interest emerge already, concerning the stage of evolution reached by 3,600,000 BP or earlier: first that some small Pliocene hominids had feet of distinctly human form, and second (from the spacing of the footprints) that those hominids had achieved 'a fully upright, bipedal and free-striding gait.' This confirms emphatically the testimony of the Lucy skeleton of the Afar triangle. So the hands of these very early hominids were already available for carrying things and for beginning to manipulate things as humans do, although there is still no trace of tools or weapons, or even of stones which might have been put to use. But cultural evolution in that direction in a line of surviving descendants was perfectly possible, and wooden clubs could have been in use already. In any case, these prehistory-making discoveries confirm at last that use of the hands helped to bring about the evolution of a big brain, rather than the other way around.

It is by now clear, from all the pieces of evidence reported in this section, that forms assignable to the genus *Homo* have existed far longer than was supposed in the 1960s – certainly at least 1,900,000 years, possibly 3,600,000 years, and most probably something in between. Judgements are handicapped by the lack of a universally accepted definition of the genus *Homo*.

Conservatively, it is safe to say that hominids of the *Homo* grade or approaching it – either *Homo* or a gracile *Australopithecus* – must have existed in different regions of eastern Africa before 3,000,000 BP. For the purposes of this book, the date of 3,000,000 BP has been arbitrarily taken as the beginning of the distinctively protohuman and human stage of our evolution.

At the same time the weight of evidence has continued to pile up in favor of the hypothesis that the immediately preceding evolution had taken place on the savannas of eastern Africa. There is still a possibility that the first members of the genus *Homo* arose somewhere else and wandered into Africa at a very early date (and it could hardly be proved that this did *not* happen), but the evidence now points with increasing persuasiveness to Africa, particularly eastern Africa, as the cradle of the genus *Homo*. Thus we have the fact that the apes in the closest line of descent, both chimpanzees and gorillas, are found only in Africa (which was almost enough for Darwin's intuitive genius a century ago, though since then specimens of *Ramapithecus* as possible ancestors of *Homo* have been found in greater number in Eurasia than in Africa); the lack of persuasive evidence that any of the australopithecines ever existed outside Africa; the fact that hominid jaws with resemblances to specimens assigned to the genus *Homo*, and footprints of fully upright hominids, have been found in eastern Africa with reliable dates of around 3,600,000 BP or earlier; the fact that the earliest undoubted stone tools now known were found in eastern Africa; the fact that a *Homo erectus* skull has been found in eastern Africa with a reliable date of between 1,600,000 and 1,300,000 BP; the fact that the earliest known Acheulean tools have been found in eastern Africa with a date of between 1,400,000 and 1,300,000 BP; and the absence of any convincing evidence of the presence of *Homo* outside Africa at such early dates. It is not surprising that the great majority of the authorities now favor the African hypothesis.

On that basis, then, and reverting to *Homo erectus*, it seems most likely that small groups who belonged to that resourceful intelligent species ventured abroad and made their slow wanderings northwards and eastwards, some of the early groups reaching Java and China and others reaching central and eastern Europe. Such movements probably took place on numerous occasions over a long stretch of time, starting sometime between 1,500,000 and 700,000 BP but continuing until much later, and from different points of origin. Although the fossils from eastern Asia and from central and eastern Europe which have been assigned to *Homo erectus* are not associated with artifacts representing an Acheulean industry, there are many archeological sites in Atlantic Europe and the Mediterranean basin containing rich Acheulean assemblages, and it is very probable that most if not all of them are the handiwork of *Homo erectus*. Thus it appears that members of that species could spread far and could thrive and survive catastrophes in widely varying environments.

One can get later glimpses of the genus *Homo* during the Middle Pleistocene in Europe and the Mediterranean basin. Although radiometric dates there are unfortunately rare, the jaws or skull fragments mentioned above as found near Heidelberg in Germany, Vértesszöllös in Hungary, and Ternifine in Algeria can safely be placed somewhere within the period 500,000 to 300,000 BP. Assigned by many workers to *Homo erectus* and by others to early subspecies of our own species *Homo sapiens*, these specimens are followed, within the period 300,000 to 100,000 BP, by several skulls or skull bones bearing marked resemblances to the *Homo erectus* pattern but widely recognized as belonging to the species *Homo sapiens*. The latter specimens include primarily the familiar Steinheim and Swanscombe skulls of Germany and England but several others as well, notably a few from Tautavel and Montmaurin in southern France. Considering all the available evidence, it is a reasonable conclusion that *Homo erectus* evolved, in the course of several hundred thousand years, into *Homo sapiens*.

In the period shortly after 100,000 BP, the principal western fossils are now usually assigned to the subspecies *Homo sapiens neanderthalensis*. These should not, however, be simply identified with the type of Neanderthal Man popularized a couple of generations ago. This latter form is known as the 'classic Neanderthal' type, classic in the subjective sense of having been the first one known and the most familiar in the past. By accidents of discovery, many well-preserved fossils of that type had been found in Europe, one of the first ones in 1856 in the Neander Valley in northwest Germany, and the type had been depicted in many imaginative reproductions with a brutish and generally alarming aspect – a robust frame, extremely heavy brow ridges, a low receding forehead, a prognathous profile, and often (incorrectly) a menacing bent-forward posture. But it is well to remember that the brain-case was also very large, actually a little larger on average than ours. In addition, the classic Neanderthalers practiced an elaborate stone tool industry, the Mousterian (named from rock shelters at le Moustier in south–central France), comprising a variety of specialized small knives and scrapers; they were resourceful enough to survive more than half of the stages of the last great glaciation; and they commonly buried their dead. Burly in appearance and heavily muscled, they were certainly not unintelligent.

Furthermore it is now usual to regard the subspecies *Homo sapiens neanderthalensis* as comprising a particularly wide range of morphological variation. Some students like to distinguish within it a 'progressive Neanderthal' type which is much less burly than the classic type, with brow ridges less heavy (in certain cases no heavier than in many modern humans), foreheads somewhat higher and more rounded, jaws lighter, and faces a little straighter. Neanderthaloid specimens showing several or all of these characteristics have been found in many parts of the world, especially the Middle East but including eastern Europe and western Asia, and also North Africa, eastern and southern Africa, and eastern Asia, with estimated dates between 70,000 and 40,000 BP. Selective pressures, not yet fully identified, may have been working more or less uniformly on many of these far-flung populations, and in addition occasional interbreeding may have taken place between some of them.

On the basis of the data now available, it seems reasonable to conclude that some of the varied Neanderthal forms became at some stage differentiated enough in the modern direction to warrant classification in a new subspecies, *Homo sapiens sapiens*, to which we and all the other modern human races belong. Thus it is probably through some of the less burly types of *Homo sapiens neanderthalensis* that we can trace our descent from *Homo erectus*, while the classic Neanderthalers – perhaps the importance attributed to them is simply a classic error in the early study of human origins – appear now to have been a unique specialized form which evolved in isolation on the western peninsula of Eurasia by around 70,000 BP and never traveled very far in place or time.

For, as many popular accounts tell it, the classic Neanderthalers of Europe disappeared around 35,000 BP – in a disappearing act that probably lasted several thousand years – with the appearance on the scene of the Cro-Magnon people. The latter were essentially a local race, of which numerous specimens have been found at Cro-Magnon in southwest France and elsewhere in Europe, of our own modern subspecies *Homo sapiens sapiens*. (Since the *neanderthalensis* subspecies no longer exists, it is not an imposture for us to call ourselves just *Homo sapiens*.)

Until more evidence becomes available, it is not clear exactly where or when the critical evolutionary steps leading to the *sapiens sapiens* grade of humans were taken. It is conceivable that in two or more different regions of the world some identical or similar steps were taken in parallel fashion, in response to similar selective pressures, but it is in principle unlikely that parallel evolution could account for all the space–time panorama of Neanderthal and *Homo sapiens sapiens* forms towards the end of the Pleistocene Epoch. It is a good guess that sometime after about 70,000 BP, in one or two of the regions where varied Neanderthaloid types existed, there were conditions so favorable to groups with *sapiens sapiens* characteristics that those groups prospered and multiplied – perhaps in temporary isolation – and developed further in the direction of the future subspecies *Homo sapiens sapiens*. It is also a good guess that sometime later, once the new subspecies was successfully established, it was able to spread very fast, carrying its lucky genes from continent to continent, into western Europe in the west, and in the east even crossing over at different times into America and into Australia, and also reaching the Pacific islands.

Drawing back a little, here, and disregarding unresolved questions about the precise assignment of particular specimens, one can see clearly the major stages of our fossil history. Between about 15,000,000 and 8,000,000 BP, primates existed with teeth and jaws showing hominid characteristics. After a long gap in the fossil record, there emerges at around 3,600,000 BP plain evidence of small-brained but fully erect hominids in eastern Africa. By about 2,000,000 BP their descendants had developed enlarged brains; they were making stone tools of distinct types, and in addition they were developing some exceptional sociocultural patterns which will be outlined in the next two chapters. Sometime around 1,500,000 BP, these descendants had in turn given rise to *Homo erectus*, a species of still larger-brained protohumans of eastern Africa, who in the course of a million years or more moved far and wide over the earth and succeeded in adapting themselves to extreme environmental changes. They then, sometime before 200,000 BP, gave rise to early forms of our own species, *Homo sapiens*. Some of these early *sapiens* forms were large-muscled and burly in appearance, but others, including our direct ancestors, came to have progressively lighter faces, lighter limb-bones, and lighter muscles, ending up as *Homo sapiens sapiens* by around 40,000 BP.

There are still some unanswered questions about the selective pressures responsible for this last trend: essentially, why did humans become less burly? A conceivable contributing factor will be suggested in a later chapter.

To return for a moment to the remains of the Cro-Magnon people in Europe, one feels a twinge of real pleasure on viewing their elegant bones – typically a very tall figure with a large and well-constructed head, forehead high and smooth, chin well formed. And still more pleasure in viewing their cultural achievements, consisting of skilfully made small tools of the Aurignacian industry (found first at Aurignac in the French Pyrenees) and the beginnings of the great school of colored drawings and engravings on hidden cave walls. The latter document several remarkable things: purposeful human thought, a sound knowledge of animal anatomy, and esthetic sensibility akin to ours.

After about 35,000 BP, human remains proliferate in many parts of the world, in sequences and relationships far too complex for the aims of this book. Persuasive evidence exists that some evolutionary changes continued to take place in physical characteristics of human beings. It is possible that a few such changes have helped to make possible the vertiginous cultural flights of the last few minutes of evolutionary time.

# 5

# *Life in the Plio–Pleistocene Part I*

Starting from the preceding chapter's sketch of the fossil evidence, it is now possible to peer a little more searchingly into the protohuman and human stage of our evolution, taken as the 3,000,000 years covering the late Pliocene Epoch and nearly all of the Pleistocene up to the time of *Homo sapiens sapiens.* In this period our ancestors increased the size of their brains three-fold, from an average of say 450 cc to an average of about 1400 cc, with a very wide range of variation at the close of the period. They also evolved the other physical and behavioral traits which are the distinguishing marks of modern humans, including especially the capacity for a great variety of cultures. In the end we were to emerge as creatures categorically different from the apes, indeed spectacularly different, while always keeping, in common with them and with other mammals, certain deep underlying layers of being.

The aim of this chapter and the next is to visualize the environments and conditions of life of our Plio–Pleistocene ancestors, which stimulated and guided their evolution, and at the same time to search out some of the basic evidence relating to the evolution of human capacities and needs for love. This will require not only prudent inferences but also many more or less reasoned speculations and some outright guesses – which, however, will not be passed off as anything better; it will not be science fiction, or for that matter *Just-so Stories.*

## *Physical environments*

In eastern Africa, where protohuman evolution is considered to have started, the hot interior of the earth was repeatedly bursting up through the crust. The present topography, including the Great Rift Valley, was being formed. When a volcano erupted, the molten lava heaved up would devastate the immediate vicinity and vast clouds of ash would settle over the surrounding landscape for distances up to several hundred kilometers.

There were moderate changes of climate. A gradual lowering of temperatures which had started a good deal earlier appears to have continued irregularly during most of the 3,000,000 years, while in humidity there were successive alternations of moderate rainfall and moderate desiccation. Africa was not covered by the vast glaciations which in the northern world repeatedly spread over large areas now temperate.

The present evidence concerning protohuman living conditions from about 3,000,000 to about 700,000 BP comes from regions of eastern Africa lying outside humid forest zones and outside deserts, that is, from environments collectively called savannas – varied grasslands and parklands ornamented here and there with scattered trees and with woodlands bordering watercourses, open landscapes supporting many species of grass-eating animals, which had several species of carnivores preying on them. There is good evidence that mammalian species living on open savannas in more or less continuous exposure to predation, and still more the predatory species themselves, are under special selective pressure to develop larger brains. Both pressures were working on our ancestors, who were at first prey and later predators.

Partly as a result of such pressures, and perhaps also as a result of environmental changes caused by volcanic activity, or of changes in cosmic radiation which could have given rise to mutations, the Plio–Pleistocene in eastern Africa was a period of rapid evolution for mammals generally, and above all for certain hominids. There was wide diversity of mammalian species in the early part of the period; by the end, this diversity had been considerably reduced, often at the expense of exceptionally large forms. One of the most curious of the early forms was *Deinotherium*, a preposterous elephant-like animal whose tusks curved downward and backward from the underside of the lower jaw. Early in the Pleistocene several genera developed gigantic varieties (such as a baboon as big as a male chimpanzee, and a pig the size of a hippopotamus, with tusks a meter long) which died out before the end of the period. Yet there were always many antelopes, other grass-eating animals, and members of most of the well-known families of mammals. The big predators included forms of hyena and leopard and the extinct saber-toothed tiger.

In some northern regions of the world, where *Homo erectus* started arriving by around 700,000 BP if not before, the environments were very different. The climatic changes were at times violent: in the course of the intermittent glaciations that started sometime after 1,7000,000 BP (there and in North America and Antarctica), the snow and ice accumulated in places to a thickness of several kilometers, immobilizing so much water that the levels of the world's oceans fell by 100 meters. In the mild interglacial phases those colossal masses slid, tumbled, crashed, and flowed back towards the oceans, cutting and eroding high ground and laying soil down on broad flood plains. Under such drastically changing conditions mammalian evolution was even more rapid. Mammoths came and went, and also bison, while protohumans and humans were among the few species that managed to adapt and survive at most latitudes – in their case with the aid of shelter, clothing, fire, and other urgent cultural adaptations.

## Hunting activities and adaptations

It has been said a thousand times, but must be said again here, that hunting was a major influence in the evolution of human behavior. It is not that it produced a species of aggressive carnivores or territorial killers; the truth, as usual, is much more complicated, and also more interesting.

No one knows today exactly why some very early hominids emerged from the forests, where they had been safe from most of the big predators, where the young especially could scramble up the trees and usually save themselves. Perhaps it was because of the gradual recession of the forests. Perhaps it was because in a period of desiccation some of the accustomed plant foods became scarce and it became necessary to search out supplementary food, including ultimately the meat of other animals.

As mentioned in Chapter 3, apes and Old World monkeys of several species, although essentially vegetarian, sometimes eat small animals with great gusto when they come upon them. On the other hand, all present-day human tribes of hunters, except some of those in the frozen north, obtain an important part of their nourishment from plant foods. In Africa today, both the hunting–foraging San people (formerly called Bushmen) roaming over desertic plains, and the savanna-dwelling Hadza, depend on plants for something like 80 percent of their food in weight; the nutritive importance of meat is due mainly to its high protein content.

Similarly, our Plio–Pleistocene ancestors are now believed to have been not carnivores but omnivores, owing their survival partly to meat but very largely to plant foods – various kinds of seeds, fruits, nuts, shoots, leaves, and edible roots and tubers. This is consistent with the evidence of their jaws and teeth, which have strong chewing and grinding equipment (quite apart from the large grinding cheek teeth of the extinct robust *Australopithecus*, perhaps almost a pure vegetarian), and canines much smaller than those of the great apes. (Speaking of teeth, the sweet tooth of many modern humans, especially children, suggests a possible adaptation of hominids who obtained part of their nourishment from ripe fruits and honey.)

It seems safe to suppose that their first animal prey, apart from insects and eggs, were very small creatures which they happened upon. Beyond that, we can only guess about the meat-procuring ways of our ancestors of 3,000,000 BP – gracile australopithecines or a very early species of *Homo* – because the archeological evidence from then until about 2,500,000 BP is extremely scarce. No stone implements reliably assignable to that period have so far been reported, and except for the series of very ancient fossils in the Laetolil Beds south of the Olduvai Gorge there is as yet no evidence of continuous or even successive occupancy of a particular locality. These are the real Dark Ages of our past. The very lack of evidence makes it seem unlikely that our ancestors of that time had any organized hunting practices.

But scavenging is regarded as a likely possibility for them, and it may have started well before 3,000,000 BP. Today the racing cheetah brings down its antelope, devours the choice parts, and then ambles off, leaving the remains for hyenas and other hunter–scavengers, ultimately for the vultures. Our ancestors of that time were much more intelligent and therefore more resourceful than hyenas, judging from several kinds of evidence including that of ratios of brain-size to body-size; they were sometimes no less hungry; and it is known that they were already securely bipedal at 3,600,000 BP, in other words able to wield clubs and throw rocks to drive off scavenging hyenas. It seems to be a good guess that they would have arrogated for themselves a place in the scavenging pattern – and that a scavenging–foraging way of life would have evolved sooner or later into hunting–gathering.

And there are archeological indications that true hunting of large game had occurred by roughly 2,000,000 BP. Part of the evidence is provided by two sites in the Koobi Fora region, both of them outcrops of the KBS Tuff, that marker horizon now given a date of close to 1,900,000 BP. According to Isaac's analysis the assemblages of artifacts found there (generally similar, as mentioned in Chapter 4, to the Oldowan industry) indicate that one of the sites was a camp or occupation-floor and the other a butchery site. At the former, rough tools and serviceable flakes and splinters are associated with significant quantities of broken-up animal bones – several species of antelope, two species of pig, a giraffe, and a porcupine. The evidence of an early stage of meat-eating and food-sharing is unmistakable. The butchery site consists of the broken-up remains of a single hippopotamus skeleton, surrounded by a patch of stone artifacts, but since only one animal is involved it could either have been brought down in the chase or found dead; what is clear is that the members of the genus *Homo* who made the associated stone artifacts were serious about eating meat.

Further evidence is provided by Olduvai Gorge. There, at sites with a clear potassium–argon date of 1,750,000 BP, large quantities of bones of large animals have been found – including antelopes, other bovids, species of pigs and horses, and the ungainly *Deinotherium* – in patterns which clearly demonstrate killing by hunters. The bones, some of them broken up as if to extract marrow, are concentrated in several areas with many Oldowan stone artifacts, suggesting occupation sites or living floors, plus in some instances fossil specimens attributed by many authorities to *Homo habilis*. Those assorted animal bones are part of what Isaac has memorably called 'the garbage record' and 'the trail of litter that leads back through the Pleistocene.'

Without, however, a Land Rover or even a gun, it was neither easy nor safe to hunt down and kill big animals and butcher them. It might have been too much for the gentle reader of this book, and it would certainly have made an end of the gentle author. To appreciate the difficulty of hunting activities, and the ways in which they helped to shape human evolution, it will be useful to try to visualize those activities from the garbage record and other evidence, and then to attempt an inventory of the physical and behavioral adaptations which they are likely to have called forth.

As to just what the hunting activities consisted of, there is no convincing evidence at present from the Pliocene or the start of the Pleistocene. In order to see the direction of evolution – culturally in hunting procedures and biologically in the related protohuman powers and tendencies – one should skip to about 1,300,00 BP and thereafter; by then a good deal of evidence is available concerning the techniques and procedures of hunting. Thus, in a bed at Olduvai Gorge dated somewhat before 1,000,000 BP, there is a deposit of clay which seems to represent an ancient backwater or swamp, and in it were found the partially articulated remains of a number of large hoofed animals, including huge extinct buffaloes of the genus *Pelorovis* with a horn spread of about two meters, and in the immediate vicinity abundant stone implements of the Early Acheulean industry, and broken-up animal bones. In the case of one of these beasts, lower parts of all four legs were found standing upright, but the trunk of the carcass had been removed: these and other details suggest strongly that a number of hunters working together had surrounded one or more large animals and driven them into the morass, where they were then killed and butch-

ered. Elsewhere at Olduvai, in a bed considerably older than
1,000,000 BP, the bones of a single extinct elephant were found,
embedded in clay with the feet at a lower level than the rest of
the skeleton. Protohuman hands had apparently hacked the
meat off the carcass, because quite a few Oldowan choppers
were found scattered among the bones. At another eastern
African locality (Olorgesailie) there is considerably later horizon, dated a little after 500,000 BP, which contained the
fragmented remains of over 50 baboons of a large extinct species –
more than 1000 identifiable teeth and bones plus 15 kilograms of
splinters – lying amid an abundance of Acheulean hand-axes
and other artifacts. This is a clear indication of effective hunting
by male teams executing organized drives or encircling movements. An oversized male baboon with great fangs would have
been extremely dangerous when cornered, as would the gigantic
*Pelorovis*, not to speak of the elephant.

These African finds have a remarkable sequel at a pair of sites
in Spain (Torralba and Ambrona) usually dated a little after
400,000 BP, where the remains of a great many elephants have
been found, plus rhinos and other large hoofed animals. Those
sites also contain at several horizons stratified remains of former
swampy surfaces on valley floors: it seems probable that the
animals were systematically waylaid, perhaps during seasonal
migrations, and driven into swampy ground where they foun-
dered and either died or were killed, and where they were then
butchered. The associated artifacts, again of the Acheulean
industry, are relatively few in number, indicating that the sites
were not habitations. (No hominid fossils have been found at
Torralba and Ambrona.)

It can therefore be said that by 500,000–300,000 BP protohuman hunters in Africa and in Spain, in all probability
belonging to the species *Homo erectus*, had developed organized
techniques for tracking, encircling, driving, killing, and butch-
ering big game, working in sizable teams. And these very
effective techniques must have evolved out of the simpler
procedures apparently employed in the Koobi Fora and
Olduvai regions some 800,000 years earlier, which themselves
had probably developed out of still earlier and simpler procedures, including scavenging. Before the Middle Pleistocene

(considered to have started around 700,000 B P) hunting techniques probably evolved rather slowly. The rates of development of stone-working techniques in the Lower Pleistocene show that at that time our ancestors were far from being rapid innovators; their tehnological progress may have been accomplished largely by virtue of occasional rather abrupt advances, separated by lengthy periods without much change. It seems likely that cultural evolution did not build up much speed until the Middle Pleistocene.

This book, however, is not concerned primarily with the successful hunting procedures themselves, which were developing through cultural evolution, but rather with the genetic adaptations facilitating them which successive generations of early hunters are likely to have been acquiring in the course of a couple of million years, under the pressure of natural selection. Incomplete as the archeological evidence still is, quite an assortment of inferences can be extracted from it. The pages now following will attempt an inventory of the most likely adaptations. Attention will be focused on the period of real hunting, say from about 2,000,000 B P onwards, because while an earlier scavenging stage would have exerted generally similar influences the pressures of real hunting would have been stronger and they are easier to visualize today.

In early protohuman populations, for convincing reasons which will soon be outlined, hunting must have been an occupation of the male sex. Consequently the inventory of adaptations which follows will have application particularly to the males. The inferred roles of females in the Plio–Pleistocene, and the principal genetic adaptations which could have been elicited by those roles, will be discussed in the next section of this chapter. Some traits must have evolved in both sexes more or less equally.

The early hunters must first of all have acquired new levels of intelligence, or, to be more specific, enhanced faculties of curiosity, observation, memory, visualization, association, reasoning, and spatial orientation. Such faculties would have enabled them to understand the habits and seasonal migration routes of the game animals, and to note and remember the topography of the hunting regions – where there were water-holes frequented by the game animals, where there were natural barriers, and where there were treacherous swamps. Successful hunters also had to acquire the ability to devise strategies for using their information, and more broadly they had to acquire a tendency to be stimulated rather than merely baffled by a psychological challenge. The hunting techniques of the big felines and other great predators are relatively simple and unchanging, in large part genetically programmed in the course of many millions of years of specialized adaptation. But the protohuman male sprang from an essentially vegetarian line and had to work out by trial and error how he could hunt, kill, and butcher successfully. He had the advantage of a higher primate's preadaptation in curiosity and opportunism, and of even greater plasticity of behavior. Meanwhile, he was himself laying down a preadaptation for today's science and technology.

In a word, the brains of the protohuman hunters had to increase greatly in size and involution. I quickly add that female roles in the Plio–Pleistocene required just as much intelligence and very possibly more, with certain qualitative differences which will later be considered.

Secondly, early hunters needed to have a number of gross physical attributes: muscular strength, a good normal running speed, a capacity for short very fast sprints and great exertion, and enough stamina and lung power to trot doggedly after a game animal for great distances – sometimes for several days, to judge from the ways of certain modern hunting tribes. At the same time the hunters had to have fine motor coordination, and they had to acquire manual skill and dexterity far surpassing that of the apes in order to fashion and use weapons and tools. It probably became useful to be able to throw with force and accuracy. Chimpanzees and some other primates are apt to throw objects when excited or angry, though only with rudimentary accuracy, and it is likely that some protohuman hunters used thrown weapons in hunting. A hypothesis has been suggested, without confirmation so far, that Pleistocene hunters sometimes threw sets of bolas – two or three rounded stones of about baseball or cricket-ball size joined to one another by thongs of leather – to wrap round and ensnare the legs of the prey. It is believed that handedness, right or left, which is a specifically human trait, may have evolved for these purposes among others, since it permits the highest development of manual skill through division of labor between the hands.

Incidentally, the habit of hunting by daylight on tropical and subtropical open plains (and female activities also) may have required a new system of body-temperature regulation – rapid evaporation of skin-surface moisture. It is generally thought that this may have been the primary adaptive value of our hairlessness (which is simply an arrested development of the body-hair follicles), and our greatly increased development of body-surface sweat glands. It is also thought that in tropical latitudes protohumans developed dark skin, through production of the pigment melanin, as a protection against excessive ultraviolet radiation from the sun. In northern regions at a later stage some quite different adaptations became necessary.

Successful hunting must also have required in the males some remarkable moral or psychological capacities, and these must have developed as the processes of biological evolution interacted with those of cultural evolution. I suggest that one of the first of such capacities would have been one for partially suspending fear – a modest capacity in most males and a great capacity in a few. As one of the basic compulsions of self-preservation, the emotion of fear is a primordial force which is almost universally present in mammalian species: most individual animals which lacked it did not live very long. Men are a special case. Apart from them, the exceptions are mainly forms which are themselves so redoubtable or so well protected that they have little or nothing to fear. Not many mammals other than humans have enough courage to fight to the death if they can save themselves by flight or surrender. In certain cases – for example, male lions fighting for a territory, or the females of some species defending their young – fear can be momentarily subordinated to another emotion, but a man's cold suppression of fear by act of will, and a man's reckless bravado, are traits of a different order.

These traits could have developed out of two early hominid patterns of behavior like those observed in some nonhuman higher primates today, mainly terrestrial species inhabiting open country. In one of the patterns adult males stand up to a dangerous predator long enough to allow the females and infants to escape, and in the other pattern young males of the same species engage in showy displays on the outer edge of a troop. Comparable behaviors may well have been practiced by hominid males on African savannas at a very early stage, and may have been vitally important in group defense against predation. If so, when the hunting stage was reached a base already existed for the development of cold courage in adult males and daring in young ones.

Plio–Pleistocene hunters probably felt no anger or hatred towards the animals they hunted; on the contrary there is evidence in the beautiful wall-engravings of the late Pleistocene in France and Spain that they felt some kind of personal involvement with those animals. Early hunters seeking confrontation with a huge *Pelorovis* buffalo or with a troop of oversized baboons were not driven by rage: some of them acted from cold calculation with foresight and deliberation, conscious of danger but managing to overrule their fear; others, especially young ones, may well have been daring to the point of recklessness. In both cases, if the males survived, their courageous genes would have been passed on to many sons; and even if they met death prematurely the same genes would often have been passed on through kin selection to close relatives.

It is tempting to guess that in the course of many thousands of generations and many periods of danger or hardship, with natural selection at work, the race of hunters gradually acquired not only the capacity for a partial suspension of fear but a real liking for the chase as a man's sport, and a lively pleasure in risk-taking for its own sake, especially when young. Since the idea is a new one it may be permissible to push it a bit further. A vestige of Pleistocene hunting seems obvious enough in the modern sportsman who drags himself out of bed before dawn and then scrambles in discomfort over the hills for hours, in the hope of bringing back an animal whose meat cannot today be eaten until it is partly rotted. But, in addition, one can speculate that a positive penchant for risk-taking gradually aquired by hunters during the Plio–Pleistocene still persists in the genes of a young man of today who defies death and society on a roaring motorcycle, or who hurls himself off the ramp of a ski-jump, or scales an unscalable mountain, or climbs into a rocket to be blasted into space, or one who simply drives too fast in his father's car. The insurance companies have statistical evidence that the road-accident risk is abnormally high in young males, and our society does not teach young males to drive recklessly; most parents try to induce their growing boys to be careful.

More broadly, it is conceivable that the ability to suspend fear is one of the factors which, as well as aggressiveness, have made organized warfare possible for men for some thousands of years. At the same time it has certainly made possible countless acts of gallantry and self-sacrifice, and the final reckoning is still to be made.

The mechanisms of the central nervous system for controlling fear are not well understood. Possibly they are of two different types, one a conscious mastery of fear by act of will and the other simply a switching off of the visualization of immediate dangers. The first faculty could serve, with training, to control other drives as well, to control the expression of emotions in general, to provide self-discipline. Perhaps these valuable faculties, which can be developed in humans to levels generically higher than in other animals, are linked together. On the other hand the mere non-visualization of dangers would be enough for recklessness in young males.

Another variety of psychological discipline, tenacity, is also necessary for successful hunting, and is likely to have been developed in males during their 2,000,000 years or so in that career. To run down an antelope must sometimes have required several days of stubborn single-minded pursuit. Sustained concentration would also have been necessary, in order not to lose sight of the prey for too long. If the original prey got away, a team of hunters would have had to fix on another one and start all over again.

In the next section of this chapter it will be shown that the Plio–Pleistocene hunters maintained home bases, to which they returned after the chase, with food for the whole group. This means that when the prey was finally brought down the hunters had to sling heavy loads on their shoulders and make their way back to the home base, without much sport or excitement, only a requirement for more tenacity, more self-discipline.

In addition to these varied traits which hunting activities seem likely to have called forth, there is a conspicuous social trait which has been strongly emphasized in the standard reconstructions of our past, and with justification, namely, cooperation among members of the hunting teams. This would have been required not only in the highly-organized maneuver of driving large animals into a swamp but also in relatively simple encircling movements. Wild dogs and other carnivores which hunt in packs are genetically programmed for this last elementary strategy, and protohuman hunters are almost sure to have improvised cooperative strategies in specific situations.

It is not known when planning was first brought into play, but it was certainly needed for the elephant drives, and it would have been useful much earlier, to take advantage of seasonal migrations or simply to prepare for an attack at a waterhole at sundown. Like teamwork in the actual chase, planning would have involved a conscious joint effort on the part of the hunting team.

Some kind of communication of intentions, ideas, and commands there certainly was. Primatologists have established that apes and monkeys communicate among themselves fluently, by vocalizations, movements, gestures, bodily attitudes, physical contacts, and facial expressions; progress has been made in deciphering and interpreting these signals. And communication among protohumans must have been at a generically higher level. A number of students have speculated that spoken language was developed during the Pleistocene in response to the need for more refined communication in hunting. The fascinating question of the origins of language – on which some evidence will be reviewed towards the end of this chapter – must remain open for the present. What matters here is that Plio–Pleistocene hunting teams had to work cooperatively, that to do so they had to communicate increasingly with each other, that as their communication became more articulate their teamwork became more efficient, and that these reciprocally reinforcing adaptations must have strengthened and deepened the personal relations among the members of a team.

A further note on hunting-team associations will be added in Chapter 12.

Finally, the hunting life would have preserved and reinforced the male trait of striving for dominance or superior status among males and among others generally, together with the underlying competitive drive, which as brought out in Chapter 3 were almost certainly part of the genetic heritage of very early hominids. The establisment and exercise of leadership would have facilitated efficient coordination and control of hunting teams. At the same time it would have strengthened the protection available to all members of protohuman groups. In addition, males of high rank would, as a rule, have had access to more females than males of low rank. Later chapters will mention evidence that this is often the case among living humans as well as among many nonhuman primates and other mammals, and in the Plio–Pleistocene this discriminatory state of affairs among our ancestors would surely have been quite open. These factors would have produced many protohuman males with genes for leadership, including a readiness to fight and a definite aggressive tendency in many cases. These factors would also have preserved, in nearly all males, the underlying competitive drive and the restless propulsive trait of striving for leadership.

## Home bases and life styles: food-sharing

There is tangible evidence that our protohuman ancestors established home bases. Evolutionary antecedents for such a practice can be found in several primate species adapted to open-country living. Herds of gelada baboons, for example, adopt cliff-face sleeping-ledges to which they repair for safety at night after foraging widely over their ranges during the day; and it has been observed that during the day the females and infants tend to remain closer to those havens of safety than the males do. There are already many examples from the Late Pliocene and the Lower and Middle Pleistocene of protohuman occupation sites resembling those mentioned in the preceding section, and the cumulative significance of their garbage record is clear. Groups of protohumans whose fossilized bones or artifacts or both have been found at the sites must have used those sites for extended periods of time, either continuously or intermittently, and their food must have included the meat of the animals whose fossilized bones have been found scattered about. The significant archeological remains are not found spread indiscriminately over the landscape but are concentrated in limited areas.

At one such site in the Olduvai Gorge with a potassium–argon date of about 1,750,000 BP, a particularly eloquent discovery was made several years ago, namely a rough ring about five meters in diameter, formed of sizable chunks of a lava that is plentiful in the vicinity. It is thought that very early hunters arranged the ring of stones to hold short stakes upright, supporting a rude shelter of branches, grasses, or hides, where a dozen or so adults and children could rest. This interpretation gains some support from the presence of hundreds of animal bones, including bones of many large animals, littering the ground outside the ring but immediately adjoining it. One large animal would have nourished a small group of protohumans for a month or two, if the meat was preserved by cutting it in strips and drying it in the sun. Many stone artifacts are also scattered about the site, and a fossil specimen attributed to *Homo habilis* has been found in the same horizon not far away.

Traces of possibly similar shelters or windbreaks have been found with Middle Pleistocene dates at certain other eastern African localities (Melka Kunturé and Kalambo Falls). In addition, Henry de Lumley has reported a particularly interesting and perhaps derivative set of dwellings at Terra Amata in Nice in France, dated provisionally at about 300,000 BP: these appear to have been a number of rather large oval huts, 7–15 meters long and 4–6 meters wide, each with an outer ring of sizable stones serving to brace a palisade of stakes driven into the ground, and each with a few stout posts planted in a row down the middle, presumably to support some kind of overhead structure.

The ring of stones at Olduvai thus seems to be an early prototype of Pleistocene living-shelters. And the chances are overwhelming that the Olduvai shelter was not the only one, or for that matter the first, built by early members of the genus

*Homo.* Indeed, there is nothing surprising about the construction of a simple shelter: even a chimpanzee and a gorilla have been observed with a roof of sorts raised over a leafy nest. The real significance of the shelters is their indication that small groups of adults and children established regular home bases and used them, in all probability seasonally or intermittently, for several years or even several generations.

Altogether, considering both the many concentrations of artifacts and animal bones and also the occasional traces of constructed living-shelters, it can reasonably be concluded that our ancestors did use home bases for upwards of 2,000,000 years, starting in eastern Africa. It is therefore worthwhile to try to visualize the patterns of life at those bases.

In order to discern some of the patterns, it will be best to start by looking in a different direction – towards problems of childbirth and care of the young. Chapter 4 reported that during the Plio–Pleistocene the cranial capacity of our ancestors was increasing with exceptional rapidity, in terms of evolutionary time. Many other mammals, especially preyed-upon species and predatory species, were increasing the size of their brains, but the extraordinary rapidity of this development in our own early ancestors was a distinctively hominid and proto-human phenomenon. It was one of the factors of the utmost importance to human evolution, since it made human culture possible. Increasing intelligence made possible progressively flexible responses to environmental shocks and opportunities, and provided the resourcefulness and learning-capacity which were needed for success in hunting and other activities. Even the areas of the brain providing for the faculty of manual dexterity are today three times as big in humans as in chimpanzees. The tripling of overall brain size in our ancestors within 3,000,000 years is a proof of the intensity of pressures exerted by natural selection and a measure of the great importance of this adaptation for survival. There is no reason to doubt that comparable advances were being made at the same time in the conformation and degree of involution of the brain.

But those successively bigger and bigger heads all had to pass through a mother's pelvis at birth. If the heads were too big at birth there was acute danger to both mothers and infants, and if the infants came to be born at too premature a stage of fetal growth there were heightened rates of infant mortality and still greater postnatal helplessness than before. The rate of perinatal mortality was certainly extremely high already, as indicated in a later section, and a further rise could well have resulted in extinction of the unlikely new genus. An adaptation which could have solved the problem was that of a substantial change in the size and conformation of the female pelvis, but this would have had a serious disadvantage of another kind: it would have impaired mothers' efficiency in running and walking, so that they and their infants would have had difficulty in keeping up with groups following animal migrations. This would often have been fatal, at a stage when protohumans were still threatened by large predators of the savannas: the standard tactic of many carnivores today, including lions and hyenas, is to fix upon an animal which becomes separated from its group and can therefore be caught more easily, especially if it is small or weak.

Although direct evidence from fossilized bones is lacking, it seems likely that this dangerous problem worked itself out gradually in a series of compromises, with natural selection eliminating all the extreme responses: the female pelvis becoming somewhat modified, leaving the mothers able to walk and run reasonably well but not quite as well as the males; the female difficulties in childbirth increasing somewhat, and culminating in the severe travail of modern women; the infants coming to be born at an earlier and still more precarious fetal stage, with the mothers acquiring a behavioral tendency for ever-greater concentration on the care and nurture of them; and possibly a slowing down in the otherwise optimum rate of increase in brain size – who knows how many larger-brained infants, and their genes, may have perished at birth as a result of this problem?

The numbers are extremely simple. Chimpanzee infants are born with a cranial capacity of about 200 cc, which is roughly doubled in the course of individual growth; human babies today are born with a capacity of something like 400 cc, and this is increased in the course of growth to about 1400 cc on average.

It was mentioned in Chapter 3 that the higher primates are distinguished from other mammals in the greater helplessness and dependency of their young. In protohumans this trend was carried still further, the infants being utterly helpless at birth and probably very dependent until six or seven years old. Among chimpanzees in the wild, as previously noted, mothers' milk provides the principal food for young animals until the age of two and half years or more; and among protohumans, judging from a good deal of fossil evidence, and from the slower emergence of both baby teeth and permanent teeth in modern humans as compared with chimpanzees, this period was even longer, at least three years, though without doubt Plio–Pleistocene children started receiving supplementary nourishment from fruits and other foods when very young. The point here is that a prolonged period of nursing must have been a major restriction on the activities of early females. And even before their nursing came to an end most mothers must have started on a new pregnancy.

Normal females of the Plio–Pleistocene, if they succeeded in surviving to an age of 45, would have been actively bearing children throughout a period of about 25 years. It will be suggested in Chapter 6, in a demographic context, that on average they gave birth to between six and eight children. This allows for a couple of miscarriages or stillbirths, and otherwise an interval of about three years between live-born children. It is well within the physiological capacity of modern women (as established by the Hutterite sect in the United States, with an average of over twelve children per married woman, and a birth interval of a little over two years), but under Plio–Pleistocene environmental conditions it implies a decidedly arduous life.

At the time when protohuman females became hairless a new problem arose. The young offspring of all nonhuman primates ride about clinging to their mothers' body hair, supporting their own weight but receiving an occasional helpful lift from their mothers. (A vestige of this behavior can still be seen in very young human infants today: they often have enough strength in their fingers so that if presented with something clutchable they can nearly support their own weight.) But infants whose mothers had lost their luxuriant covering of body hair could not do this. They would have had to be carried in their mothers' arms, a considerable further emcumbrance of the mothers.

(This, incidentally, would not have been possible before our ancestors had become fully bipedal, so hairlessness must have evolved sometime after that.) Theoretically the babies could have been strapped to the mothers' backs or fronts, but this would have required an invention difficult and highly improbable in the Plio–Pleistocene. And the growing children could not have kept up with adults on the move until aged five or six; therefore they also must have been carried much of the time.

This digression about the problem of childbirth and child-care yields at least three conclusions of practical and philosophical consequence. The first is that the brains of our protohuman ancestors grew larger not only with great evolutionary rapidity but also despite many problems and at substantial cost: this is nature's proof that nurture has been of immense importance in human affairs. The second conclusion is that protohuman children were much more vulnerable than the juveniles of any other primates, even chimpanzees; they needed a longer period for growth and development, and in a savanna environment they were much more exposed to dangerous predators than forest-dwelling apes were: this means that whereas the young of other primates, including chimpanzees, had a good chance of surviving with only a mother's care, protohuman children needed also the protection and support of an adult male.

The third conclusion leads back to the original subject of Plio–Pleistocene patterns of social life. Baldly stated, this conclusion is that protohuman females did not, as a rule, participate in big-game hunting. Those who survived were strong and resistant, but they were developing in a different direction. Their pelvis was evolving for childbirth rather than efficient running; their babies were completely helpless and their older children long dependent; both babies and small children had to be carried; and throughout their reproductive years they were either nursing or pregnant, at times both.

To be sure, there must have been exceptional young females, and if for some of them those burdens were not sufficient, then no doubt they hunted with the males, and sometimes outran them – but then they left relatively few surviving children, and perpetuated relatively few of their genes. The fact that today the articulation of women's arms is much less adapted than men's for throwing with force and accuracy is consistent both with a supposition that protohuman males developed this unique faculty because it was useful in hunting, and also with the conclusion that females did not as a rule take part in the chase. In short, natural selection was persistently weeding out hunting propensities in females, so that after a million or so years the great majority of them preferred to do other things, at or near their home base with their babies and young children. Indeed one can now infer, I think, that these problems of birth and protection of the young were among the principal reasons why it was advantageous to use home bases in the first place.

Starting from this point it perhaps does not require too much guesswork to visualize some of the patterns of life developing at Plio–Pleistocene home bases. The bases themselves were probably not permanent domiciles. The hunters must have followed the seasonal movements of game animals for consider-able distances. Over longer periods of time, with changes in climate and food availability, protohuman groups must have moved from one region to another. Probably it is best to think of them as semi-nomadic, establishing provisional bases and from time to time moving on, or back.

It was essential that early home-base groups should be small, not only during foraging–scavenging times but throughout most of the long period of hunting–gathering, because on savannas plant foods for hominids were much more sparsely distributed than in forests, and because the game animals on which protohumans depended for their protein were themselves widely dispersed. This has been tentatively confirmed by analyses of Plio–Pleistocene sites in eastern Africa, which have indicated that the groups using the sites were consistently within a range of approximately 12 to 50 individuals. It is reasonably inferred that home-base groups were typically made up of between two or three families and six or seven families, the families averaging six or seven individuals each, including infants and children. (There are indications that much later, towards the end of the Pleistocene Epoch in Europe, many populations of humans began to exploit the hunting of large migratory mammals in herds, particularly wild cattle, and that this permitted the formation of much larger social groups, facilitating perhaps the ultimate transition to pastoral and agricultural life.)

As for the range of daily movement, the fact is that large game animals did not present themselves at the front door, so to speak, to be slaughtered and eaten. On the contrary it would seem that a hunting team typically had to set out at daybreak and range over considerable distances. On several living floors at Olduvai and elsewhere a number of smallish unworked stones, 'manuports,' have been found which are not indigenous and which must have been carried there, it is not known why, from points of origin perhaps more than 20 kilometers away. The practices of some present-day hunter–foragers suggest that it would often have been necessary for Plio–Pleistocene hunting teams to pursue their prey for several days. And since large assemblages of the bones of big animals have been found at home bases, it is evident that after a kill the hunters must have shouldered heavy loads and carried them back to their bases and shared them with the females and the young.

Paleoanthropologists generally postulate at this stage a division of labor between the sexes, the males hunting and the females gathering plant foods as well as feeding and caring for the young. While this attribution of food-gathering to the females as a differentiated occupation is speculative, it is supported by some evidence. Primarily, it is the standard pattern in present-day tribes of hunter–gatherers. Scholars of the present generation wisely eschew any tendency to view the ways of a few such tribes as unchanged survivals from the Pleistocene; but it is entirely permissible to infer that their pattern has practical adaptive advantages in any hunting–gathering economy. It seems probable from the evidence that our Plio–Pleistocene ancestors obtained a large part of their nourishment from plant foods, and it is unlikely that the males would or could have done the time-consuming work of gathering plant foods for the group as well as hunting big game. The hairlessness of women today could mean that in the Plio–Pleistocene tropics the females as well as the males lived an active and arduous life in the heat.

One can here press forward a bit further in speculating on the life-styles of Plio–Pleistocene females, especially now that an unconscious male bias which sometimes produced distortions has been exposed and counterbalanced by some able women of science. To cite one of these, Adrienne Zihlman of the University of California at Santa Cruz has rejected the conventional family daguerrotype in which 'mothers and their young ate and survived through the protective, hunting, and sharing activities of males.' She has proposed instead that the gathering of plant foods by females may have been the basis for the emergence of hunting, that 'the sharing of plant foods, developed initially between mothers and offspring, was probably the source for expanding sharing patterns to include adult males,' and that 'perhaps tools for hunting developed from those used in gathering.' If females used sharpened sticks of wood for digging up edible tubers, those digging sticks would inevitably have perished. And no one disputes Zihlman's observation that fossilized animal bones are much more durable than plant refuse, and that the archeological record in consequence may have tended to overstate the importance of meat in protohuman diets.

It is extremely probable that the basic feeding pattern of the very earliest hominids, like that of chimpanzees and baboons today, was one of peripatetic feeding on plant foods (and perhaps insects and eggs), supplemented opportunistically by small animals. In that primitive pattern, however, each hominid fed itself on the spot, and no food was collected systematically for later consumption. The food-sharing pattern visualized at home bases by around 2,000,000 BP may have been a relatively new development at that time. It could have arisen in cultural evolution in various ways. If mothers were sometimes able to leave some of their children at home bases, they would certainly have collected any food those children were able to eat and would have carried it back to them – perhaps improvising for this purpose trays of bark or sacks of animal hides. And it is evident that when a stage of active scavenging or hunting had been reached the protohuman males on their part did carry meat back to home bases. Future studies may be able to throw light on just how and in what sequence those practices evolved.

In the meantime, it can be agreed that by around 2,000,000 BP protohumans in eastern Africa were living in small groups, commonly using home bases where food of all kinds was shared, and that in general the gathering of plant foods was done by the females, while the males engaged in hunting – described by Zihlman as 'a dangerous activity requiring high energy output with unpredictable return,' though the 'potential payoff was equally great in producing a large source of utilizable protein.'

Such a division of labor, permitting the development of specialized skills, would surely have been advantageous to all members of protohuman social groups. And it would have created strong selection pressures for increased intelligence in the females as well as in the males – in fact quite possibly more in the females since they lacked some of the muscular strength and physical capabilities of the males. Thus, the females would have had to develop a capacity for efficient and rapid collection of plant foods, including resourcefulness in devising for that purpose tools and carrying-utensils. They would have needed acutely sensitive perception and instant responses to danger. The most successful of them must have had enough intelligence and intuitive tact to manage the dynamics of their social relationships with adult males and others in their groups without the use of force. Above all, the females had to be capable of continuous awareness of the needs of their young.

Even with food-gathering as their specialized activity, the females undoubtedly devoted most of their attention to nurture of the children. Apart from feeding their young, and actually carrying the growing ones until they could trot along fast enough to keep up, the mothers must have kept them under constant surveillance. They must have protected them, comforted and reassured them, played with them, scolded them, prepared them for life, and taught them how to behave in respectable Plio–Pleistocene society.

At least as much as the males of that time and very possibly more so, the females must have been under strong selection pressure to develop improved faculties of communication. And improved communication required increased intelligence, while increased intelligence demanded improved communication.

The preparation of food must have been very rudimentary until fire came into use, but it is usually reasoned that this was also part of the females' work at home bases. And since they spent more time there than the males it is likely that they concerned themselves more than the males did with keeping the bases reasonably sanitary and attractive. (To any feminist champions aroused by these inflammatory remarks, I quickly acknowledge that owing to the marvelous plasticity of our species the male can very easily be trained, today, not only to cook or wash the dishes but also to make the beds and even to prepare and administer the baby's bottle.)

Continuing with a reconstruction of patterns of life at home bases reasonably sanitary and attractive. (To any feminist other ways also. Hunters with broken bones, individuals afflicted with food poisoning or parasitic infections, not to mention females in accouchement and their newborn, could rest there, cared for and shared with, until they were able to move about safely. In the merciless environment of a savanna ecosystem, with large carnivores always looking for exposed and faltering prey, this must have saved countless lives at times when predation was an important danger for our ancestors. Again, individual males and females who managed to reach old age could continue to live there although no longer active, and to make their experience and their memory of other times and places available to the group; probably it was because of the usefulness of this resource that honor and prestige were accorded to the old until our own time (in which knowledge is being accumulated at an ever-accelerating rate and the old need to learn from the young).

In a word, the home bases contributed substantially to the survival and reproduction of members of our genus. They were probably a central feature in the lives of those groups from which we are descended. We owe to Isaac a comprehensive vision of our past, in which home bases were part of a highly adaptive food-sharing complex which involved scavenging or hunting, food-gathering, division of labor, the use of tools and other equipment, and very probably improved communication of some kind. The complex as a whole served as a base upon which the superstructure of modern culture and technology could be erected.

# 6

# *Life in the Plio–Pleistocene Part II*

## *The beginnings of love*

Social arrangements at home bases must have included forms of marriage and family, though obviously these words are not used in the sense of the institutions sanctified in modern Christendom. The home bases were primarily places where small groups of adults and children came together for eating and sleeping, and since the biological function of that pattern of life undoubtedly included as a major element the protection of growing children it is highly probable that tendencies developed to hold small groups together for periods of several years.

The question asked here is what held the groups together: could it have included rudimentary forms of love? The intense emotional bond between a modern mother and her child can be traced back many millions of years into our primate and mammalian past, but when did the love between adult males and females first become established in the human line of evolution? *A priori* it might be assumed that the underlying emotional tendencies are at least as ancient as the genus *Homo* itself. But to preserve a steadfast objectivity it is preferable to look for factual evidence of some kind.

Chapter 3 reported that nonhuman primates show great variety in the relationships between males and females. Signs of a preference of a particular male for a particular female and vice versa are found sometimes in Old World monkeys and apes, including relatively promiscuous species, notably chimpanzees. Certain species form harems which hold together for months and sometimes for several years, and in other species observers have found some clear cases of a special attachment between particular males and females lasting beyond an estrus period. And the acrobatic gibbons often live for several years in their small monogamous nuclear families in the treetops. The tentative conclusion reached in Chapter 3 was that Old World monkeys and apes may long have had a genetic potentiality for forming individual preferences in mating and perhaps for developing male–female bonds in situations where they would be particularly advantageous, and that such a potentiality may have been part of the genetic heritage of very early hominids.

Professor C. Owen Lovejoy of Kent State University has recently put forward some very novel and provocative suggestions concerning the early hominids. Making use of one of these ideas, one can note that today the minimum interval between births of children in human females (less than two years) is substantially shorter than it is in female chimpanzees (about three and a half years, according to the best observations). If an adaptation of that kind arose in early hominids, it would have conferred a reproductive advantage great enough to compensate for serious handicaps of other kinds; and the point is that in early hominids such an adaptation could most readily have been developed *after* a rudimentary bonding tendency had been established in adult males and females: a lengthened attachment between a male and one or more females would have provided each female and her young with enough protection and support so that she could successfully start on a new pregnancy before the last-born infant was able to take care of itself. This suggestion seems to merit careful consideration and study.

In the meantime one can only guess about the life-styles of the first hominids – either *Ramapithecus* or some related form not yet discovered. There is reasonable evidence that *Ramapithecus* sometimes lived in or near savanna environments, perhaps lacking the relative safety of forests. If so, they, and especially their young, were more exposed than the purely forest-dwelling primates to predation by big carnivores. In any case there is plain evidence in the fossil record that very early hominids lacked the size and strength of chimpanzees or gorillas, and also the fleetness of antelopes. Consequently one can guess that if some very early hominids in savanna environments did have an incipient tendency to form lasting associations between a male and one or more females this would have had some significant survival value for their vulnerable offspring.

But one can already attempt something better than guesses concerning the protohuman stage of evolution in the Plio–Pleistocene. Starting at the end of that period and working backwards, it will be pointed out in Chapter 8 that the ardent, consuming love between a man and a woman which we know in our Western civilization is no novel or merely local phenomenon, that on the contrary essentially similar basic emotions have been found in all the past civilizations of which we have good historical knowledge and in many extremely varied cultures existing today on all the continents and in all the island regions of the world. This very wide distribution, seen against the background of the behavior of nonhuman primates and the emotional resources of higher mammals generally, makes it permissible to conclude that basic tendencies of males and females to form an emotional bond had been planted genetically in the human line (and undoubtedly reinforced by cultural evolution) sometime before the dispersal of *Homo sapiens sapiens* across the world. This carries the inquiry back to the closing chapters of prehistory, but it leaves open the question whether emotional bonding tendencies may have existed in the Pliocene.

For this, it is useful to revert to the instance of the tired hunters: to the phenomenon of a team of Plio–Pleistocene hunters, after a long and arduous chase, electing to sling loads of meat on their shoulders and carry them back to their home bases. It may be added that this action must have been one of the conscious purposes of the expedition from the outset.

That phenomenon is really an extraordinary one. Food sharing exists in other animals, but it is always of a different order. Careful observations of free-ranging chimpanzees have established that when one of them has caught and killed a small animal it will usually concede a few morsels or even a portion to a couple of its companions, but only after it has been insistently pestered by them, and as if it wanted to buy peace. Birds bring food to their nests for their young, but birds have been evolving in a separate evolutionary line for a quarter of a billion years and they are a highly specialized class of animals with rather rigidly programmed behavior. Many carnivores are known to carry meat back to their young, but even they are forms specialized for hunting, in which this is a program of behavior established genetically over many millions of years. Protohumans, in contrast, would have had very few rigid programs of behavior. They were descended from a line of primate vegetarians, and they were not specialized for anything – unless it is considered that they were becoming specialized for culture, which would give them the widest scope for choosing their behavior. What protohumans must have had was a set of mighty protean drives and emotions, plus enough plasticity and enough intelligence to devise and modify their behaviors within wide limits.

On the other hand, in Plio–Pleistocene times protohuman males were not yet socially or culturally commanded. They had acquired faculties of self-discipline and tenacity, and each early hunting team was probably directed and coordinated by a leader, but there was no higher-level authority which could effectively command the leaders. And the early hunters individually could hardly have been inculcated with a social conscience or a sense of duty such as that which bears down so oppressively, though not always effectively, on us today.

In short, when protohuman hunters at the end of a chase carried heavy loads of meat back to their home bases, often kilometers away – a small gazelle was not too heavy, but a *Deinotherium* weighed five or six tons and large joints of its meat must have been heavy burdens even for hunters a good deal more muscular than we are – they did this because fundamentally they *wanted* to do it. And perhaps they wanted to do it because they felt some kind of attachment with the females and children at the home bases.

Some stony anthropologists reason that the members of a home-base group were held together simply by a nexus of economic self-interest. This was surely a factor; and in a broader sense the division of labor and the differentiation of roles must have given substantial advantages to the members of early groups practicing them; they must have enabled the members of those groups to prosper and increase in numbers, and they must also have had the effect of helping to hold males and females together in such groups for extended periods. But the economic factor alone could not account for the carrying home of big game: a team of hunters who had a month's supply of red meat in their hands were not likely to want to carry it a long distance merely in order to trade part of it for fruit and vegetables; it would have been easier to gather some fruit and vegetables themselves.

Given, then, that carrying home large game for sharing it with the females and children required strong exertion, that it was a volitional act without specific genetic programming, that it cannot be accounted for merely by social or cultural compulsion or narrow economic self-interest, the concluding inference drawn here is that the basic motivating force must have been provided mainly by the great mammalian resource of emotion. More specifically, I suggest that some of that vast resource was channeled into an affectional potentiality which early hominids may have possessed in common with some other primates and may have developed further, or, to be flatly explicit, that an adult male's tendency to love a female existed already in some degree in the earliest days of big-game exploitation – 2,000,000 years ago and perhaps earlier.

All this is far from saying that hunters of the late Pliocene and early Pleistocene felt longings and tenderness like those known in our highly elaborated, highly sensitized culture. They certainly did not. But perhaps, as a guess, when the members of a hunting team ate or felt hungry some of them thought of eating with the females and children. Most probably, a very confident guess, each of them thought from time to time of copulating with a particular female, or of winning her admiration with a shank of *Deinotherium*. Conceivably some of them thought of playing with a baby, tossing it in the air and catching it, or of roughhousing with older children, or bringing along an older boy on a future hunt. Since faculties of memory and visual imagery must have existed – they were necessary for successful hunting – such states of consciousness were perfectly possible. And, assuming stong selection for tendencies which favored bringing food home, then such states of consciousness would have developed in time into a composite which can with some legitimacy be called the beginnings of love. Inborn tendencies of that kind would have been transmitted genetically from adult males to some of their own children, and would also have been transmitted through the operation of kin selection to still others, since many of the protohumans sharing a particular home base would have been related to each other by various ties of kinship.

It is highly probable that in the male the symptoms of affection which developed first were those of attraction to an adult female, because the copulatory drive had to be very powerful and it could have found expression in a variety of ways. Here there are one or two physiological and anatomical facts to guide speculation.

In most mammalian species all sexual activity of the females is concentrated into the limited periods of estrus in their hormonal cycles, engendering a festival of copulation for them during those days and inactivity during the rest of the cycle. In many mammalian species both sexes are inactive during most of the year. Higher primates show much variation in effects of the estrous cycle, and even in some of the primate species in which estrus is powerfully signaled externally, copulation has been observed at other points in the cycle. In modern women, estrus as a sign of ovulation has practically disappeared, and sexual receptivity in the female and excitation in the male can be aroused at almost any time, in some situations with delicious frequency. The meaning of this is that the loss of estrus, a change which appears to have started in the primate stage of evolution, must have developed much further during the hominid stage, or sometime after say 15,000,000 BP. Probably the development was completed by 3,000,000 BP, because in general the distinctive sexual adaptations of humans are complex and rather fundamental, so that some of them must be of very ancient origin. They include a special kind of sexual dimorphism, in which the female is only a little smaller than the male on average but marvelously different in secondary sexual characteristics; in particular the transfer of the female sexual signals from the rear to the front with the disappearance of the flamboyant sexual skin on the behind found in some primates and the development of enlarged and rounded breasts and ultimately delicate facial features and complexion. These must have started to take place as a consequence of face-to-face interactions accompanying the bipedal posture of early hominids.

It seems most likely that the biological reason for the loss of estrus in hominids was the greater vulnerability and the longer dependency of hominid infants and juveniles: when genetic mutations caused a particular female to lose the symptoms of estrus during the period surrounding the time of ovulation, and to be receptive to male advances during all of her hormonal cycle, she could have dispensed with the former frenetic round of copulations throughout a week or more of estrus. As a result her existing offspring would have had a better chance of surviving. The mutant genes would have been favored by natural selection. On the other hand such mutations would have had no particular value at that time for non-hominid primates, because their infants were becoming self-reliant at earlier ages; for most of them it would have been sufficient to have estrus suspended during the period of lactation only, as it is for their descendants today.

In any case, the loss of estrus is likely to be very ancient. Probably during all of the 3,000,000 years explored in this book the protohuman and human females were accessible continuously (except during part of the period of nursing), and the males were surely vigorous producers of seminal fluid at all times. Thus, it must have been easy to establish consortships lasting longer and longer.

In such circumstances the reproductive impulses of protohumans could sometimes have broadened out enough to include a preferential emotional bond lasting years, between a male and one or more females who shared a home base. And their singularly slow-growing and vulnerable children would have had better probabilities of survival. The separations during hunting expeditions could have produced in the male not only a build-up of the sexual urge but also a sense of personal attachment; in the female, who was dependent on the male's protection and support, and who was already profoundly adapted for emotional tenderness, it would have produced a mixture of anxiety and pining. So each of them would have felt some sort of pleasure, possibly elation, when they were reunited. Natural selection would have strongly favored such feelings and their appropriate consummation, until in the course of time the tendencies became general and in some individuals intense. At all stages, the rapid processes of cultural evolution would certainly have been reinforcing this development, to the advantage of individual children and of whole populations.

There is a good deal more to say about love life in the Plio–Pleistocene, but it can best be left for later chapters. At this point it is necessary only to add a word about the bond which was probably developing between adult males and the children surrounding them. As reported in Chapter 3 the adult males of certain species of nonhuman primates seem to possess a potentiality for paternal solicitude and possibly affection; in nearly all mammalian species the very young emit eloquent signals of their presence and need for care, and in many primate species these signals must reach an adult male as well as the mother. With this background, all that was needed in the human line of descent was that an adult male should devote some continuing attention to one or more particular children. This is just what must have been happening in the groups sharing Plio–Pleistocene home bases, especially in cases where a bond existed between the adult male and the mother to whom the young were attached. And once the beginnings of real paternal affection appeared (in the broad sense of affection felt by an adult male for particular children attached to a female consort), those beginnings must have been seized upon and developed intensively by natural selection, because the exceedingly dependent children must certainly have survived in greater numbers when they had the benefit of emotionally-motivated support and protection by an adult male as well as motherly care. It would nevertheless have required a great many generations for the genes underlying that new variety of affectional bonding to spread through most of the male sex. Cultural evolution must have made an important contribution here also.

To conclude, I repeat that in the earliest male–female emotional bonding, just as much as in the later development of paternal affection, the vital biological point is the survival of protohuman children. The primary reason why men and women of today have a tendency to love each other is that among their early ancestors the rudiments of such a tendency made an essential contribution to the survival of children, increasing the chances that they would live through the perilous years of infancy and childhood and then reproduce in turn. Men and women fall in love today because of the needs of their early ancestors' children.

## Demographic speculations

Since demography is preeminently 'a science of big numbers,' one cannot get very far in it with the tiny numbers of proto-human fossils of the Plio–Pleistocene. Nevertheless, using what facts are available and applying indirect reasoning and a little judicious speculation, it is possible to form a few demographic notions of evolutionary significance.

One such notion is that protohumans and early humans developed inborn tendencies to arrange themselves in a pattern of small, separated social groups. There are at least two reasons why such tendencies would have been advantageous in the Plio–Pleistocene. The first is very direct and definite: it is the fact that early home-base groups had to be small in order to find enough food in a foraging–scavenging or hunting–gathering existence in savanna environments. No doubt intelligent proto-humans would have developed a pattern of that kind culturally, through trial and error, but a genetic predisposition would have helped them; and their own smaller-brained hominid ancestors on savannas would have been under selective pressure to acquire a genetically-influenced tendency.

The second reason why such tendencies would have been advantageous is less obvious but even more compelling in the long run. It will be set out in this section and the next. To start with, it is known that the total protohuman population of the Plio–Pleistocene was generally in a state of equilibrium, in the sense that it had an average rate of increase of almost exactly zero. It is commonly estimated that the total human population of the world at the end of the Pleistocene Epoch, around 10,000 BP, was of the order of a few millions; and the total hominid population at 3,000,000 BP was probably not much less, judging from fossil evidence of the comparative numbers of baboons, large carnivores, and hominids in eastern Africa in the Plio–Pleistocene. (Indeed, even if the total hominid population then had been only of the order of a few thousands, a gross underestimate, the overall average rate of population growth over the ensuing 3,000,000 years would still, owing to the magic of compound interest over very long periods, have been so close to zero that it would have taken 1000 years for 1000 proto-humans to increase to 1002.) And some very interesting conclusions follow from the fact of zero population growth. The principal one is that the rate of infant and child mortality must have been somewhere between 53 percent and 65 percent. To justify this inferential leap, I must cite a pioneering study carried out in Hungary by Professors György Acsádi and János Nemeskéri during some 20 years of work together in demography and anthropology. Their findings are reported in *History of Human Life Span and Mortality*, published in Hungarian in 1964 and in English in 1970. In this admirable work they constructed life tables for certain medieval and prehistoric populations by applying up-to-date demographic techniques to skeletal samples of those populations, classified according to age and sex. Although the available fossil samples of some of the prehistoric populations were regrettably small, Acsádi and Nemeskéri were duly cautious in drawing conclusions, and other experts have not been able to fault them in any fundamental way. One of their more reliable findings was that in a good-sized sample of a hunting–gathering population in savanna country in the African Maghreb at the very end of the Pleistocene the rate of mortality before the age of 14 was 53 percent. Based on regrettably small samples, they estimated that that rate was 55 percent for a Neanderthal population in Europe, and 68 percent for *Homo erectus* in China.

These figures are derived from a combination of zero population growth and estimates of the average number of children born to each female. Zero growth results when the average female's children include exactly one daughter who survives to reproductive age; but in the Plio–Pleistocene the average female was giving birth to substantially more than one daughter, and the rest of them were dying before reaching reproductive age. Acsádi and Nemeskéri estimated, on the basis of all the information available to them, that in a *Homo erectus* population in eastern Asia a female who lived to the end of her reproductive life would have given birth to 8.0 children, on average. Adjusting this to reflect deaths of some mothers before the age of

45, on the basis of the life tables given, and assuming that just half of the children born were daughters, I estimate that the number of daughters born to a female, on average, was 2.84; if the number surviving to the age of 14 or 15 was exactly 1.00, the intervening mortality rate would have to be 65 percent. Acsádi and Nemeskéri estimated that same mortality rate, of course more accurately, at 68 percent; but they calculated elsewhere that an infant and child mortality rate of 68 percent was at or close to the extinction rate for any human population, so I stay with my rough-and-ready calculation of 65 percent as a pragmatic upper limit.

It is possible that the estimate of an average of 8.0 children per *Homo erectus* female in a full lifetime is a little too high. Nancy Howell of the University of Toronto has just published a very searching demographic study of a group of San (Bushman) hunter–gatherers of the Kalahari Desert in Africa, the Dobe !Kung. (The exclamation point signifies not astonishment but a click sound used in the language of those appealing people.) For Dobe !Kung women in the 1960s and 1970s, the corresponding figure (even after a minor technical rectification) was a shade under 5 children. Although that level may be exceptionally low, in consequence of the desertic environment and the exceptionally low reserves of body fat observed in Dobe !Kung women, yet it will be prudent to envisage the possibility that the average for our female ancestors of the Plio–Pleistocene may have been as low as 6 children. Taking this figure and making the same adjustments for females dying before the end of their reproductive years, the infant and child mortality rate which would have resulted in zero population growth is 53 percent. This, however, seems clearly to be the lowest mortality rate which can be considered likely, since it is underpinned by the 53 percent rate in the Maghreb population at the end of the Pleistocene. It is confirmed also in several other ways, including that of studies of the modern Samburu, a pastoral people living in dry country in eastern Africa, which show that in their case the infant and child mortality rate has been about 52 percent in recent times (a calculation which is possible because the Samburu obligingly keep records of ages for tribal ceremonies).

The conclusion that the infant and child mortality rate

among our Plio–Pleistocene ancestors averaged somewhere between 53 percent and 65 percent is tantamount to a judgement that, overall, somewhere between half and two-thirds of all their live-born children died before reaching the age of 14 or 15. This would have been the consequence of many different hazards, starting with loss of maternal care and, especially in the early part of the period, predation by large carnivores; other hazards would have been infections, undernourishment, accidents of birth and of early life, violence, and inborn defects. (The specific hazards, for protohumans of all ages, will be reviewed in a later section.) Certain ethnographers have taken much interest in the infanticide practiced by some stuggling tribes in modern times, but it is inconceivable that infanticide could have been a major factor in the very high rate of infant mortality among our ancestors generally. It would almost certainly have been a derivative phenomenon, resulting from environmental hardships or insufficiencies; it would also have been resorted to in cases of malformed babies, and possibly in cases of twin births when only one infant could be cared for.

The high rate of infant and child mortality undoubtedly resulted in a very short life expectancy at birth, namely between 15 and 20 years. As one student of prehistoric demography has observed, life expectancy at birth has approximately doubled twice in our evolutionary past, starting at under 20 years in the Plio–Pleistocene, rising irregularly to 35–40 for recent pre-industrial civilizations and to 70–75 for today's privileged societies.

This seems at first glance to support the portrayal of life in the Plio–Pleistocene as 'nasty, brutish, and short.' But in reality it was probably not that bad. Acsádi–Nemeskéri curves indicate that Maghreb hunter–gatherers of the late Pleistocene who managed to survive the extreme hazards of infancy and childhood had a fairly good chance of living on for a good many years – about half of them until their late 30s, about 40 percent of them until 45, and perhaps some 10 percent of them even into the 60s. Strong and resistant enough to survive the childhood years, they apparently could confront with success many hazards and hardships of adult life. And our early protohuman ancestors, like some hunter–gatherers of modern times, may often have been able to enjoy life as adults. The experience of losing half to two-thirds of their live-born children, shocking as it may seem to us today, would not have been a cause of prolonged distress; it was simply one of the facts of life which had to be accepted.

Moreover, it will be well understood that the overall growth rate of zero is only a mathematical abstraction, an average grossly smoothed. It masks wide differences between different populations in a given period, and differences between overall rates in different periods. Plio–Pleistocene environments were varied and changing, in factors affecting protohuman survival. Some populations must have been thriving and increasing in numbers while others were decreasing in numbers or dying out altogether.

For most of our early protohuman ancestors the crucial danger was that of infant and child mortality, which emphasizes once again the vital importance of all the adaptations which tended to keep that mortality rate below the extinction level. The point is that because of this crucial vulnerability our evolutionary line was in real danger of extinction. Although some of our ancestors did survive, and although their descendants did number probably a few millions by the time when *Homo sapiens sapiens* was starting to spread over the world, yet it may be that they only just barely made it. Long before that, many populations must have died out, and very likely all of them would in fact have died out if any of the important adaptations contributing to survival – starting with strengthened affectional tendencies and enlarged brains – had never evolved.

## *The beginnings of segregationism*

In all of the foregoing one can discover, I would like to suggest, one of the genetic factors underlying certain baneful phenomena of our contemporary world. This point seems interesting enough – borrowing a useful criterion from the *Guides Michelin* – to be worth a short detour.

The precarious situation of our ancestors during a great part of the Plio–Pleistocene – especially in the early part of the period, when the hazards were especially serious, as suggested in the next section – meant that our ancestors would not have had much chance of surviving, in varied and changing environments, unless some of them happened to develop very reliably a pattern of small separate breeding populations rather than a single all-inclusive population in a state of panmixis, in other words unless they formed and maintained for many generations small isolated gene pools with quite limited flows taking place between them, instead of a single large lake. This is because separate breeding populations (each one made up, perhaps, of a few home-base groups not too far from each other) could, in the shortest possible period of evolutionary time, diversify and differentiate, could develop among them a range of varied new genetic traits, and could also, much more rapidly, diversify and differentiate culturally. Only then was there a good chance that members of some of the breeding populations would survive and increase in numbers under varied and changing environmental conditions. For example, certain populations developed superior hunting methods, and certain others developed enough male–female bonding tendencies to provide superior protection and support for the dependent young: other things being equal, such populations must have prospered while others were declining in numbers or dying out. In promoting these and many other advantageous cultural and genetic characteristics, selection at the breeding-population level would have supplemented and reinforced selection at the individual level.

Consequently, for these reasons as well as because of the need to separate into small groups in order to find enough food, there must have developed in all of our ancestral populations which survived the first perilous million years or so a strong behavioral tendency to segregate into separate breeding units and to maintain the segregation permanently. As an expression of such a tendency, the members of each unit would have formed a sense of solidarity among themselves and an attitude of suspicion, rejection, or hostility towards other groups and their members – as in the heavily loaded 'us' and 'them' of our time. (There are some recent reports of very hostile interactions between chimpanzees belonging to different communities. If further studies confirm that these are a common occurrence, they may possibly mean that the tendency suggested here is at least as ancient as the hominid line.) An early tendency of this kind, a primordial segregationism, could have continued to have positive selective advantages for an additional million years or so, and it could well have been further strengthened in various periods of protracted danger still later, notably in the northern world during the long glaciations.

On this basis I suggest that an ancient segregationist tendency is one of the major underlying causes of the racism, nationalism, tribalism, and other group antagonisms which afflict our world today. They cry out their presence, one or more of them, on every continent and at all levels of material welfare. They can be reinforced visually by differences of skin color, and they thrive on ignorance; they become most destructive when combined with aggression, violence, or oppression. Since these group antagonisms are so widespread, showing up in some way and in some degree in almost all societies despite enormous diversity of environments and cultures, and persisting long after they could have been of positive value for survival, there is reason to believe that a genetic propensity of some kind underlies them, and that this propensity has helped cultural evolution to make its important contributions.

The suggested segregationist tendency can be recognized today in a variety of pleasanter forms also, for example in a fondness for forming and preserving distinctive customs and beliefs, folk music, folk dances, and other folk arts. Most remarkably of all, it survives everywhere in an unmistakable propensity for developing local dialects, for originating them quickly and then in the course of long periods of time converting them into distinct languages. This last phenomenon leads to segregation through differences of speech, which in the past has been particularly effective in preserving the separation of gene pools, and which in the contemporary world is still helping to keep certain senseless animosities alive. It has even been further reinforced by a laughably genetic inability in most adults to learn to speak a new language without a foreign accent which can easily be detected by others (whereas children can usually learn to speak a second language perfectly).

It is quite true, to follow this detour back to the main route, that our species shows also some tendencies of an integrationist nature, including impulses to reach across racial and other boundaries to communicate, to understand, to help, and even to love. Such tendencies have become particularly noticeable in very recent times, but I dare to suggest that they too could have a genetic base (and a cultural base) in human prehistory. When a certain stage of evolution had been reached – sometime after 1,000,000 BP, say, when survival had become significantly less precarious, and after many diversified gene pools had been securely established – the merging of separate gene pools may have resulted in new biological advantages. Modern studies have found, through experiments with plants and animals and through observation of human cases, that hybridization between different strains very often results in increased size, reproductive ability, or resistance to disease. The phenomenon is referred to as 'heterosis' or 'hybrid vigor.' Consequently, when once the survival of members of the genus *Homo* no longer depended critically on living in small groups and on diversification and differentiation of breeding populations, natural selection may well have tolerated and finally encouraged the development of some tendencies to interbreed or unite. If so, this could help to account for genuine integrationist tendencies in many men and women of today. At the present moment of history the segregationist tendencies seem to be still predominant, but we can well be thankful that the other potentiality exists and is available for cultivation and use.

## Dangers and challenges

It may be asked what specific hazards our ancestors had to contend with in the Plio–Pleistocene. During the time of gracile australopithecines and early members of the genus *Homo*, in Africa, predation must have been a very great danger, especially for the young. There were many large carnivores on the African savannas, notably leopards, hyenas, and saber-toothed tigers, which survived by seeking out and killing exposed and weak creatures of all kinds. At one of the archeological sites in South Africa (Swartkrans) the skull of a juvenile *Australopithecus* has been found with holes punctured in it at points corresponding closely to the positions of a leopard's canines. The protohumans who survived in that environment were alert, intelligent, and resourceful, and they undoubtedly sought safety in group life. Protection by strong adult males must have been crucial.

As hundreds of thousands of years passed, the adult males acquired enough experience and skill so that the dangers of predation were progressively reduced. Before 1,000,000 BP, males of the species *Homo erectus* had become reasonably effective predators themselves, and one may wonder whether hyenas had not by then already begun to acquire their present fear of humans. It was probably in the period before 2,000,000 BP that our ancestors came closest to extinction.

Hunger was undoubtedly another important hazard in the earliest days, especially if one reason for venturing out of the forests was that traditional plant foods were becoming scarce. The discovery and gathering of new kinds of plant foods and the occasional capture of small animals or scavenging of large ones would not have been very efficient at the start. However, when in the course of evolutionary time some new abilities in hunting had been acquired, hunger should not have been a major problem: usually there was a fair supply of game on the African savannas, and limited numbers of skilful hunters and their families should have been adequately nourished.

A more serious problem could have been the picking up of new parasites, to which no immunity or resistance had been acquired, when there was a change of diet, especially meat. (Even measles, when introduced into America by the Spaniards, caused catastrophes among the Indians.) In addition, long-established parasites would always have taken some toll. Many of the parasites to which humans are subject are found also in apes and monkeys, and are believed to have been evolving, millennium by millennium, along with their hosts; they include various intestinal worms, lice, and bacteria. Other serious bacterial infections, including anthrax and botulism, must from time to time have been picked up from handling animals, with disastrous consequences. On the other hand, infections like smallpox were probably not common, for epidemics and plagues striking large numbers could not have existed in hunting–gathering times. On the savannas, some jungle diseases such as malaria and yellow fever should not have been a problem.

After our primate ancestors came down from the trees they suffered far fewer broken bones than before (gibbons are known to have a great many). Later, in savanna days, the potential dangers of sprained ankles and other temporary disablements were greatly reduced whenever home bases came into use.

At intervals, perhaps sometimes more than once in a generation, volcanic eruptions in eastern Africa may have taken many lives. The most widespread cause of death was probably not that of frying in molten lava, or smothering under a heavy fall of ash as at Pompeii, but rather that of famine after large areas had been scorched and laid waste.

For the rest, mutations and accidents of birth must always have caused a certain number of deaths. Observations of the San and other living hunter–gatherers suggest that malformed infants were commonly put to death as soon as they were born, and when they were not they could hardly have survived for long. In Africa climatic changes were generally not so sudden or drastic as to be a major threat in themselves, though they must have caused changes in the kinds of food available. There could hardly have been organized wars until after pastoral or agricultural life had produced sizable communities and the accumulation of goods, but there was surely recurrent fighting between members of different breeding groups and even a single group, resulting in deaths.

In northern regions there was quite a different situation. We do not yet know when or why protohumans, members of the species *Homo erectus*, penetrated into Europe and northern Asia. Perhaps they were following game; perhaps they simply drifted from campsite to campsite, generally moving northwards, and then happened upon ecological niches where they could prosper; perhaps they were pushed from some center of dispersal by populations at that time better adapted; perhaps they were propelled by that inborn penchant for exploration and discovery which is a trait of some monkeys and many men.

All we know is that by the Middle Pleistocene some representatives of *Homo erectus* were present in northern China and in Germany and Hungary. The sites where their remains have been found are now dated provisionally at 700,000 BP, 500,000 BP, or later, well into the age of glaciations. There is no way of knowing at present whether these represent the earliest foot-holds in northern regions; it is perfectly possible that some groups had arrived there several hundred thousand years earlier. Other groups surely arrived later in Atlantic Europe and the Mediterranean basin.

In Europe, where Middle Pleistocene conditions are best documented at present, those adventurous protohumans were to encounter unimagined environmental challenges. Presumably it was during interglacial or possibly preglacial times that they intially ventured northwards, but for great portions of the ensuing hundreds of thousands of years their descendants were exposed to severe cold, and – much more seriously – to severe scarcities of plant foods, so that they became heavily dependent on the hunting of big game. A great many of them, and many small population isolates, must have perished during the intermittent glaciations, while the hardy survivors doubtless flourished and multiplied rapidly during the warm intervals lasting many tens of thousands of years. The pressure of natural selection must have been exceptionally intense.

Since the margins of time available for responses were usually too short for genetic adaptations, the first hope for survival lay in cultural adaptations, which, if possible at all, can become operative in a few generations or even in one. Fortunately for us, those ancestors were already at a level where successful cultural responses were possible. One of the first of these, especially if the ancestors were already hairless, must have been learning to clothe themselves with animal skins and furs.

Another response must have been fire. In Africa there is no positive evidence of the use of fire before about 200,000 BP, though archaeologists today are inclined to think that chemical characteristics of the soil in many regions could have erased charred remains, and that there is consequently no way of knowing when it was first used. But definite evidence of fire has been found at the *Homo erectus* sites in China and Hungary, and there fire was certainly needed. Clear traces of fire have been found at important Acheulean sites in Europe a little later (Torralba and Ambrona in Spain and Terra Amata in France). Such traces are common at Neanderthal sites, and there is evidence that Neanderthalers cooked their food. In the beginning, protohumans may have captured fire and kept it alight without knowing how to produce it artificially. Living pre-literate tribes have been found in that situation, and traditions of sacred flames are widespread. Ready-made fire could have been obtained from conflagrations started by lightning, volcanoes, or tree falls.

The possession of fire had important secondary advantages. It made it safe to establish home bases in rock shelters, which otherwise seem to have been avoided: the fire kept nocturnal predators away, and the shelters provided additional protection from the cold and the long snows. And when the cooking of food was regularly practiced the range of usable foods was extended and the danger of pathogenic parasites was reduced.

With the pronounced dependence on big-game hunting during cold periods, and the increasing rigors and challenges of hunting in those conditions, the division of labor between the sexes may well have evolved further. The males must have devoted much more time to hunting, and their techniques of hunting are known to have evolved. In addition, natural selection must have promptly favored male roles involving increased support and protection of the females and children.

The females for their part may well have taken on responsibilities for preserving fire, for taking care of the home bases (which were probably more permanent when rock shelters were used), probably for preparing hides and stitching them together as garments, and in due course for cooking. The gathering of plant foods would have been abandoned for many months of the year during glaciations. Perhaps it was at this stage that home-making became a sufficiently complex and important undertaking to start that tradition of womanly activities. Such activities were then so exacting and so vital to the survival of family groups that they would have been held in honor both by the males and by the females themselves, as indeed they were in the settling of the American West.

While these cultural adaptations were being urgently improvised, the more gradual processes of genetic change were surely set in motion. Many generations may have been required for them to take effect, often hundreds of thousands of years. A conspicuous change would have been the loss of the previous dark pigmentation of the skin. In the increasingly filtered sunlight of northern regions with long winters, there must have been selection for light-colored skin. This permitted absorption of ultraviolet sunlight which could synthesize needed amounts of vitamin D, not otherwise obtainable without vitamin pills.

The other genetic adaptations would have been less visible. As a guess, they may have included higher levels of physical energy and resistance to exposure, higher levels of resourcefulness and inventiveness, possibly strengthened propensities for group cooperation and new propensities for group discipline.

## Language

Early hominids, like the apes, certainly communicated with each other by means of gestures, bodily movements, facial expressions, and vocalizations of some kind. But the great evolutionary Rubicon was the invention of a language of words, and in recent years a spate of technical theorizing has arisen over that subject. In the early 1970s certain scholars issued the arresting proposal – supported by a panoply of anatomical evidence which was promptly disputed – that Neanderthal Man, judging from a plaster cast of one skull of the classic type, did not possess a pharynx capable of articulating and resonating certain vowel sounds needed for human language. After several years of technical debate the initial proposal has been considerably toned down. In its 1977 form it says, in effect, only that the classic Neanderthalers were not 'physiologically equivalent to modern humans' in speech capability and that their phonetic range differed 'slightly.' Even this mild handicap is not imputed to the progressive Neanderthalers. Consequently there now seems to be no reason to question the judgement of Jane Hill in an authoritative review published in 1972, concluding that so far as vocal tract anatomy and brain development are concerned 'the earliest origins of true language might be several million years old.'

In then seems useful to search for other clues. Concerning the Neanderthalers, the first and most important one is that they often buried their dead. More than a dozen Neanderthal burials have been found in Europe and western Asia, including several burials of children and several burials in which offerings were placed with the dead – in some cases animal bones which may have had meat on them, in one case a whole animal, in several cases stone implements, in one case flowers, in another a ring of stones encircling the head, in another a pattern of ibex horns, in another a pattern of bear skulls. Thus it appears that the Neanderthalers had convictions of some kind about death, about a life after death, or about what we call magic. Could such beliefs have taken form, and could they have spread widely in a human subspecies, if there had been no language of words?

The other clues about the Neanderthalers are more tenuous. At one of the burial sites (San Circeo in Italy) it was found that the opening at the base of the skull had been artificially enlarged. This has led to a guess that the brain had perhaps been extracted and eaten ceremonially. Another clue, a little more significant because of frequent occurrence, is that Neanderthalers made much use of red ochre. This is an earthy iron ore such as hematite which occurs naturally in lumps and can be sharpened into pencils or pulverized and mixed with liquid to form a paste; if it is fired or heated its redness is intensified. In the words of E. E. Wreschner, 'Ochre is closely connected with the rituals, magic beliefs, and symbolic behavior of Upper Paleolithic, Epipaleolithic, Neolithic, and modern man.' Evidences of the collection and use of ochre have been found in numerous Neanderthal living sites in six countries from Spain to Russia, and in three of the burial sites just referred to it figures among the grave goods left with the dead. It is very tempting to regard it as an accompaniment of abstract ideas and purposeful symbolization, and hence of words. Here it would be well to have confirmatory evidence of some sort.

As for *Homo erectus*, the immediate progenitor of the Neanderthalers, it may be asked whether the planning of hunting expeditions, or the advance organizing of strategies for separating an elephant from its herd and driving it into a morass, could have been accomplished without at least rudimentary verbal communication. (Verbal communication was probably needed more at that planning stage than for the exchange of signals during the actual chase.) Similarly, it may be asked whether the teaching and transmission of behavior connected with fire would not also have required spoken language of sorts: keeping a fire alight, kindling a fire, establishing home bases in rock shelters under the protection of fire, using fire to prepare food. As a tentative conclusion, there seems to be a very good possibility that *Homo erectus* had at least a rudimentary language of words. If so, this extraordinary capacity would most certainly have been pursued and developed; indeed it would go far to explain the remarkable success of members of that species on three continents in varied and sometimes extremely harsh environments. It will be remembered that the range of their brain size overlaps with that of modern humans.

So far as is now known, however, they did not bury their dead. Among the *Homo erectus* remains found in northern China some of the bones and skulls had been split open: this has suggested ceremonial cannibalism (which would surely represent the most ancient of eucharists), but other interpretations are equally possible. It may be a little more significant that there is evidence of ochre collection and use at two Acheulean occupation sites of the Middle or Late Pleistocene at Terra Amata in Nice and at Hunsgi in southern India. No protohuman or human bones were found at either of those sites, but at both there was a convincing assemblage of Acheulean artifacts, an industry commonly associated with *Homo erectus*.

Perhaps someday it will be possible to trace the origins of spoken language back still further, to *Homo habilis* in the earliest days of meat-eating and home bases, that is, 2,000,000 BP or earlier. As noted at the end of Chapter 5, significantly improved communication of some kind probably formed part of the complex of food-sharing cultural adaptations of that time; certainly that complex created new opportunities and new needs for improved communication.

There are not enough clues to justify guesses on this question concerning the gracile australopithecines. In the case of the robust species of *Australopithecus*, however, the rather static fossil record suggests a definitely negative answer. Indeed one could argue that it was partly because of *not* having a capacity for language that the robust forms were doomed.

On the question of how – in what situations and in what ways

– spoken language originated, the possible answers are intriguing but decidely speculative at present. In the past, many anthropologists tended to assume that verbal communication evolved from the limited number of calls and cries and other vocal sounds of nonhuman primates, each vocal sound having one or more specific complete meanings. Now, however, it seems more likely that articulated words arose in other ways, possibly as an advantageous aid to each individual's own processes of imagery and conceptualization, surely as an accompaniment to progressively developing relationships among members of small social groups – between particular males and females who formed lasting attachments to each other, among the members of hunting teams, among the females who remained close to the home bases, among the juveniles who played endlessly together, and perhaps especially between mothers and their children.

There are some appealing clues concerning the last combination. As Chapter 9 will report, a large number of psychological tests of modern boys and girls have shown that by and large the girls do better than the boys in verbal tests, that is, in the learning and use of language, while the boys' superiorities lie in other fields. It is conceivable that this represents a talent which was developed in females as an accompaniment of the exceptionally close association between protohuman mothers and their children. If this should be so, one could speculate that the vocal sounds exchanged between them during the months and years of early childhood came to acquire gradually differentiated meanings, in other words that one of the germs of human language lay in the happy babbling and cooing between infants and their mothers. A little support for this notion seems to be provided by the exceptional ease with which children today can learn to talk. As all parents know, small children pick up their 'mother tongue' without being taught, and they can usually learn a second language quite easily – surely a genetically bestowed talent. In addition, the babbling-cooing hypothesis may derive a little support from another observation that has been reported by certain students of children's behavior: that infants and very small children of widely different cultures seem to have a very similar quality of voice and to make very similar sounds, almost as if there were a universal style of baby-talk.

Confirmation is needed, but if it should be forthcoming one could speculate that the distinctive infantine sounds had evolved out of the primate adaptation of noisy infant vocalization mentioned in Chapter 3, which confers the advantage of signaling the presence of infants needing adult care. And the interesting implication would be that protohuman children may also have been especially active vocalizers, as modern school-children most certainly are when they are set free after an hour or two of restraint. But while juvenile apes and monkeys were not capable of taking the next step of developing language, it may not be too far-fetched to suppose that some protohuman children, with their larger brains and the different anatomical form of their mouths and throats, did take that momentous step, helped and encouraged by the protohuman mothers who loved them.

In short there are two or three different phenomena which together allow one to speculate that the interaction between protohuman mothers and their small children may have made a significant contribution to the development of human language, and thus to the rise of human culture.

# 7

# *Love Between Parents and Children*

The evolutionary background of mothers' love has been amply discussed, and there is very little to add. That background explains a mother's tireless solicitude for her baby's comfort, her readiness to confront any danger in order to protect it, her pleasure in seeing it smile, her delight in playing with it, caressing it, and exchanging sounds with it, her physical pleasure in holding it to her breast.

It can quickly be acknowledged that mothers are not all alike. Humans are eminently variable in their behavioral traits, and even in the maternal tendencies there are many differences between individuals; some perfectly normal women who are mothers plainly do not experience all of the feelings commonly associated with motherhood. Yet there is significance in the fact that so many distinct kinds of maternal feelings exist. Taken together they seem to be a complex arising not from one gene alone but from a number of additive separate genes or gene-combinations. In this context as in many others, nature has achieved an advantageous redundancy: if some of the standard genes or gene combinations are missing or fail to reach phenotypic expression in a particular woman, one or more of the others can suffice to assure the necessary minimum of nurture and protection for her children. Although statistical information is wanting, the proportion of women lacking every one of the maternal tendencies is, in all probability, extremely small.

There are several lovely propensities of the average human female which can be seen as a kind of overflow or diversion of a little of the great stream of maternal emotion: a continuation of motherly care for grown children long after they need it, a visibly pleasurable response to another woman's baby, a ready concern for any creatures that are weak or suffering or in need, a fondness for small animals, for flowers and plants, sometimes a weakness for diminutive things a general. A little girl's care of her doll surely belongs in this category, even though her behavior is doubtless reinforced by parental encouragement and other social influences. It is evident also in an old Southern Baptist story about a little boy who went to Sunday School for the first time: when his mother afterwards asked him who the teacher had been, he hesitated and then said, 'I think it was Jesus's grandmother' – because she had a picture of Jesus and kept talking about him all the time.

The proposition that some minimum of maternal tendencies is nearly universal in human females may need to be reconciled with the phenomenon of infanticide, which ethnographers have reported as practiced in certain preliterate societies. The explanation is that infanticide is not necessarily a sign of absence of maternal love; it can sometimes result from a mother's intense concern for the needs of several children already alive and growing. Many of the societies for which a common practice of infanticide has been reported are societies living close to the edge of survival, for example certain Eskimo tribes a few generations ago. In the Plio–Pleistocene a similar response in similar situations could have been favored by natural selection because it resulted in a net saving of children's lives.

Emotionally, there may be a parallel in a modern young woman who has an abortion. She is not necessarily lacking in maternal impulses; she may have an abundance of them, combined with a pragmatic realization that she is not currently in a position to give a child the kind of care which is necessary in our society.

As for the babies, they are born with a scream, and it is almost true to say that they have been wired to cry afterwards whenever they are hungry or in pain or discomfort. A little later still, they are predisposed to babble and to make their presence heard. Human infants also have very mobile faces, and the early smiles of small babies are often construed by ethologists as an adaptation which has the function of attracting the mother's attention and stimulating her interest and affection. This is indeed probably the reason why natural selection has established the trait, as a part of facial mobility in general, though it is still permissible to suppose that a baby simply smiles with happiness because it perceives that its mother is near. With the exception of those cases where a baby is deprived of a normal mother or foster mother, every baby knows that through its mother it is assured of protection, nourishment, solace, and love. Indeed it often knows of nothing else in the external world; its entire experience may be limited to this. Meanwhile, in boy children, those internal hormonal secretions which will engender aggressive behavior later in life have not yet been released. The extreme innocence and trust of early childhood, which Wordsworth, living in another century and another world, could see as an intimation that we come from heaven, trailing clouds of glory, we can see today as an intimation that we come from a mammalian past in which for many millions of years mothers have nourished and loved their young.

This happens to be one of the few areas where there is at present some fairly good quantitative information about human emotional tendencies and needs. There is now a wealth of evidence that a child is apt to suffer lasting impairment if, at an early age, it does not receive loving care from its mother or a mother-figure. Uncertainties and differences of opinion exist among psychologists concerning the details, but from many hundreds of classified case histories the major facts are clear: that intensive mother–child interaction during the first two or three years of a child's life is a necessary condition for optimum development, that if at that stage the interaction is lost for an extended period, or if it is seriously deficient or distorted, the resulting deprivation is so serious that it is apt to retard the child's mental development and may also damage its personality more or less permanently.

The conditions of deprivation can occur in a great variety of situations, including that of parental neglect or maltreatment. One type of situation where the evidence has been relatively accessible to quantitative study is that of children placed in institutions in infancy and kept there for extended periods. Orphanages of course vary considerably (and in the special case of some Israeli kibbutzim, collective child-rearing has worked rather well), but it can be said that very commonly, or at least in a large minority of the orphanage children, there are IQ scores substantially below average and low scores in other tests of overall development. The major cause is the deprivation of maternal care: as a general rule the institutions provide adequate nourishment for the children and satisfy their other basic physical needs; and when particular children are taken out of the institutions and placed in adoptive homes before the age of one year, sometimes even two years, there is a consistent tendency for their low IQ scores to rise after a year or so, usually to average levels and sometimes higher. Some degree of vulnerability may remain; the exact extent to which the early impairment can be reversed by relief from deprivation is still under study.

Some children are apparently able to escape or resist the ill effects of maternal deprivation, and in those who are not the impairment can take many different forms, affecting general intelligence, language ability, the mental capacity for 'abstract function,' or the quality of interpersonal attachments. It has repeatedly been found that the early damage is the most marked and the most difficult to reverse in the areas of language ability and interpersonal relations – as if development in those two areas depended on favorable conditions at a particularly sensitive early stage of life. Children who remain in depriving institutions after the age of two years are commonly deficient in the capacity for strong affectional ties, and in later years some of them turn out to be 'affectionless' and occasionally delinquent.

Evidently what a child needs is interaction with a particular mother-figure, normally though not necessarily the child's own mother. The greatest damage is done when each child has several different caretakers in the course of a day, and when each adult caretaker has partial responsibility for many children. (There is, however, some evidence that an average child can develop quite satisfactorily when two or more mother-figures provide attentive care, working in turns but with some continuity.) For this reason it is very difficult for a large institution to provide adequate maternal care; it is a social problem which has not yet been solved.

The human child's need for interaction with a mother-figure is undoubtedly more intense, complex, and long-lasting than that which the Harlows demonstrated in experiments with rhesus monkeys, mentioned in Chapter 3. At both levels, natural selection developed the compelling emotional needs because infants lacking them failed to attach themselves sufficiently to a mother-figure and consequently were often unable to survive.

Human children also need interaction with a father-figure, but up to now there has not been enough factual research on this subject to warrant definite statements. There are indications that a child's interaction with its father is important mainly at a later stage of development, possibly between the ages of five and ten. One study has found that delinquency is linked more with insufficiencies and distortions in father–child interaction than with maternal deprivation.

The father's love for his child, although usually powerful and compelling, seems to be different in several ways from the mother's. It is probably less universal; if we has statistics they might show that the percentage of men seriously deficient in parental love is higher than the percentage of women. The father's love probably shows more individual variation, ranging from an intensity greater than the average woman's to an intensity far lower, and encompassing wide differences in general character also. Often, for example, it seems to take hold not immediately when the baby is born but months or even years later, when the growing child's personality is manifesting itself. Certainly the father's love is not physical or sensual as the mother's is. Although it is usually accompanied by a lively sense of responsibility, it is less continuous; it does not need to be expressed around the clock, every day. No doubt the immediate cause here is the typical difference in occupations, in other cultures as well as our own, but it is conceivable that if the parental impulse were as continuous and immediately compelling in fathers as it is in mothers the occupational difference would be less general than it is.

If the above differences are allowed on a provisional and illustrative basis, they can be largely accounted for by differences which have been noted in the evolutionary background: a father's love for his child has a much shorter evolutionary history than a mother's, and a different one. It is unknown among the lower mammals; its antecedents appear mainly in some of the nonhuman primates, where the adult male is seen to assume a generalized responsibility towards all the young animals in his troop. And later, at the stage of Plio–Pleistocene hunter–gatherers, the beginnings of real fatherly affection could have appeared; but even then any males who had a parental attachment as continuous and immediately compelling as that of the females would have been under a considerable handicap as hunters, and would have provided considerably less meat for their dependents.

Perhaps a word can be hazarded concerning the effect on the young, in the Plio–Pleistocene, of the affection which it is suggested that they received from the adult males looking out for them. Basically it must have given them an additional sense of security – security of being fed, and security against dangers like the saber-toothed tiger, exceeding their mothers' powers of protection. It must have engendered a tendency to feel respect for these father-figures, possibly to regard them as benign and all-powerful, at least during the years when their support and protection were most needed. And since the father-figure usually had a good deal more physical strength and aggressiveness than the mothers, the young must have felt also some fear or awe of them. Such attitudes as these would have manifested themselves first as simple responses to immediate stimuli, but they doubtless had a certain survival value in themselves. They could therefore have been somewhat favored by natural selection and in the end established as genetically-influenced tendencies occurring in human children with moderate frequencies. This could help to account for certain father-figure phenomena of our own world, remote though it is from the hunt and the saber-toothed tiger.

In our world, again, there is another phenomenon which seems to occur fairly regularly: that of adolescents breaking away from parental authority. Even before the present moment of history, in which traditional values and norms of Western societies have lost much of their relevance for current life and are being thrown out kit and caboodle, it was common for young people, especially boys and young men, to assert themselves against their parents' authority, especially their fathers'. This could possibly reflect genetic predispositions, again of moderate frequency. In the boys and young men, it could be associated with rising levels of sexuality, aggressiveness, competitive dominance-seeking, and adventurousness or risk-taking – all activated by the great hormonal events of adolescence, which are of course genetically based. (The parallel in nonhuman primates will not be overlooked.) In the young of both sexes, the phenomenon could also result partly from exposure of the inherent fallacies in the mystique of the father-figure, and possibly the smaller fallacies in the mother mystique. And from Plio–Pleistocene times up to this afternoon one can see solid biological value, on balance, in tendencies of these kinds – for experimentation with new ideas, for discovering new values and establishing new norms, and thus making it possible for cultural evolution to take place.

In our world it seems to happen fairly often that when the young reach full maturity the underlying affectional bonds are rediscovered and renewed, based on a new strength-relationship – the parents recognizing that their children are different and independent, bound to make their own decisions and their own mistakes, and the young acquiring a protective attitude towards their parents. One can only guess whether something similar was apt to happen in the Plio–Pleistocene.

In this discussion of the love between parents and children, attention has been focused on the genetic component. But obviously all human cultures have also contributed substantially, first of all in transmitting acquired information considered useful for the care, protection, and upbringing of children, but also in establishing social norms and superimposing magical, religious, or legislative sanctions to enforce them, and eventually to providing organized assistance for needy children. But such cultural constructions appear to be essentially reinforcing or supplementary; it seems reasonable to suppose that they were easy to establish because they accorded with a complex of emotional tendencies developed genetically.

# 8

# *Love Between Men and Women*

Scientific research has done wonders with the atom and the DNA molecule, and not badly with visual–spatial abilities in children, but it has not made much progress yet with love between men and women. We have a universe of ancedotal information about it – derived from personal experience, from personal observation, and from literature including psychoanalysis – but we have very little quantitative information about the frequency, duration, and correlations of the emotional states which men and women regularly experience in love at successive stages of their lives.

A generation or so ago Alfred Kinsey and his associates made a quantitative analysis of the sexual behavior of large samples of contemporary American men and women, in terms of manifest physical acts. Their work, despite its limitations and flaws, is still a great landmark in the scientific study of sexual behavior. Other workers, both before and since, have made valuable additions to it. But in the domain of the emotions – where to an even greater extent human lives are enriched, tormented, or even destroyed – a comparable analysis is still awaited. When one finally does appear, many of the suppositions of this book will have to be reconsidered. It will therefore be prudent, for the present, to focus on gross emotional experiences, so familiar that they are not likely to be questioned (though even that is not a guarantee against error), and to speak with extra circumspection when less widely recognized experiences are discussed.

The present dearth of quantitative information is especially regrettable because there is such enormous variation and plasticity in individuals. Owing to the plasticity, some of the most familiar patterns of love between a woman and a man are heavily influenced by cultural factors; that is, they are constrained by the precepts or social mores of a particular place and time, and conditioned by the traditions and models of a particular culture. These circumstances make it hard to identify with certainty the genetic factors whose evolution we might like to explore.

The next chapter will deal with major differences between the sexes, where, as it happens, there is considerably more factual material at hand for interpretation in terms of biological origins. Here the concern is with various conspicuous phenomena which can be considered without much attention to sex differences.

## The bonding tendency

To put matters in perspective, it should be recognized that love between a man and a woman is not merely a contemporary or local phenomenon. There are explicit records of its existence in all of the great literate civilizations of early historic times, from Egypt and China to Greece and Rome. In Egypt of the New Kingdom, starting before 1500 BC, there were *Songs of Love* expressing with freshness and grace the ardors, joys, and sorrows of young lovers; in China in the Early Chou Dynasty, starting before 1000 BC, there were love poems and love songs of great sensitivity and delicacy; and the much more abundant literatures of Greece and Rome include many chronicles of love, from the legendary devotion of Penelope to the passion of Dido and Aeneas.

And as regards the preliterate societies existing in modern times, love between pairs of men and women figures in the great majority of reports of travellers and ethnographers. In the absence of any comprehensive collation of such reports, a random sampling may serve to give a superficial overview: Edward Westermarck's three-volume classic on human marriage quoted or summarized a total of 83 early reports in which the subject of love was dealt with, relating to preliterate societies in the Americas, Australia, Africa, India, Indonesia, and the islands of the Pacific; 68 of these reports, or 82 percent, testified that emotional attachments between men and women existed in the societies described, ranging from settled conjugal affection to suicidal passion, while only 18 percent were negative (these stating, for example, that the women were regarded as men's possessions, used for breeding or for work).

In ethnography as in other fields, however, solid information about love is lamentably scarce. Early anthropologists had an ebullient interest in everything under the sun, including love, but generally lacked the techniques of a modern scientific discipline, while most of the modern practitioners, many of them working with meticulous thoroughness and employing advanced mathematical procedures, have so far not had much time for love. And the outlook is not good, because most of the world's remaining preliterate societies, with increasing exposure to our own, are in the process of becoming literate or extinct or both.

Probably the best single treatment of this subject in the ethnographic literature is in Bronislaw Malinowski's 1929 work, impressive for that time because of its thoroughness and sensitivity, written on the basis of two years of investigation in the Trobriand Islands northeast of Australia. The following excerpts speak for themselves:

> Toyodola, the nicest man I knew in Oburaku, was for weeks anxiously watching his wife's illness and hoping for her recovery. When she died, he behaved first like a madman, and then, during his mourning confinement, in which I often visited him, he wept so bitterly that his eyesight suffered.
>
> Love is a passion to the Melanesian as to the European, and torments mind and body to a greater or lesser extent; it leads to many an *impasse*, scandal, or tragedy; more rarely, it illuminates life and makes the heart expand and overflow with joy.

Then, following numerous specific instances of romantic attachment, devotion, jealousy, unhappiness:

> In these examples we find elements of what we ourselves mean by love: imagination and an attempt to woo the heart through the imagination rather than by a direct appeal to the senses; steadfast preference, and repeated attempts at possession. In many of them, there is a pronounced appreciation of the personality loved and of its power to enrich life or leave it empty. These elements certainly appear in unfamiliar combinations and in a perspective strange to us. The attitude to sex is different... A platonic attachment would be

impossible. Above all most of the personal initiative in wooing is replaced to a considerable extent by the practice of magic.

To guard against overstatement it needs to be said that among the totality of cultures ancient and contemporary there are some where ardent love has been reported to be very rare, possibly nonexistent, and that even in the cultures where it is observed it is never universal. In conditions of material hardship there may be few opportunities for the blossoming of romantic love. Indeed, in our own richly favored societies there are unquestionably some men and women – no one knows at present how many – who never in their lives experience the exultant joys, the aching griefs, of which most of us are capable in love. And in any case 'marrying for love' has not always or everywhere been the prevailing pattern: many past or present societies, perhaps most of them, have given preference to other criteria in match-making.

This should not be taken as evidence that the tendencies of men and women to love each other are lacking in a large proportion of individuals. In some cases conjugal affection may develop in marriages initially loveless, in others love affairs may occur outside marriage, and in still others there may be valid emotional tendencies which simply do not reach fulfilment. Quantitative information is lacking at present.

What can safely be said, with due recognition of nature's exuberant inventiveness in individual variations and the plasticity of every human being, is that the predisposition for love is very widespread, that the great majority of women and men are born with a genetic capacity and need for forming durable attachments of an emotional character. Some sizable majority have a propensity for sustained love. In some the need for love is compulsive; they must always have a close emotional relationship with some person of the opposite sex, cannot get along without such a relationship.

The evolutionary explanation, it will be remembered, is this: that our early ancestors acquired tendencies to form an emotional bond between a male and one or more females because the end result was to provide nurture and protection for several years for their exceptionally helpless young. According to the reasoning in Chapter 6, the tendencies already existed in some degree about 2,000,000 years ago, and from then onwards were very strongly favored by natural selection. It is even possible that the development of rudimentary emotional bonds had started in very early hominids.

To elaborate the evolutionary process, some of our early ancestors happened to have as much of these tendencies as the most attachment-prone of the other primates, some had a little more, and some had less or none at all: those in whom the bond-forming tendencies were most marked, other things being equal, stayed together longer in a family group with their young; and those particular ancestors left many more offspring who survived the perilous years of infancy and early childhood and lived to mate and reproduce in turn, often passing on some of the bond-forming genes. Since other things were never exactly equal, the cycle had to be repeated a great many times, but in upwards of 2,000,000 years there were plenty of repetitions for ensuring that the tendencies became well implanted in the protohuman stock and that the genes favoring durable male–female bonding came to be present with an elevated frequency in the collective protohuman gene pool.

The Plio–Pleistocene evolution of the male–female bond as envisaged here had a wealth of emotional resources to work with, in the form of the ancient attachment between a mother and her child (and if the suggestions in Chapter 6 are confirmed, father–child affection was evolving soon after the emotional bond between adult male and female). Evidence that nature did in fact make use of parent–child love in this context may be found in the traces of that kind of love which exist today in the relations between women and men. It appears most simply in the protective tenderness of each partner towards the other. Other traces can be detected in the fondness which lovers often have for pet-names and diminutives, in some happy cases for children's play and children's tales. But the strongest evidence is in the warmth of each partner's response to helplessness, vulnerability, need, or tears of the other, in the fact that love is never so tender as when a partner's weakness is sensed.

It is essential to remember that at the protohuman level mere copulation would not have been sufficient, no matter how irresistible the urge, how fierce the pleasure. The primordial copulatory drive could have guaranteed plenty of pregnancies, and many of these would have been carried through in due course to a successful birth; but if males and females had not been attached to each other in parental roles during a period of several years thereafter – by love, in the absence of any other adequate force – the exceptionally helpless and vulnerable young would have had poor chances of surviving until adolescence. From a demographic standpoint, the rates of infant and child mortality would have risen from say 53–65 percent to levels insupportably high. This is why most of us today have strong tendencies to love as well as to make love.

As a matter of fact the two tendencies seem to be closely associated. Although reliable quantitative information is lacking, there are abundant indications, both in literature and in common experience, that there is a definite link between the physical and the emotional attachments of a man and a woman. An emotional attachment demands consummation in physical union; and also, perhaps more fundamentally in a biological sense, when a man and woman have been joined together in the blinding intimacy of that union there is often a tendency, on one side or both sides, to form an emotional bond. The inference is that the association exists today (and in our culture it has undoubtedly resulted in some ill-considered marriages) because it had solid adaptive value in the Plio–Pleistocene world.

## Overflow

The propensities for love between males and females proved so advantageous, and were developed by natural selection in such plenitude, that they not only assured male–female bonding but also overflowed into many other areas of experience. Thus in modern humans they have long been manifested in areas which we know as the arts. The arts, it is true, have also served the human purposes of magic and religion, perhaps from a very early time, but love is probably older than the supernatural.

Music, as Darwin first speculated, may have had its origin in mating activities. Singing may have served in the Plio–Pleistocene to express and arouse sentiments of love, to plead courtship or seduction, possibly to voice the delight of possessing and being possessed. Love calls, love songs, serenades, laments – and also, be it noted, lullabies – may well have assisted significantly in the reproduction of the genus *Homo*. The difference between men and women in the musical pitch of the voice is a type of sexual dimorphism a great deal more marked in humans than in other animals, and it is noteworthy that it makes its appearance just at the onset of the reproductive age. This clearly supports the notion that vocalization played a part in courtship from very early times. In our world the singing voices of some women and some men (possibly even their speaking voices) are full of erotic meaning for peculiarly susceptible or practiced ears. Most past and modern songs are explicitly centered on love.

Dancing may also have long given expression to love, since today it figures prominently in courtship and mating. In many existing preliterate societies it is a special feature of marriage rites or festivals of sexual license, and in our own case it is used both as an avenue to marriage and a prelude to seduction. The erotic content can be conspicuous in all types of contemporary dancing, from Balanchine or Béjart to discothèque. At some stage much later, love overflowed also into painting and other graphic arts, and of course finally into literature.

These familiar facts indicate what a vast flood of emotion was channeled by natural selection into love between protohuman males and females, fundamentally because it had the effect of binding them to one another while their children were young.

Nor will it be overlooked that in modern times, and probably always, the exertions which men have made in all kinds of pursuits, from sport to politics, from paid work to crime, have been augmented by the desire for women's affections. Sometimes it has made itself felt directly, but more often indirectly in the form of increased ambition for prestige, power, or property. On the women's side the efforts to attract and hold men have been more direct and no less assiduous. In both sexes, finally, blocked reproductive impulses have been diverted into other channels, some beneficent, some destructive, some pathogenic.

In short, the combined and associated reproductive impulses, physical and emotional, developed in protohumans through natural selection, are among the most powerful and engrossing of all the forces actuating human beings. Despite a very wide range of intensity and quality in individuals, they have had a mighty effect on the behavior of men and women and have pervaded all the realms of their activity.

## *The sexiest animal?*

Are we, then, the sexiest animal, whatever that may mean? Some say we are, citing the continuous accessibility of human females. Others have been pleased to point out that the human penis is bigger than a gorilla's, and that only in humans is the female capable of orgasm.

But the subject is more complex than that. It is true, as mentioned in Chapter 6, that the cyclical estrus within which ovulation takes place has for all practical purposes disappeared in the human female, and that coition can take place at all times, thus providing a high birth-rate despite the loss of estrus. It is also true that the human penis is bigger than a gorilla's, though this would seem to be simply a mechanical adaptation to the position and length of the vagina in a bipedal female; it is perhaps more relevant that the human male's nervous system has developed far enough so that he can do without the penile bone or cartilege of most apes and monkeys. Finally, it is true, as nearly all authorities agree, that in the females of other mammalian species orgasm is either nonexistent or very doubtful; this does appear to be an important human adaptation, though it is highly variable, and not universal, among human females.

But the reproductive drive is no less compelling in other animals, at the appointed seasons or times, when it can be more violent and uncontrollable than it is in humans generally. The fact that the human species has been increasing its numbers at a dizzy rate in the latter part of the industrial era is the result not of extraordinary sexiness but of extraordinary mastery of the environment and the causes of mortality.

In the absence of a valid measure of sexiness, perhaps the conclusion should be that under stable conditions every species is sexy enough so that its reproduction is assured. Every animal is an integrated system. One whose behavior is rigidly pro-grammed in inherited reflexes or instincts simply does what is necessary for the production of offspring, perhaps without great pleasure. At successively higher, more elaborated levels of development, with successively wider ranges of choice in behavior, species which have survived have acquired more elaborate and more pleasurable reproductive drives. In hu-mans, sexuality has had to evolve in order to retain priority over hundreds of new capabilities, interests, and desires. We pro-bably have far more intense pleasure in sexual activities than other animals have, just because we are more capable of many kinds of competing other pleasures.

From the viewpoint of this book, the really great expansion or enrichment of the reproductive impulses in humans is the evolution of a tendency in most men and women to love each other – more precisely, the tendency of one particular man and one particular woman to love each other for some extended period of time. When today a pair of close-clinging lovers whisper that they need each other terribly, it is probably quite true, not a romantic fantasy but a biological fact. They are products of 2,000,000 years or more of nature's selective breeding for the formation of emotional bonds between males and females. The lovers have a real and intense need to love and to be loved.

Moreover, at the level of humans, the relationship has to be a rather selective one. No doubt the lovers are floating a little above reality when they feel that they could never love anyone else, for humans are exceedingly malleable and human life is now rather long; but men and women are so much more complex psychologically than other animals, their individual needs and idiosyncrasies so numerous, that for many of them it may in fact be difficult to find a partner with whom they can share a deep and enduring love. There are undoubtedly many cases in our society where, under conditions of wartime, say, or in situations of special enchantment, a true emotional bond is formed between a man and a woman who in ordinary life would seem very ill-assorted, and of course this has happened regularly among the yearning and inexperienced young. Such cases are simply a confirmation of the compelling need of men and women to love and be loved. But if, as is usually the case, the state of love comes to an end on one side or both sides when the special conditions no longer exist, this is a demonstration that an enduring emotional bond between a man and a woman depends upon a rather careful assortment of partners or else a great deal of good luck.

## Loosening the bond

For how long, then, is there a biological reason for a pair bond to last? As a short answer, natural selection required that it last long enough in the Plio–Pleistocene to provide a reasonable chance of survival for infants and small children. In a monogamous family with one child this might have meant six or seven years. But probably a great many successful Plio–Pleistocene families were not monogamous, as indicated on later pages, and they certainly had more than one child. In these circumstances the biological imperative for the maintenance of a pair bond could have been a little flexible. There was surely very intense selection for bonds lasting at least a couple of years, ensuring male protection and support during one pregnancy and early infancy; and there was doubtless selection, probably a little less intense, for bonds lasting some years more.

A little less intense, probably, because in the Plio–Pleistocene there could sometimes have been offsetting advantages in retaining some degree of polygamous tendencies. Those individuals with the best qualifications for successful reproduction – for example, males with marked leadership capacities and females with abundant maternal tendencies – would in any case not have been left very long without partners for reproduction. On the contrary, a possibility of change would have permitted a particularly capable male to take on a new female, perhaps keeping the first one as well; and a possibility of change would also have permitted a mother to attach herself to a new male better able than the first one to provide protection and support.

If strong emotional attachments were formed and later disturbed, jealousy must have made its appearance on earth as a bitter emotional torment. Certainly jealousy is not a mere refinement of civilized societies, though civilization has no doubt refined and intensified its tortures. The emotion is extremely widespread today, in all parts of the world. There may be significant differences between men and women in the nature and power of jealousy, but it seems to be nearly universal in both sexes. The sampling of ethnographic reports found in Westermarck's work indicates that jealousy on the part of men has been reported in more societies even than men's conjugal love, presumably because in some of the societies men were reported to regard their women more as possessions than as objects of love. And the same ethnographic reporting sample shows that on the women's side jealousy was very common and often of tragic intensity. The evolutionary point is that jealousy, bitter as it has been for the individuals concerned, has had substantial value in terms of the survival of children, as an additional mechanism for prolonging the close association between the parents or protecting that association from being too easily or too lightly ended. In most societies, moreover, evolving cultures have exerted an additional influence favoring the maintenance of conjugal and family bonds, by condemning and punishing adultery (more seriously in women than in men in most cases). In general, this has also contributed to the survival of children.

It may be useful to pause for a moment over the plain contradiction between tendencies to preserve male–female bonds and tendencies to loosen them, both tendencies being here mentioned as having advantages. If some intermediate tendency was the biological optimum, why didn't nature select for that optimum instead of working in two opposite directions? Indeed, why not forget about natural selection altogether and attribute everything to cultural factors, or for that matter to chance? Actually there is a sustainable answer to those questions, based essentially on the fact that natural selection is blind and never knows where it is going or what the optimum is.

A similar puzzling antithesis of opposing and partly inborn tendencies can be seen in many other areas of human behavior, some of which have been mentioned already: segregationism and integrationism; aggressiveness and a tendency to form ties of affection; resistance to change and a taste for novelty and experimentation; fear and the control of fear. The reconciliation offered here is that genetic factors underlying the opposing tendencies could have been acquired in some cases at different periods of evolutionary time and under different sets of environmental conditions, in some cases at different stages of individual development – for example, during early childhood or in adolescence or maturity. In other words, the optimum, whatever it may be, is not an absolute; it changes. Yet once a behavioral tendency is established genetically in a species it persists for a long time, unless it turns out to have disastrous effects in a new environment. In addition, I suggest that when nature happens to furnish a species and even a particular animal with a pair of opposing genetic predispositions, the subsequent processes of cultural evolution (not to mention individual adjustment) can operate more quickly and flexibly in responding to changing conditions than they could with a homogenized intermediate predisposition. Thus it would appear that natural selection may sometimes have actually favored situations of opposing tendencies. Nature is as inventive as it is blind.

And of course it is never perfect. The pairing of antithetical tendencies in the same species produces sooner or later some social confusion, and when an antithesis is planted in the same breast there can arise disturbing internal conflicts and sometimes harmful psychological stresses. Such by-products have evident disadvantages, but it would appear that the disadvantages have in the evolutionary past been less important than the advantages; it is the balance that counts.

## The anatomy of love

A book like this one, written in literal prose and concerned with the biological foundations of love as revealed or suggested by scientific knowledge, should not presume to add to the vast and rich poetic literature which already exists and which will continue to pour forth as long as men and women continue to live and fall in love. All that it can becomingly do is to try to suggest some of the ways in which science can view known experiences of love, compounded as they are of inborn capacities and needs and of contacts with the outside world.

Take, for instance, an experience of particularly rarified

essence: many of us, perhaps most of us, have discovered in early adolescence the strange and sweet euphoria associated with the mere prescence of a particular girl or boy, and countless times in later life the warm impalpable excitement of finding ourselves near an attractive woman or man. Seeking to describe these light-as-air sensations, people sometimes talk of vibrations, radiations, electricity, chemical reactions. Some of those forces are indeed operating, but internally for the most part rather than across space. What really happens is something like this: after the onset of puberty the hormones which generate reproductive inclinations flow into the system in increasing volumes whenever elicited by the presence of an appropriate stimulus; although the processes are well hidden, it is known that they are very complex, involving neural perception, transmission of nerve impulses to the brain and from one nerve cell in the brain to another across a synaptic connection, activation of the hypothalamus at the base of the brain, activation in turn of the pituitary gland just below that, secretion of hormones into the bloodstream, transport of the hormones throughout the system (back to the brain, and elsewhere) and reception of them at key points, heightened general tonicity, and finally psychic states – all developed over millions of years because of their contributions to successful reproduction, and all vastly more marvelous than a modern magician's ability to bend spoons.

When two people actually fall in love, when their private miracle unfolds, the same physiological processes are at work on a much more massive scale. In addition some vitally important and uniquely human psychological capacities come into operation, above all those of prolonged memory and of vivid imagery or visualization, enabling intense emotional states to be maintained or evoked for long periods of time and over great distances. Superimposed on all this, cultural and environmental factors exert their powerful influences; in part, they supply traditional or normative models of feeling, which can range from crudeness to exquisite delicacy, from emotional mediocrity to soaring passion.

The external factors include also moralistic constraints on behavior, and these can be important. If there are no social constraints applying to the lovers – if they are mature and free, or if they are still young but living in the Trobriand Islands or in a contemporary British or American university – they can dedicate a good fraction of their energy to making love. In other situations they may be much less fortunate. Some cultures may in effect prescribe a prolonged chase, or the expedients known in American sociological literature as 'petting,' or even indefinite starvation. The stern restraints of the Victorian or Puritan culture in the West produced an assortment of unintended results, from warped lives to a flowering of literature – sometimes, as in the illustrious case of the Brontë sisters, both at once.

There is very strong anecdotal evidence that a refined culture combined with an intermediate régime of moralistic constraints, as in some European cities in modern times, favoring restraint during the initial stages of courtship but also eager sharing of erotic delights after love has been well established, provide a climate favorable for the ultimate raptures; it is known that in that sort of climate an oceanic tide of love can sometimes rise between a man and a woman, flooding back and forth and filling both of them to the uttermost limits of human feeling. One can hope that such experiences are still within the reach of some of the young of today, even though they may be momentarily disoriented, disinhibited, and disenchanted, and incidentally assailed by commercialized pornography and commercialized violence.

As the years pass, the later course of love is also determined by a combination of genetic factors of ancient origin and a variety of external factors. The most familiar experiences include the satisfaction found in joint parenthood and in other shared life experiences, the occasional susceptibility to the charms of others and the ensuing minor or major infidelities, the rather frequent occurrence of serious new loves, in most cases a gradual slowing down or cooling off as in the anguished prevision of the young Rupert Brooke's poem 'When love has changed to kindliness.' Some of the basic biological factors underlying these experiences will be suggested in the next section and in the two chapters which follow.

*Marriage patterns, including polygyny*

It is usual to think of human marriage institutions as cultural structures; certainly cultural forces are responsible for their extremely varied formal rules. Yet there can be little doubt that genetic factors have also been at work. Essentially, the innate bond-forming and bond-protecting tendencies of human females and males would seem to have been the underlying dynamic forces which made marriage institutions inevitable.

Cultural structures tend to vary widely within the limits of genetic capabilities, and to change greatly with the passage of time. If mating patterns were purely cultural in origin, one could expect to find some contemporary societies living naturally in a state of promiscuity, without marriage of any kind. But there are practically no reported societies, past or present, in which complete promiscuity (or, obviously, complete celibacy) has been the rule for all its members, apart from some unlucky preliterate tribes whose institutions have been corrupted or destroyed by contact with ours. This is because the great majority of adult men and women are so constituted that complete promiscuity is not what they want, that the bonding tendencies implanted in them by natural selection have demanded the formation of durable attachments. It is as if the essential contribution of culture had been to devise a great variety of systems of marriage, polygamous and monogamous, experimenting actively until a system evolved which was ideally suited to human nature and the conditions of human life. Quite evidently, that system has not yet been discovered; more experimentation seems to be needed, and indeed seems to be taking place.

There are some clues, though obviously no proofs, concerning the patterns of mating which may have been prevalent during the Plio–Pleistocene. And since those patterns must have left residual traces in our emotional nature, it will prove worth the effort to turn back to prehistory in search of them.

It will be remembered that in the apes and Old World monkeys there are diverse mating patterns, most of which fall into three categories: promiscuity modified by dominance ranking among the males, promiscuity modified by brief consortships and sometimes individual preferences, and harems which remain stable for lengthy periods, sometimes for several years. Very likely all three of these patterns were followed by the earliest hominids, at least in different populations.

At the protohuman stage later on, owing to the exceptionally long dependence of the young, most surviving populations probably followed a pattern of harems – more correctly, polygnyous arrangements of some kind in which two or more adult females were associated for an extended period with one adult male – or else a pattern of one-male–one-female consortships which had gradually become prolonged to a couple of years or more. As a guess, the second pattern would generally have been adopted as a first stage in a majority of the protohuman populations, but it would itself have developed in some cases into a polygynous pattern: if consort pairs stayed together for several years they would sometimes have developed into polygynous units.

The last point needs a little justification. It has already been inferred that Plio–Pleistocene mothers usually nursed their young for three years or more (as women of present-day hunting–gathering tribes do). A more speculative inference can now be added: that Plio–Pleistocene hunters probably had little or no sexual interaction with their consorts during a significant portion – say a year or more – of the period of nursing. The possibility that a behavioral tendency of that kind would have been adaptive in the Plio–Pleistocene is suggested by the physiological fact that ovulation is suspended in chimpanzees for something like four years after an infant is born, and in modern women during a period of at least several months of nursing. The inference is supported by the ethnographic fact that in a significant proportion of today's preliterate societies – about one-third, according to a random sampling by J.–F. Saucier in 1972 – the men leave their women alone for a year or more while they are nursing. Further support is provided by a different sort of consideration. Protohuman mothers must have had an exceedingly arduous and exhausting life – going through numerous pregnancies during their reproductive years, nursing each surviving child for three years or more, carrying one or two of their youngest children in their arms when away from the home base or on the move, and contributing substantially to the support of the group by gathering plant foods. It is easy to conjecture that nursing mothers of that time may not have had much energy, or interest, left over for sexual dalliance.

Thus there are some suggestive indications, though hardly more than that, to the effect that Plio–Pleistocene males often left their females alone during a considerable part of the long period of nursing. If they did, it is virtually certain that they had recourse to polygynous arrangements of one kind or another: the sexually tranquil male gibbon may be able to go six months without imposing himself on his mate, but the great majority of healthy protohuman males would certainly not have gone a year or more without imposing themselves on somebody; even a month or two may have been too long for them. Resorting to uninhibited guesswork, one can imagine a sequence like this: a particular nursing mother showed little interest in copulation, her male consort refrained from forcing her excessively but was soon attracted to a more responsive female, and if he was after all a capable and kind protector–provider the nursing mother was sometimes inclined to accept the polygynous situation, though perhaps not happily.

In this confection of inference, speculation, and gossamer guesswork, the first clues point, albeit waveringly, towards a probability that polygynous arrangements occurred with some frequency in the Plio–Pleistocene. A few somewhat stronger clues – what I would call circumstantial evidence – can be extracted, with an effort, from ethnography.

Types of marriage are among the subjects covered in George Murdock's comprehensive *World Ethnographic Sample* of 1961. The *Sample* is designed to be as representative as possible of the entire known range of human cultural variation, taking into account the quality of the descriptive literature; it includes every distinctive cultural type for which reliable information is available, even when there is only one example. It covers all areas and sub-areas, and includes about a dozen examples of ancient civilizations such as the Babylonians, Egyptians, Hebrews, and Athenians. It also includes a geographic sampling of contemporary civilizations of the industrial world, but the great bulk of the information relates to the preliterate peoples of the world on which there are valid ethnographic reports. Altogether, the *Sample* includes and analyzes 554 societies for which definite marriage data are available.

This huge mass of ethnographic information has been systematically sorted and cross-tabulated by A. D. Coult, always without any weighting by size of population. The marriage patterns are broken down into certain different categories of polygyny, plus straight monogamy and straight polyandry. The first facts that emerge are these: that polygynous patterns are surprizingly widespread in the world, some system or degree of polygyny being found in 75 percent of the 554 societies; that straight monogamy is much less widespread, at 24 percent; and that general polyandry – two or more husbands for one woman – is very rare, 1 percent.

The cross-tabulations of marriage patterns against other data are particularly interesting. One of these shows the correlation of different marriage customs with different economic patterns. Among societies where hunting–gathering is either dominant, co-dominant, or important as a means of subsistence (267 societies in all), 83 percent in each of those three categories have some system or degree of polygyny, and only 17 percent have an exclusively monogamous system; polyandry is not an established pattern in any of the hunting–gathering societies. On the other hand among societies at the other end of the spectrum (132 in all), where hunting–gathering is absent or insignificant, only 59 percent have a system of polygyny; the proportion of straight monogamous patterns rises to 39 percent and polyandry appears in 2 percent. These figures reveal an obviously significant correlation between hunting–gathering as a way of life and polygyny as a pattern of marriage. The correlation might or might not be a cultural survival from Plio–Pleistocene times, but it is in any case a strong indication that polygyny commends itself to populations at the hunting–gathering level, whether Plio–Pleistocene or contemporary.

The geographical correlations are also revealing. The most striking figures are these: of the 116 reported societies in Africa, 94 percent have some system or degree of polygyny; and of the 77 societies included as representative of Europe and the areas around the Mediterranean, only 44 percent are in some degree polygynous and 56 percent are monogamous. This region including Europe is the only one where a majority of the societies have monogamy as the established system; in each of the other regions – the Americas, East Eurasia, and the Pacific – the proportion of societies which are monogamous is 26 percent or lower.

To summarize this ethnographic material:

1. Various degrees and systems of polygyny are very widespread.
2. The incidence of polygyny is especially high among hunting–gathering peoples.
3. The incidence of polygyny in Africa is extremely high.
4. The Europe–Mediterranean region is the only one where polygynous systems are found in less than half the societies and where straight monogamy is found in a majority.
5. Polyandry is extremely rare.

These points lend fairly solid support to the probability that polygyny occurred with some considerable frequency among the hunting–gathering protohumans of the African savannas during the Plio–Pleistocene.

One can go a little further. Additional points are hidden in the meaning of the terms polygyny and monogamy as used in the *Ethnographic Sample*. A society is classified as monogamous if plural marriages are either forbidden or else not preferred and not frequent; in other words there may be traces of polygyny even in some of the societies classified as monogamous. As for the societies classified as polygynous, it needs to be noted that in a great many of them a majority of the men have no more than one wife. The *Ethnographic Sample* distinguishes general polygyny and limited polygyny: a society is placed in the former category if polygynous unions are both preferred and common, where 'common' means that over 20 percent of the men actually have such unions; a society is placed in the limited category if such unions are favored by the culture but are in a practice relatively infrequent, under 20 percent. It can be inferred that in both categories, and especially in the limited one (accounting for over

40 percent of the polygynous hunting–gathering societies), polygynous unions tend to be a privilege of men of above-average power, status, or wealth. The next chapter, dealing with differences between the sexes, will reinforce this inference. In short, even though all the pigs on that farm are polygynous, some of them are more polygynous than others.

This point is of considerable importance not only to the pigs but also to the farm. The conspicuous result of such a system, in a population of human pigs as in a population of apes or monkeys, is that the most successful males – in general the dominant or high-ranking males – will obtain more than one dependent female each, and will each produce more offspring than the average. In a population with roughly equal numbers of males and females there will not be enough females to go around, so that some of the non-dominant males will leave fewer offspring than the average or none at all. At the same time, males possessing genetic capacities for dominance or leadership, and also the females and young attached to them, will have better chances of survival than the others.

Among protohumans biological evolution and cultural evolution would have been working together to favor the spread of both polygynous systems of mating and also dominance or leadership traits in males. The proportion of males with inborn capacities for dominance or leadership would have tended to rise faster in populations with mating systems of unequal polygyny established culturally, and populations with a preference for polygynous systems would have tended to increase faster than other populations. Both points will become clearer in Chapters 9 and 10.

In conclusion, then, it seems a justifiable working hypothesis that polygynous mating systems were widely adopted by protohumans, that during the Plio–Pleistocene natural selection was promoting tendencies in males to seek more than one female consort, and was at the same time favoring cultural systems of polygyny. Very possibly it came about that most males were born with a tendency to wish for two or more females, even though in practice this privilege was generally reserved, as in polygynous societies today, for males with traits for dominance or leadership. Chapter 10, dealing with differences between the sexes, will touch upon still more fundamental factors which would have favored polygyny.

Of course, if it is accepted that during the Plio–Pleistocene males and females were developing tendencies to form durable emotional attachments to one another, the suggested polygynous patterns must sometimes have caused distress to individuals: it must have happened sometimes that a female suffered acutely because a high-ranking male for whom she had a fondness was pleased to maintain one or more additional consorts, that a low-ranking male had to live without a particular female or perhaps any female at all, and that a female conceived a tenderness for a low-ranking male but was not permitted to attach herself to him. And even though such situations must have entailed anguish or conceivably death for some individuals, it would again have been a question of the overall balance of advantages and disadvantages. Human unhappiness did not originate in modern times, though like human pleasures it has been elaborated and intensified.

Ethnography yields an easy additional clue about marriage patterns in the Plio-Pleistocene: great variety. Human cultures are immensely variable. The *World Ethnographic Sample* distinguishes several varieties of polygyny as well as the broad categories of general and limited polygyny. In the first category there are numerous sororal polygynyies, in which a man is encouraged to marry two or more sisters, and just about as many non-sororal polygynies, in some of which the ladies so favored should never be sisters. And limited polygynies are sometimes reported as preferably sororal and sometimes not. The rare pattern of polyandry, with a frequency of less than 1 percent overall, is surely a remarkable invention, though not a very promising one. And among monogamies the variety of patterns, and the rules concerning kinship categories preferred, permitted, and prohibited for marriage have proliferated around the world to a degree that has in the end become comical. With all this variety of patterns in historic and modern times, it seems hardly conceivable that any one pattern was universal in Plio–Pleistocene times. Unequal polygyny probably became the most frequent pattern, with various sub-patterns, but proto-human cultures were probably already experimenting actively, engaged on the unending quest of the ideal pattern.

In this light, a few comments may be added concerning our own Western marriage institutions. The unique ascendancy here of the monogamous pattern can to some considerable extent be ascribed to Christian teaching. The pre-Christian tribes of Europe were sometimes polygynous, and certainly one of the main ways in which the Christian Church placed its stamp on Western society was that of outlawing polygyny. But monogamy in the strict sense of exclusive lifelong emotional and physical attachments between two people has always been more of an ideal than an earthly reality, and today the radiance of the ideal seems to be fading. There is little need to elaborate on the varied escapes and subterfuges practiced in Western societies in order to stretch the confines of monogamy – divorce, annulment, permanent liaisons, clandestine love affairs, casual infidelities, active flirtations, platonic intimacies. There are probably few marriages in any Western society which do not at some time undergo one or more of these expansions in the course of a long lifetime.

In certain European countries where divorce has been difficult or impossible, extramarital liaisons have been the general rule. The United States, being mainly open and non-traditionalist, has preferred divorce and remarriage, and according to US Census Bureau statistics the rate of divorces per 1000 married couples has been rising substantially in the past 20 years, increasing about 140 percent between 1960 and 1979. The best measure of the current prevalence of divorce in the United States is obtained by taking the proportion of women aged 30 who are already divorced and adding a further proportion based on the divorce experience which older women have had in recent periods after passing the age of 30. Applying this method to the latest detailed census estimates for 1975, the senior demographer of the Census Bureau, P. C. Glick, calculated in that year that about one out of every three women who were 30 years old and married would ultimately have had a first marriage end in divorce. This compares with about one in four based on Census estimates for 1971. Moreover, most of those women would have remarried and some of them would have had a second divorce. Finally, the Census estimates for 1975 indicate that for every 100 divorced women there were 65 who were still legally married but living separately from their husbands.

Putting these figures together, one can say that if conditions remained as in 1975 something over half of all young women who married would ultimately have their first marriage break up in divorce or separation, and a few of them would be divorced or separated more than once. Actually, divorce rates in 1979 were perceptibly higher than in 1975, according to sample statistics of the Census Bureau. An additional allowance might be made for the numerous couples who are emotionally or physically estranged but who continue living under the same roof for reasons of loyalty or duty, for financial or professional reasons, or out of simple inertia.

Partly, no doubt, these bitter statistics are attributable to the fact that human life is by now rather long for lifelong love. During the centuries when the Church's influence was at its height the average life expectancy of young adults in Christendom was probably a good 25 years shorter than it is today, and a lifelong marriage was correspondingly easier to sustain.

In any event, in our institution of monogamy there seem to be distinct elements of polygamy, including elements of the unequal polygyny which prevails in most other past and present human cultures and which is here provisionally imputed to our common ancestors in the Plio–Pleistocene. In recent centuries a significant minority of Western men have arranged relationships with two or more women and have either voluntarily or under societal influences provided some measure of support and protection for all of them – a wife and one or more mistresses, one or more divorced wives and a new wife. The institutional forms are different but some of the underlying realities, and the genetic tendencies which they imply, bear resemblances to those suggested for the Plio–Pleistocene. One is tempted to say that our monogamy contains quite a bit of crypto-polygamy.

At this moment in the history of Western culture the institution of marriage seems to be evolving rapidly, under the influence of the pill, antibiotics, and other new forces. Consequently special interest attaches to patterns now being worked out by the liberated young of post-industrial societies, who today seem so well able to reject cultural influences other than their own. What catches the eye first is the tendency towards promiscuity among the teenaged young, especially the boys, on which some statistics are given in Chapter 10. The existence of such a tendency has not previously been acknowledged in our culture, but it is not new in the world at large. Adolescent promiscuity has been observed in many preliterate societies, including the well-studied Trobriand Islanders. There is even a faint hint of a physiological trait associated with it, namely the fact that fecundity in adolescent girls, that is, the probability of conception, is low in the first year or more after menarche and does not reach its maximum until several years later: this could be a protective adaptation during the early years of adolescence; conceivably some degree of promiscuity in early adolescence was advantageous in the Plio–Pleistocene (before cultural guidance had become powerful in this area) because it gave the young enough time for experimentation so that they could assort themselves into reasonably stable pairs before the age of maximum reproduction.

But that is obviously guesswork. What will be more worth observing in the somewhat promiscuous young will be the frequency with which in maturity they form one-to-one attachments lasting several years. This has already been reported to occur in many cases, but it is too soon to know how high the normal frequency is. If young people largely emancipated from the prescriptions of any culture except their own should in time show a general tendency to settle down in durable attachments, this would confirm that the genetic bond-forming tendencies which underlie marriage institutions are indeed compelling.

## Incest avoidance

Through all the prolific variety of marriage patterns in human societies there is an interesting thread of unity: the incest taboo and the avoidance of incest. Incestuous matings are known to occur in most societies, but they are rare, and they are nearly always forbidden. Almost universally, sexual activity and marriage are prohibited between mothers and sons, brothers and sisters, fathers and daughters. Indeed, ethnographers and cultural anthropologists who have labored to make sense out of the bewildering complexities of kinship terms and marriage regulations in preliterate societies have often concluded that they are essentially based on the incest taboo. Thus Robin Fox, after years of wrestling with kinship systems in such societies, has written of the incest taboo, 'It lies at the back of all systems of kinship and marriage, and represents a basic ground rule of such systems.'

In addition, alongside the taboo, the great majority of us seem to have, at least from mid-adolescence onwards, a pronounced psychological tendency to avoid incest, varying in intensity in different individuals and sometimes amounting to a revulsion which is much stronger than any cultural precepts. Although there is no scientifically controlled information of a quantitative nature on precisely this point, a suggestive collateral indication is provided by good data on a different subject, namely the tendency of children reared together in Israeli kibbutzim to avoid marrying each other: marriage records of thousands of Israeli adults brought up in those agricultural collectives (as reported by J. Shepher in 1971) contain not a single case of marriage between a man and a woman reared together throughout childhood; the only exceptions involve pairs who had been separated and placed in different kibbutzim for a large part of their childhood. According to many young people who have had the experience, boys and girls reared in the same kibbutz feel no sexual attraction for each other.

Why? How did these extremely widespread prohibitions and inhibitions originate? It there a biological basis for them too? Yes, there is, and it is of major interest for this book because it illustrates how genetic factors can have a far-reaching but invisible and unsuspected influence on human behavioral tendencies and even on human cultural precepts.

Psychoanalysts brought a wealth of creative imagination to bear on the incest taboo, starting with Freud, whose intuitions were flashing at a time when certain cardinal scientific facts were still unknown; and by now there exist many more or less colorful explanations of the phenomenon. Now, however, it is reasonably clear that the primary explanation is to be sought in genetics.

Human populations carry a rather heavy genetic load of harmful recessive genes. Such genes are harmless or sometimes even beneficial to an individual carrying them when they are heterozygous – that is, when present on only one of a particular pair of chromosomes, either on the chromosome received from the mother or on the one received from the father. But they cause early death or serious physical or mental defects on the rare occasions when they are homozygous – that is, when the genes at the same particular locus of both the maternal chromosome and the paternal chromosome of that pair are of the same harmful type, resulting in a double dose. It has been calculated that the average person carries several harmful recessive genes – up to ten or more, depending on the degree of harmfulness taken into account, equivalent collectively to more than two lethal genes. (Harmful genes originate in mutations. Those which are called 'dominant' instead of 'recessive' tend to have their bad effects in every case, and therefore do not last very long in a population.) Recessive harmful genes are transmitted from generation to generation over long periods, in principle doing no harm except in those tragic cases where an individual happens to inherit one of them in a double dose, from both parents. Under the laws of chance this will happen very rarely if there is no inbreeding; but it will happen much more often if the two parents are closely related, because in such cases there is a much higher probability that both parents will possess through common inheritance the same harmful gene.

Studies made in the 1960s of 31 children born to father–daughter and brother–sister unions in the United States and England established that 6 of the children died early and that 12 of the survivors had severe mental or physical defects – making a total of 58 percent of the 31 children, as compared with 8 percent in a control group of children whose parents were not consanguineous. A later study of 161 children born of incestuous unions in Czechoslovakia showed that 9 percent of them were stillborn or died within a year, while an additional 36 percent suffered from severe physical or mental defects, making a total of 45 percent who, in a Plio–Pleistocene environment, would most probably have died before reaching reproductive age.

In all those cases together, even though different students doubtless meant slightly different things by 'severe mental or physical defects,' it looks as if double doses of harmful recessive genes were responsible for either deaths or severe defects of some kind in between 35 and 50 percent of the children of incestuous unions, over and above the percentages attributable to other causes.

And these figures cannot be dismissed as derived from non-representative samples, because they are corroborated by large quantities of data concerning children of first cousins. Half a dozen varied studies have been made in several countries on the medical history of large numbers of children of first-cousin marriages, and all of those diverse studies have reported rates of early mortality and of physical or mental defects significantly above the rates in children of unrelated parents. Extrapolation from such figures to estimate the far greater probability of homozygosity in children of incestuous parents, using well-proven formulas of modern genetics, yields results compatible with those in the studies cited above.

Starting from such figures as those, it can be calculated that during nearly all of our 3,000,000 years the rates of infant and child mortality would not have stayed within a tolerable range such as 53 to 65 percent but would have risen to extinction levels in many populations where individuals were not restrained from brother–sister and parent–offspring matings by either incest-avoidance tendencies or cultural incest taboos, or both. Incest-avoidance tendencies and cultural incest taboos, whenever they appeared, must have been decisively favored by natural selection.

Starting a generation ago, anthropologists have cited many social factors to explain the incest taboo, for example the elimination of a major cause of conflicts within family groups, and the valuable social consequences of matings between members of neighboring populations. Such factors have un-doubtedly contributed to the spread of the incest taboo, but on more recent evidence the recessive-gene factor has almost certainly been the most important one.

There is now general agreement, among scientists who have studied the genetics of the question, that this factor has been mainly reponsible for the very widespread distribution of both the psychological tendencies and the taboo opposing incest. This conclusion is supported, moreover, by persuasive evidence in primatology that the avoidance tendencies were already being developed before the hominid stage was reached: tendencies to avoid mother–son and brother–sister matings have been reliably reported in the 1960s and 1970s in several species of monkeys and apes living in natural surroundings, notably rhesus monkeys, Japanese macaques, and particularly chimpanzees. In addition many studies of primates living in social groups in the wild show that the young animals of one sex or the other tend to emigrate to a different social group before mating. This of course has the same effect (or even more, since in some cases it precludes father–daughter matings also); it may well be that the tendencies evolved primarily for this reason. Similar tendencies have also been reported, in the same recent period, for many species of vertebrates below the primate level. (The very extensive data now available on incest avoidance can be found in sources listed in the Bibliography and referred to in the Index.)

Reflecting the great increase in pertinent information in recent years, John Maynard Smith of the University of Sussex has handsomely written (in a book review in *Nature* in November 1978), 'Ten years ago I regarded incest avoidance as an entirely cultural phenomenon; only a bigot could hold this view today.'

It is quite true that some animals, including the unspeakable laboratory rat, engage regularly in incestuous matings without ill effects. The explanation is that if a population is somehow able to survive the loss of many individuals that are homozygous for harmful recessive genes (for example because large numbers of young are produced, or because the shelter of a laboratory is provided for all of the survivors), the harmful recessive genes will be gradually bred out and will ultimately disappear from the population. But there is compelling evidence that early hominid and protohuman populations could not have withstood the deadly losses.

It is recounted that in historic times certain dynasties successfully practiced incestuous marriages. But the historical evidence may not withstand critical inquiry. In the celebrated case of the Egyptian Ptolemys in particular, the Pharaonic children were often adopted and very few of them were reported as actually born of incestuous unions. And of course strong and healthy children can be born of such unions in half or more of the cases.

I like to fancy that if Freud himself were living today he would tell his more undeviating followers that some of the phenomena on which he erected for them the rococo edifice called the Oedipus complex can now be explained more simply and directly: although tendencies to avoid incestuous relationships are inherited by most humans, they are normally *latent* during infancy and young childhood – along with the mating impulses – because in our evolutionary past there was no need for either of them at those ages, or indeed until adolescence, and because on the contrary it was advantageous to a small child to try to form the closest possible emotional attachment with each of its parents regardless of sex.

While further study is always desirable, the most reasonable conclusion from all the information now available is that human incest-avoidance tendencies and the cultural incest taboo have both been established in the long past, by biological evolution and cultural evolution working together, owing primarily to the load of harmful recessive genes in our genetic heritage. The moral is that powerful genetic factors can operate invisibly.

# 9

# *Differences Between the Sexes Part I*

Everybody agrees that there are differences between men and women in psychological characteristics; the arguments arise over the question of whether or not the differences are inborn and important. Some intelligent people, champions of women's rights, seem to hold that the psychological differences are sometimes inborn and sometimes important, but never both. Certain zealous champions even seem to believe that it would be advantageous to women to be considered exactly like men. This book, also an earnest advocate of women's rights, reaches the conclusion that some of the psychological differences are both important *and* largely inborn, and also rooted in our evolutionary past.

It must be mentioned that at a scientific level there is an environmentalist school of medical psychology in the United States, including very eminently Dr. John Money of the Johns Hopkins University Hospital, which appears to hold that the psychosexual differentiation or 'gender identity' normally acquired by children before the age of four or five may be caused predominantly by environmental determinants such as the influence of parents and others. In that thesis, the evidence 'indicates that genetic and prenatal hormonal determinants do not, in general, override postnatal determinants.' The clinical evidence, however, which is adduced in support of the thesis is of one kind only: the successful results usually obtained in steering towards either a male or a female gender the development of certain individuals who are marked by abnormalities of chromosome-complement, sexual organs, or hormonal function, reflected in various types and degrees of hermaphroditism or physical ambiguity in sex, including cases which sometimes end in sex changes assisted by surgery.

Although it would be rash for an outsider to become embroiled in the technical arguments, there are two major reservations which even a generalist can propose. The first is that all those cases of hermaphroditism or sexual ambiguity represent collectively less than 1 percent of the total human population, and that generalizations based on them – rare individuals on the borderline between the two sexes in anatomical structure or physiology – cannot reliably be extrapolated to conclusions about the remaining 99 percent of our species. Incidentally, in those borderline cases the 'postnatal determinants' which are shown to be effective include often lifelong 'hormonal therapy' compensating for an inborn hormonal discrepancy.

The second major reservation is that even in those hermaphroditic or ambiguous cases there are usually two different sets of factors which may have an influence on the development of each subject's gender identity, namely anatomical or hormonal factors on the one hand and environmental factors such as parental influences on the other. Either of these sets of factors, or both of them together, will influence events, and if they are both working in the same direction it is wrong to assume that the environmental factors are the predominant ones unless a systematic separation of the effects of the two sets of factors is somehow achieved and it is shown that the other factors are less important. (Julianne Imperato–McGinley and others have reported some unique cases in which, or in at least some of which, the factors *were* separated, and working in opposite directions – and there the anatomical and hormonal factors were predominant over the environmental ones.)

Meanwhile, for many ordinary people it is easy to draw faulty conclusions in this domain because of the baffling complexities created by enormous individual variation and pervasive cultural influences. When it is a question of a conspicuous, easily measured characteristic such as physical height, people have no difficulty in recognizing that men are generally a little taller than women, even though both sexes vary widely and a considerable proportion of women are taller than the average man; but when it comes to psychological characteristics, subtle, difficult to measure, and much influenced by the environment, many people are inclined to give it up as hopeless. Here, let us be more optimistic, or more stubborn, while always remembering that in every psychological characteristic where sex differences are found there is a large area of overlap between the sexes.

First, it may be recalled that differences between the sexes in the more visible features of anatomy and physiology are by no means limited to size and the external and internal reproductive organs and functions. Anthropologists working with human bones, fossilized or recent, make use of a large number of skeletal measurements and ratios to determine sex – 30 standard measurements in a study by the Hungarian team of Acsádi and Nemeskéri, with results tested and confirmed as better than 95 percent correct on large random samples of skeletons whose sex was separately and independently ascertained. The differences in musculature, hair growth, and distribution of fatty tissue are familiar to everybody. Standard differences occur also in basal metabolism, blood pressure, and red-blood-cell count. There is in fact a sex difference in the nucleus of every cell in the body, the chromosome complement of every normal human male including an XY pair of sex chromosomes and that of every normal human female an XX pair, and this chromosomal difference begets among other things differences in hormonal constitution which are of crucial importance. It would be exceedingly odd, then, if in psychological characteristics there were no inborn differences between the sexes.

## Psychological differences

In Chapter 5 it was suggested that the hunting of large game developed in Plio–Pleistocene males a partial suspension of fear and that protohuman females were evolving in the direction of ever-increasing care and nurture of the young. Now it can be suggested that the females were actually being selected for caution, for visualizing or anticipating possible dangers. An early differentiation of this kind can help to account, I think, for the more vivid consciousness of possible dangers on the part of most contemporary women, and the greater daring or recklessness of most contemporary men, especially young ones. These characteristics can be observed every day on streets of a dozen countries, in the contrast between young women and young men in their respecive styles of motorcycling – the young women typically using their machines for getting from one place to another conveniently, and the young men using theirs quite commonly for generating speed, power, and noise. In addition, contemporary psychiatric studies report a preponderance of women among patients suffering from fears and phobias. This suggested difference in awareness of dangers, like most other psychological differences between men and women, has undoubtedly been increased by cultural influences, perhaps substantially.

In aggressiveness, a characteristic which may be related to the suspension of fear, and for which early origins can well be visualized, there is reasonable scientific evidence of a genetic difference between the sexes. About 50 independent research studies (collated by Roberta Oetzel in 1966) have been carried out in order to measure this unlovely but originally valuable characteristic, most of them on children but in a few cases on adolescents and adults; almost without exception the studies found that it is more marked in boys and men than in girls and women. This outcome is confirmed in the report of the National Commission on Violence established in the United States in 1968, showing that in the American cities studied at that time the rate of arrests for homicide was 5 times as high among men as among women, and for robbery 20 times as high. That massive difference must have been the result of interaction between an important underlying genetic difference and societal factors.

The outcome of the 50 studies mentioned above is confirmed also by a more recent review of available research on sex differences in behavior published by Eleanor Maccoby and Carol Jacklin in 1974. Following their review the authors consider the three possible sources of aggressive behavior: genetic factors, social influences, and imitation. Their conclusion is stated as follows:

We have argued that the male's greater aggression has a biological component, citing in support the fact that (1) the sex difference manifests itself in similar ways in man and subhuman primates; (2) it is cross-culturally universal; and (3) levels of aggression are responsive to sex hormones. We have also found, surprisingly, that there is no good evidence that adults reinforce boys' aggression more than girls' aggression; in fact the contrary may be true . . . The available evidence is that adults do not generally accept or approve aggression in either sex. Either their reaction is equally negative for the two sexes, or they react somewhat more strongly to boys' aggression, on the grounds that boys are stronger and more given to fighting and therefore must be kept under closer control . . . This does not mean that we believe aggressive behavior is unlearned. There is plentiful evidence that it *is* learned. We argue only that boys are more biologically prepared to learn it.

This same careful study also makes these comments about the factors underlying the general run of psychological differences between the sexes:

It is tempting to try to classify the differential behaviors as being either innate or learned, but we have seen that this is a distinction that does not bear close scrutiny. We have noted that a genetically controlled characteristic may take the form of a greater *readiness to learn* a particular kind of behavior, and hence is not distinct from learned behavior. Furthermore, if one sex is more biologically predisposed than the other to perform certain actions, it would be reasonable to expect that this fact would be reflected in popular beliefs about the sexes . . . It is reasonable, then, to talk about the process of acquisition of sex-typed behavior – the *learning* of sex-typed behavior – as a process built upon biological foundations that are sex-differentiated to some degree.

Among the many other psychological characteristics which have been studied for sex differences, the Oetzel summary mentioned above reveals a distinct superiority of little girls over little boys in nurturing behavior (such as helping or comforting smaller children), an underlying everyday commonplace which in the perspective of this book is likely to be due more to our ancient mammalian and primate past than to the fact that modern parents give little girls dolls to play with instead of guns. The studies also show a distinct superiority of girls in feelings for others (probably related to nurturing), in perceptual speed (perhaps a compensatory adaptation of the sex which is less muscular and less aggressive), and most clearly of all in verbal abilities.

This last female superiority becomes evident in a great many tests, mostly given to children and young people; they are given very frequently because verbal ability is relatively easy to test and measure in children. The great majority of over 100 different sampling studies have found females superior, on average, in specific verbal abilities such as fluency, articulation, grammar, spelling, reading, and learning a new language. If expanding knowledge someday confirms the idea mentioned in Chapter 6, that human language originated partly in the loving vocalizations exchanged between mothers and their very young children, it will be clear that women's verbal propensities have been of enormous value to all of us.

Finally, there have been numerous tests for anxiety, and a few for conservatism in judgement or in risk-taking, and the great majority of them have resulted in higher average scores for females.

One of the characteristics where most tests have resulted in higher average scores for men is the faculty of visualizing spatial relationships. And here some genetic studies have found that the patterns of frequency of this talent in the two sexes, and of its association with certain other traits, suggest a rather widespread recessive gene on the X chromosome (like ordinary color-blindness, which for the same genetic reasons occurs much more often in men than in women). Such a talent would have been of considerable value in males of the Plio–Pleistocene because of their far-ranging pursuit of large game and because of the semi-nomadic movements of their family groups.

Psychological tests have also shown that males above the age of about 14 are often superior to females in quantitative and mathematical abilities, and especially in mathematical reasoning. In a small number of tests designed to measure curiosity and creativity, a majority have shown males to score higher. Similarly, a few tests have shown them to be superior in dealing with mechanical problems. In all these last cases, however, there is reason to suspect that the male superiority may be due partly or even wholly to longer periods of education or to special training.

Meanwhile, tests of many other faculties have yielded negative or contradictory results. In particular, tests have indicated that there are no clear sex differences in memory, abstract reasoning, or computation. By definition, there should be no significant difference in overall IQ scores, on average, because the standard IQ tests (Stanford–Binet) have purposely been adjusted so as to eliminate such a difference – otherwise, gentlemen, we might well be outpointed.

A recent and very readable review of numerous surveys of sex differences, including some of those referred to above, is contained in a book by C. Tavris and C. Offir, published in 1977. A more technical but very penetrating analysis by Helen Lambert of Northeastern University, 'Biology and Equality: A Perspective on Sex Differences,' is contained in a 1978 issue of the magazine *Signs*. (Detailed references to all the studies mentioned can be found in the Bibliography.)

Many important psychological characteristics have not yet been tested systematically. An especially interesting one is competitiveness. Few will deny that by and large, disregarding the inevitable overlap between the sexes, men are much more seriously afflicted by this restless, itchy, propulsive trait than women are. As one looks out over the landscape of our Western society, one sees innumerable scenes in which men are struggling to surpass each other, to excel in wealth, power, fame, or prestige, to win contests of a thousand kinds. For a comparison with women it would be nice to have some scholarly research and some cross-cultural information. Lacking that, one can have recourse to the *Guinness Book of Records*. In the 1975 edition of that unrivaled compilation, one finds that men outnumbered women at least 7 to 1 as holders of records in 'human performances' – from space travel to deep sea exploration to banana eating (63 in 10 minutes, by Mr. Michael Gallin in Australia in 1972) or goldfish swallowing (300, live, by Mr. John Parker in Los Angeles in 1974). This sort of thing looks like an inner compulsion stronger than reason; it would be hard to attribute it primarily to cultural influences. The ratio of male to female record-holders seems to be still higher in the world of sports. Obviously women also engage in competitive struggles, but less universally, it would seem, and to a less insensate degree; most women seem to be less tormented by the competitive impulse than most men are.

If this last is valid, the explanation can easily be seen in the evolutionary background. The phenomena of dominance-ranking among the males of higher primates indicate, according to the reasoning of Chapter 3, that in all probability competitive tendencies were possessed by the males of very early hominids, while in the higher primates generally such rank-order hierarchies as exist among the females are less universal and less important in group life. And in the protohuman stage of evolution the tendency of males to strive for dominance or leadership must have been just as strongly favored by natural selection as it had been in earlier stages.

Overall, the conclusions that can be drawn at present are these: that there are a number of marked differences between the sexes in psychological characteristics not obviously sexual, that most of the differences appear to be in some considerable measure genetically determined, and that for most of them it is possible to visualize an evolutionary origin.

## Primary psychosexual differences

But there are even greater differences in behavioral traits closely connected with the reproductive functions of the two sexes, and since natural selection would never have left the regulation of reproductive functions to the vagaries of culture, one can expect to find again that the differences are in large measure genetic.

Most fundamentally of all, there is an inborn difference in the strength and urgency of the spontaneous sexual impulse. (This spontaneous impulse is not to be confused with the capacity to respond to stimulation, discussed later. Probably a large majority of experienced adults find this difference so unmistakable that they need no persuasion, but there are some who have doubts about it, and in recent years quite a few newly-liberated girls and young women have denied that any major inborn difference exists, living out or living up in their personal lives, sometimes with a valiant effort, the doctrinal assertion that there is no such difference. Since many of the inferences and speculations of this book are based on the proposition that the difference is not only real and in large part inborn but also of great importance in the complex relationships between men and women, it seems essential to supply some of the factual evidence. Readers who are already convinced may wish to skip to page 175.

For quantitative information, the Kinsey reports are still the richest source, even though limited to a particular culture at a particular time. Their great merits include the fact that the samples investigated were not only carefully assembled but were very large, several thousands from each sex, so that many detailed breakdowns could be made without losing statistical reliability. It is today most regrettable that the vast research was carried out mainly between 1938 and 1952, before the sexual revolution; comparable research in the present juncture is badly needed, to show what has changed and what has remained the same.

The Kinsey reports showed first of all that there were great differences among individuals within each sex, differences in intensity of erotic response, in sources of arousal, in kinds of sexual activity, and especially in overall levels of activity. The overall *range* of differences, from the extreme low in a particular measured experience to the extreme high, was found to be very great in men, and considerably greater still in women. Consequently one must be especially cautious in making generalizations in this domain. Nevertheless, major differences between average men and average women in the United States a generation or so ago do show up clearly in the voluminous Kinsey data.

Squarely on the question of differences in the force and urgency of the spontaneous sexual impulse, there is such a wealth of information in the Kinsey reports that one can choose comparisons where statistical distortions and the strength of cultural influences are likely to be at their minimum. Thus various comparisons can be made between men's and women's frequency of 'total outlet,' meaning the total number per week of sexual experiences of all kinds which culminate in orgasm. If one limits the comparison to young single men and to young women who had been married but were widowed or divorced, one obtains samples where the members of each sex had a more or less independent choice of the level of activity and where the young women were both experienced and also relatively free of parental and societal restraints. If one limits the age groups taken into consideration to those of 21–25 and 26–30 in both sexes, one has samples large enough (numbering from 200 to 1500) and representative enough so that sampling errors are not great; and all of the subjects would have grown up or reached adolescence in the period of relative sexual liberalization following the First World War. And if one takes the figures for medians instead of arithmetical means, one eliminates distortion of the results due to inclusion of extreme individuals; in effect, one has a description of the average individual man and the average individual woman in each age group. On this basis, then, the finding was as follows: that the young women's total outlet was about 21 percent of the young men's, in each of the two age groups.

One peculiarity of the 21 percent figure is that the young women's median was pulled down substantially (from 36–46 percent of the young men's) by the fact that a good many of them discontinued sexual activity altogether after the end of their marriage. That fact is in itself quite a persuasive indication that their spontaneous sexual impulse was not very powerful or urgent. Kinsey had these comments, in comparing previously married men and women:

Once married, a male largely retains the pattern of the married male, even after marriage ceases to furnish the physically convenient and legally recognized means for a frequent and regular sexual outlet. These data are in striking contrast to those available for the widowed or divorced female who, in a great many cases, ceases to have any socio–sexual contacts and who, very often, may go for long periods of years without sexual arousal or further sexual experience of any sort.

Although up-to-date research (as well as cross-cultural research) is certainly needed, it seems likely that the large difference in spontaneous sexual impulse indicated above will not have been wiped out by the sexual revolution, and may not even have been greatly reduced. The revolution has enabled many teenaged girls to free themselves of parental and other restraints, and has also made it easier for women aged between

21 and 30 to have love affairs when they want to. But even back in the 1940s – which were wartime and postwar years, incidentally – most previously married young women were sufficiently released from traditional restraints to be able to have a love affair if they wanted to. Most of them had had experience with contraceptive techniques. Consequently the provisional conclusion which I think can be drawn is that the average young man's spontaneous sexual impulse is substantially stronger, more urgent, more dominant over opposing tendencies or influences, than the average young woman's (not forgetting the great range of individual variation), and that this difference is mainly inborn and only secondarily learned.

The question of inborn differences in the compulsive force of the whole complex of sexual inclinations becomes a good deal more difficult when a second factor is brought into account, namely that of erotic response to stimulation from a sexual partner or some other outside influence, because this factor of response tends to increase with experience. There is good objective evidence, as well as prevailing professional and lay opinion, that most women have a potential capacity for sexual response which can be greatly developed, and that such a capacity has in fact been developed in most women of our societies in recent generations, even since the time of Kinsey's studies. Some of the objective evidence will be mentioned later.

In the supplementary statistical findings which will now be reported, it is likely that the two factors – spontaneous impulse and response to stimulation – are both important, and are also thoroughly mixed up together. Consequently these supplementary findings cannot be taken as evidence of inborn differences between the sexes until after some adjustment – now unknown but perhaps substantial – has been made. Subject to such an adjustment, however, the supplementary data which now follow provide partial confirmation, valid even when the two factors are both at work, that there is some real inborn difference between most men and most women in the compulsive force of their total sexual inclinations.

In the course of their thousands of searching interviews with married men and women, Kinsey and his associates acquired an overall view of differences in sexual appetite. Their general finding was expressed in these words in 1948:

A great many husbands wish their coitus were more frequent, and believe it would be if their wives were more interested. That this may be an expression of fact is peculiarly corroborated ... by the large number of wives who report that they consider their coital frequencies already too high and wish their husbands did not desire intercourse so often.

Similar findings were made, and measured statistically, by two other serious research studies carried out in the United States, unfortunately at still earlier dates, one by L. M. Terman and others and one by Katherine B. Davis, published in 1938 and 1922 respectively.

The Terman study focused on 792 married couples whom the authors believed to be 'reasonably representative of the middle and upper-middle classes of urban and semi-urban Californians'; they averaged about 39 years of age. In this case the study was made by a group of psychologists using a questionnaire, with guarantees of anonymity for the respondents; the answers were subjected to numerous checks for internal consistency and truth.

To a question about the degrees of sufficiency or insufficiency of sexual activity felt by the husbands and wives, there were answers which can be summarized as follows:

|  | Husbands (%) | Wives (%) |
|---|---|---|
| Marked to moderate degrees of unsatisfied hunger | 44 | 22 |
| Optimum sufficiency | 53 | 54 |
| Moderate to marked degrees of over-satiety | 3 | 24 |
|  | 100 | 100 |

Another question, exploring the 'relative passionateness' of the husbands and wives, produced results which can be boiled down to this:

|  | Cases (%) |
|---|---|
| Husbands in varying degrees more 'passionate' | 66 |
| Equality | 17 |
| Wives in varying degrees more 'passionate' | 17 |
|  | 100 |

The Davis study was conducted by an experienced woman social worker in the New York City area, based on the responses of over 1000 married and 1000 unmarried women to a questionnaire mailed to 20,000. The questionnaire was directed so far as possible to 'normal' women of good standing in their communities, a high percentage of them being graduates of Eastern women's colleges, aged generally between 25 and 55 (with the result that all of them had been born before 1900 and had therefore been molded by a vastly more restrictive code of behavior than women of today, a circumstance which is useful for comparing the results with those of later surveys). Two questions addressed to the married women and inquiring about the intensity of their sexual appetite as compared with that of their husbands and about the frequency of their respective desires for love-making yielded results roughly as follows:

|  | Cases (%) |
|---|---|
| Husband's greater | 63 |
| About the same | 30 |
| Wife's greater | 4 |
| Uncertain | 3 |
|  | 100 |

A more recent study, by George Winokur in 1958–9, was concerned primarily with some psychologically disturbed women, but contained also information on 100 normal women about 40 years of age who were included as a control group for comparison with the disturbed women. These normal women are of interest here. When they were asked whether they enjoyed making love as much as their partners the proportion replying Yes was 63 percent, more than twice as high a percentage as in Davis's 1922 sample, implying very substantial development of the capacity for sexual response in the later group, but still well below the 100 percent which would represent equality with their male partners.

In a study made in England by Michael Schofield in 1965, 193 teenaged boys and 102 teenaged girls with experience were asked, 'Do you enjoy sexual intercourse?' and the answers came out with rather touching results:

|  | *Boys* (%) | *Girls* (%) |
|---|---|---|
| Very much | 72 | 52 |
| Sometimes | 23 | 23 |
| No, but I enjoy giving pleasure to the other person | — | 9 |
| Not really | 5 | 16 |
|  | 100 | 100 |

A number of more recent surveys of sexual behavior were published in popular or semi-anecdotal books in the 1970s. While these are not helpful in a quantitative sense they do contain many interesting details. They have been well summarized in the Tavris and Offir book already cited.

Since in all such studies there is not only a likelihood that changing social attitudes may have influenced the results but also an uncertainty about the exact meaning of key words used in the questions and the answers, a pair of sociologists at St. Mary's College of Maryland, Paul Cameron and Patt Fleming, attempted in 1975 a promising experiment. The respondents – 174 people of both sexes, aged 18 to over 65, mainly 'cluster samples' in three small Maryland communities – were presented with a list of 22 pleasurable activities and asked to rate each one of those actually engaged in, on a 5-point scale according to the amount of pleasure derived from it. The real target, Sex, was hidden amid Being with my Family, Eating, Being out in Nature, Listening to Music, etc. Although the samples were very small and some of the techniques employed rather approximative, the results are so striking that a summary seems warranted. In each of the subgroups shown below there were from 48 to 88 responses; they ranked as follows the pleasure derived from the different activities engaged in (omitting here the activities ranked lower than Sex):

|           | *Ages 18–25* | *Ages 26–29*     | *Ages 40–55*            |
|-----------|-------------|------------------|-------------------------|
| *Males*   | Music/Sex   | Sex              | Family                  |
|           |             |                  | Nature/Sex              |
|           |             |                  |                         |
| *Females* | Music       | Family           | Family                  |
|           | Nature      | Nature           | Music                   |
|           | Family      | Traveling/Music  | Nature                  |
|           | Traveling   | Job/Sex          | Traveling               |
|           | Sex         |                  | Visiting/Job/Reading    |
|           |             |                  | Hobbies                 |
|           |             |                  | Church                  |
|           |             |                  | Parties/Eating/Sleeping/ |
|           |             |                  |    Housework/TV         |
|           |             |                  | Sex                     |

Interesting if true? No, sensational if true, especially considering that the sexual revolution had already had its effects by the time of this inquiry. And there are some internal evidences of validity, such as the top rating of Family among women of 26 and over, and the consistent Family–Nature–Music–Traveling combination among women of all three age groups. Certainly, as the authors remarked, the results explain the complaint that 'Sex is all you men are ever interested in.' It can be added that in the age groups above 55, among both men and women, Sex slides further and further down in the ranking order, but the numbers in those samples are too small (9 to 30) to be reliable.

It is a great pity that the total sample in this study had to be so small, presumably because of budgetary limitations. One may hope that more ambitious and more rigorously controlled studies will be undertaken using a similar approach. Research organizations and foundations could well note the possibilities which novel and resourceful techniques can open up for exploring the fountainheads of human behavior.

Finally, a non-academic French authority, one who has directly or vicariously tested a larger sample of men than Kinsey, has something to say. This is Madame Claude, a convent-educated career woman of Paris whose memoirs were published in 1975. She had been for a time a prostitute, and for 15 years the manager of a call-girl operation so well patronized and so chic that it had been mentioned frequently and not unfavorably in the Paris press. Madame Claude was not given to statistical refinements but she had a good eye for what were for her the important facts. She believed that 90 percent of all women cannot feel the pleasures of sex as strongly as men do, and she could well have added that the number of prostitutes serving men exceeds always and everywhere by far the number serving women.

Enough on that subject. The point has been made. But there is another point which also needs to be recognized as beyond doubt, namely that the degree of sexual adjustment between a man and a woman figures prominently in the success or failure of their relationship. Nothing should be taken for granted, even this, but there is some statistical confirmation of it. The Terman study mentioned above was actually designed for the purpose of identifying the factors correlated with happiness or unhappiness in marriages. While primary attention was given to certain personality traits, the questions asked also yielded results showing that sexual adjustment was highly important. The statistical tool used was a numerical score for marital happiness, constructed by the authors from answers to a long list of questions about the attitudes and states of mind of each husband and wife. The overall average of the 'happiness scores' was around 68–9, and about three-quarters of the respondents scored above 60.

In connection with one question, asking each husband and wife how much release or satisfaction he or she usually experienced in sexual contacts with the other, the results were approximately as follows:

| | Husbands | | Wives | |
|---|---|---|---|---|
| *Answers* | % | *Average happiness score* | % | *Average happiness score* |
| Entirely complete | 62 | 73 | 46 | 74 |
| Fairly complete | 25 | 66 | 26 | 69 |
| Moderate | 9 | 53 | 13 | 65 |
| Little or none | 4 | 39 | 15 | 55 |
| | 100 | | 100 | |

Similarly, in Terman's analysis of unsatisfied hunger or over-satiety in sexual activity, it was found that the average happiness scores of both husbands and wives were well below the overall average in cases of unsatisfied hunger (57–62), above the overall average in cases of optimum sufficiency (72–3), and again below the overall average, though less so, in cases of over-satiety (61–8).

These figures give clear support to the widely held opinion: sexual harmony is one of the decisive factors in marital happiness, especially for men.

In recent years there has been an inordinate amount of public discussion of the subject of women's orgasm, and one should not add to it without having something new to say. Since, however, deficiencies experienced by many women in that regard undoubtedly account for part of the less compelling force of women's sexual inclinations, they cannot be completely ignored here.

It is well known, and substantiated in many studies, that women vary enormously in the experience of reaching orgasm in sexual intercourse, and that in the great majority of them the capacity can be substantially developed with experience. Kinsey reported in 1953 that about 9 percent of the women in his sample had never had the experience at all, while some 14 percent regularly had multiple orgasms, a few of them a dozen or more in a single love-making bout. In Kinsey's earlier sample of men about 98 percent were reaching orgasm invariably, though less than 10 percent of the adult males were capable of more than one orgasm in a short span of time. The results of numerous more recent studies of women in the United States or England, published from 1956 to 1977, have been well summarized by Donald Symons in his 1979 work *The Evolution of Human Sexuality*, which I recommend to any who want a full and up-to-date report on the female orgasm. Putting these recent studies together, one can say very roughly that 5–10 percent of the women in our culture never experience orgasm at all, that nearly half of them experience it usually or frequently in making love, but that the proportion who experience it always or nearly always is significantly less than half.

In conclusion, then, on the whole question of an overall difference in the compulsive force of total sexual inclinations, it is clear enough that in Western societies the average man's spontaneous impulse is a good deal more powerful and urgent, and that his responses are a good deal more intense or assured, than the average woman's – though the question remains of just how far the overall difference is due to external factors and how far it is due to inborn biological determinants. There is plenty of evidence that most women have a potential capacity for sexual response which can be greatly developed, and also that in our culture, over the span of eventful years since 1922, many of the differences observed between men and women have become substantially narrower. On the other hand there is nothing to indicate that cultural or experiential influences could account for more than a moderate part of the substantial differences which still remain between the average man and the average woman.

The most sensible conclusion is that in all these matters both genetic and environmental factors are involved, and that we simply do not know enough today to make a precise assessment of their relative proportions. The genetic factors are certainly fundamental and very important. They establish in men and in women certain strong needs and certain finite capacities for development, not yet measured with precision, and within similarly uncertain limits external influences can either check or encourage development.

There are, most definitely, evolutionary causes for the genetic factors, but before speculating about those causes it will be best to consider a difference in the *kind* of sexual need felt by the two sexes, specifically the relative importance of the physical and the emotional needs in men and in women. Probably one of the things that every woman knows is that the emotional component of a sexual relationship is for her more important than the physical component, but at present there is deplorably little quantitative scientific information on the point. The Kinsey interviews did not investigate directly the strength and importance of the emotional bond, and unfortunately there is so far no reported study which does investigate it with a thoroughness and reliability comparable to Kinsey's – a shocking fact, considering the importance of this subject in human lives.

Paul Gebhard, a member of the Kinsey interviewing team and at present Director of the Institute for Sex Research at Indiana University, has summarized (in personal correspondence in 1976) the impressions which he and his colleagues received while making their thousands of searching interviews:

These impressions are simply confirmation of what has always been suspected in our culture: that females value the emotional relationship above the physical erotic relationship; that males place a higher value on the physical than females do; and that for females the usual sequence is for affection to lead to sexual contact whereas this sequence is less typical of males.

Indirectly, the Kinsey reports do contain a clue about the differences between men and women in the importance of the emotional bond – if one is willing to venture into malodorous places in pursuit of knowledge. It is contained in an analysis of more than a thousand graffiti or inscriptions on the walls of public lavatories for men and for women: 86 percent of the drawings and inscriptions on the walls of male lavatories were sexual or erotic; but not more than 25 percent of those in the female lavatories were of that nature, and the great majority of them either referred to 'love' or joined names together ('John and Mary') or were roughed-lip impressions or drawings of hearts. Remarkably similar overall tallies, in spite of the sexual revolution (and disregarding significant discrepancies in certain socio-economic classes), were recorded in a 1976 study by Elizabeth Wales and Barbara Brewer, conducted in the segregated lavatories of four public high schools in Cincinnati. The differences between the sexes in this covert behavior no doubt reflect cultural as well as genetic factors, but the anonymous record in female lavatories is confidential testimony of the importance of emotional relationships for many women and girls. Light can also be thrown on the question by the stereotypes of characteristics which people attribute to the two sexes. One of the best investigations on this subject is a European research project reported in 1964, on the preconceptions of 245 French and German university students, both male and female, all unmarried and under 30 years old, most of them majors or graduate students in psychology. Each student was given a list of 154 adjectives and descriptive phrases, and asked to indicate for each one whether it was most applicable to men, to women, to both, or to neither. The students in this study were almost certainly expressing their own opinions more than their parents', and they were at a level where they must have acquired a fair amount of knowledge concerning themselves and each other. As might be expected, the published results attributed predominantly to men characteristics such as combativeness and a taste for risks and to women intuitiveness and various qualities involved in nurturing. Compassion, loving behavior, and sweetness were attributed predominantly to women. But the main point in the present context is that such qualities as tenderness, emotionality, and need for love were attributed in good measure to both sexes but much more heavily to women than to men – especially by women themselves in the case of need for love. Sensuality was attributed to both sexes, but more to men than to women, especially *by* women.

One of the very rare attempts at a serious exploration of this question in the United States in recent years is a study published in 1970 by Eugene J. Kanin, Karen R. Davidson, and Sonia R. Scheck on 'male–female differentials in the experience of heterosexual love,' a study based on 679 replies to a questionnaire sent to a large number of students at a midwestern state university. The relevant findings were that the male 'scores high on speed of involvement,' while the female 'chooses and commits herself more slowly than the male but, once in love, she engages more extravagently in the euphoria and idealization dimensions of loving.'

The provisional conclusion reached is that the widespread impression is still essentially correct today – that for most women the primary need in relationships with men is emotional rather than physical or erotic.

The corresponding need for an emotional attachment with women is of course present in modern men too, and present with equal intensity in a considerable proportion of cases. No one knows at present, unfortunately, in what proportion. Sometimes a man is even more deeply engaged emotionally than his partner. But in the average man the existence of a powerful and urgent spontaneous physical impulse creates a very different balance of tendencies. Later some evidence will be presented indicating that men are somewhat more promiscuous than women, especially in adolescence. Without any doubt, the average man is more quickly and decisively aroused physically than the average woman: in the absence of prior loyalties of overriding strength, he would often like to jump into a bed at once with an attractive woman, but she, the average woman, would usually prefer not to jump so quickly; in principle her tendency would be to wait at least until she had developed an emotional interest in him, and he in her. Moreover, if the inferences and the reasoning here are upheld, these differences are fundamental and largely inborn; changing cultural influences and personal experiences substantially modify them, and there is always the great individual variation, but on average the underlying predispositions are there to start with. Sooner or later, by and large, they make themselves felt in human populations. Why are they there to start with?

## The biological basis

In the domain of human reproduction, one of the most fundamental of all biological realities is the fact that a female is capable of giving birth to only one child (or only one set of twins or quintuplets) in a period of one to three years, whereas in the same space of time a healthy young male could easily father hundreds of children. This stark physiological discrepancy underlies some of the most important psychological differences between the sexes.* Most directly, it results in what biologists call 'differentiated reproductive strategies' – a valuable professional term for something rather complicated but not at all strategic in any ordinary purposive sense. What is actually involved can be grasped most easily by asking the following question: what are the physical and behavioral characteristics relating to reproduction, first in a male and second in a female, which under Plio–Pleistocene conditions of life – given the fundamental difference in potential rates of reproduction – would have assured to the individual the largest possible number of offspring able to survive infancy and childhood?

There are of course many characteristics, starting with good health, which in both sexes would always have been essential for producing the largest possible numbers of surviving children. In a male the *special* characteristics assuring him of the largest possible number of surviving children would have been strong and somewhat promiscuous sexual vitality and sexual aggressiveness, accompanied and partially restrained by protectiveness – enough sexual vitality and aggressiveness to be disposed to impregnate many females, but enough protectiveness, including a capacity for forming emotional bonds, to want to stay with one or more particular females and their young for extended periods and to protect and support them. In a female, however, obliged in the Plio–Pleistocene to devote over three years to the production and nursing of a single child and an additional three years or so to taking care of it, and needing the protection of an adult male during those years, the *special* characteristics would have been moderate sexual receptiveness, accompanied by a stronger tendency to attach herself rather permanently to a particular protecting male, accompanied by

*Robert L. Trivers and some other sociobiologists like to deal with this discrepancy, along with associated facts, in terms of 'parental investment.' While that metaphor is a convenient shorthand expression for specialists, and has become established in the professional literature, it is apt to be confusing to non-specialists; it has even occasioned errors by the specialists themselves, one of which has been pointed out by Richard Dawkins and T. R. Carlisle. John Maynard Smith has written that 'the concept of investment can be misleading and is always hard to apply correctly.' It adds complications to an already complex subject. Nevertheless, for readers who wish to pursue the idea of parental investment, and the more sophisticated idea of 'evolutionarily stable strategies,' important bibliographical references can be found at the back of this book with the help of the Index.

the imperatives of maternal devotion. She would have needed enough interest in sexual relationships so that she would attract a capable male, hold on to him, and keep producing young regularly, but not such a compelling sexual appetite as to risk the loss of any of her children already living.

If the above proposition is correct, it is highly probable that the greatest numbers of surviving children were born to males and females of the respective types described. And thus it would appear that after our 3,000,000 years most men and women living today are, in all probability, descendants of males and females who possessed tolerably good combinations of the respective sets of behavioral traits. This is a way of saying that in the course of our evolutionary past natural selection developed certain important differences in behavioral tendencies in the two sexes – 'differences in reproductive strategies' – arising from the vast discrepancy in their potential rates of reproduction. And it is obvious that those differences are essentially the same as the differences observed in our own time.

Since this is a key point, it may be useful to try to visualize some of the ways in which the evolution may have taken place. On the side of the males it is easy enough. The eager readiness, not to say randiness, of the average young man of today was certainly at work already in his Plio–Pleistocene forefathers, and in their early environment such tendencies would have kept the birth-rates high; if the females of particular groups were monopolized by older males, the young males would have been driven to challenge their elders as soon as they had a chance of success, or alternatively would have broken away from the groups and gone off on their own to look for available females elsewhere – either way contributing to elevated birth-rates and the renewal of their own genes. At the same time, some proportion of the males would have been predisposed to form lasting attachments with one or more particular females: in the case of those males, the resulting children and other close kin would have had superior chances of surviving to adulthood and of passing on some of the valuable bonding genes.

On the side of the females the picture is a little more complex. They were already richly endowed with tenderness, compassion, and affection; and a little evidence has been offered that today those gentle qualities come into play as one of the mechanisms for binding particular females to particular males. But affection does not spring into being instantaneously; even in stories of love at first sight it grows and develops with the passage of time, and in most cases it is established gradually. Some protohuman females would surely have tended to hold back in their relations with males, from fear or caution, until an emotional attachment had been started. Those who did so would in effect have been testing the reproductive qualifications of particular males – their sexual energy, their bond-forming tendencies, and their dominance or leadership characteristics. The latter, it will be remembered, included both fighting ability and also qualities such as protectiveness, intelligence, personal appeal, and always a very strong competitive drive. Females who were able to select their mates on the basis of the latter's overall reproductive qualifications would have left more surviving children than other females. (The workings of sexual selection will be discussed later.) Furthermore, females with a tendency to hold back until an emotional bond was formed – and also, incidentally, females who could go for long periods without sexual activity – would have been less likely than other females to enter upon a flighty sexual adventure or elopement at the expense of existing children. In short, there would have been very important biological advantages in female tendencies to be governed more by slow-forming and durable emotional attachments than by a quick-acting and relatively uncontrollable physical impulse. Females with such bonding tendencies would have left more surviving children and close kin, and the valuable genes would have been transmitted with normal frequencies to successive generations of daughters.

Yet as mentioned above it would have been adaptive for protohuman females to have some degree of sensual arousability. They had lost the riotous ways of the periodic estrus of other primate females – also for the good of the extremely dependent protohuman children, it is thought – but unless some substitute adaptation had been developed, ensuring that the average female would be disposed to attract or hold a male and to accept the ultimate physical intimacy with him in appropriate circumstances, the birth-rate might not have remained high enough to permit survival of the line leading to humans. (What happened, of course, was simply that females lacking such a disposition left fewer children.) To some large extent the necessary impulsion could have been, and probably was, furnished by a strong tendency to form mating attachments based on emotion or tender sentiments, but something more may well have been needed, a physical or erotic reinforcement, contributing to a readiness to continue bearing children throughout all the arduous reproductive years.

It would seem to be a good guess that nature's answer to this problem was the female orgasm. So far as our present knowledge of animal physiology goes, females of very few if any other mammalian species have developed this capacity. Signs of it, or possible signs, have been observed in a few species, and experiments with some primates in captivity have yielded evidence of a very rudimentary potentiality – which suggests that necessary preconditions may have long existed in various nonhuman mammals. It is practically certain, however, that there is today no other mammalian species in which the capacity has been or can be as fully developed or as widely diffused among females as in humans. Some other reinforcing adaptations may also have taken place in protohuman females for the same reason, including heightened sensitivity to other kinds of erotic stimulation.

Heightened responsiveness in the protohuman female must have been of great value in the Plio–Pleistocene. Developed originally because it led her to continue bearing children to the end, it undoubtedly had an additional effect which has rightly been emphasized by many writers: it must have reinforced the emotional bond uniting her with a male, by enabling the two of them to share in some degree the physical delights of that bond. And given the loss of estrus this shared experience could be renewed continuously, nearly all of the time except when she was nursing a small baby, and could thus have served to strengthen the bond and extend its duration.

# 10

# *Differences Between the Sexes Part II*

## *More on polygyny*

It will not have escaped notice that the differentiated tendencies which could have been evolving in the Plio–Pleistocene as a result of the vast physiological discrepancy in potential rates of reproduction – in the average male a substantially more powerful and urgent spontaneous sexual impulse, a more intense or assured response to sexual stimulation, and a leaning towards promiscuity, but in the average female a greater dependence on slow and lasting emotional bonding – would also have fitted in well with the inferred prevalence of polygyny at that time. In fact the differentiated tendencies might often have given rise together to polygynous arrangements. If so, it is likely that the physiological discrepancy was itself one of the original causes of polygyny in protohumans. A similar vast difference in potential reproduction rates of the two sexes is of course common to all other mammals, and it will be remembered that the great majority of other mammals whose mating habits in the wild are known either practice polygyny, in the sense of establishing animal harems, or else form no attachments lasting more than a few days (prolonged attachments being not necessary in their cases for the survival of the young).

The difference in reproduction potential would have favored polygyny through the action of natural selection working directly on inborn tendencies of individuals, because the greatest numbers of surviving children in successive generations would have been born to parents possessing behavioral tendencies which were conducive to polygyny. But in addition one can now see more clearly how cultural institutions of a polygynous nature could have been favored in cultural evolution: other things being equal, the highest rates of birth-and-survival would have occurred in populations practicing unequal polygyny, the lowest rates in those practicing polyandry, and intermediate rates in those practicing monogamy. And unequal polygyny would in turn have had the great advantage of facilitating the propagation of the invaluable traits of dominance or leadership in males. Thus biological evolution and cultural evolution would have been supplementing and reinforcing each other, here as elsewhere.

With the addition of these last notions, the cumulative weight of clues and evidence pointing to polygyny among protohumans becomes quite persuasive – speculative clues concerning Plio–Pleistocene situations, ethnographic evidence, considerations concerning propagation of leadership traits in males, the fundamental physiological difference between the sexes in potential rates of reproduction, and the effects which that difference would have had in higher rates of birth-and-survival associated with polygyny. Consequently the conclusion proposed is that polygyny, unequal polygyny of various styles, was the predominant pattern of mating or marriage among our hunting–gathering forebears on the savannas of Africa and later in the northern world.

If this is correct, that pattern has not only played an important part in the survival and development of our species but has also marked the emotional lives of many men and women of today, sometimes with felicity, often with pain or frustration. The most important mark, I propose, is that some of the males' original leaning in the direction of promiscuity has been preserved genetically by the prevalence of polygyny for extremely long periods, so that many men have remained until now somewhat less monogamous than women.

Probably most people share the opinion that men are inherently somewhat more promiscuous than women (in the ordinary sense of being disposed to enter into relations with more than one sexual partner), but since many may be doubtful and since the point is an important one it may be worthwhile to sample the evidence available. This difference between the sexes, assuming that it does exist, is not always easy to observe, partly because it is in an areas where individual variation is great, and partly because every normal man or woman has both a capacity for forming a fixed bond with a member of the opposite sex and also a capacity for feeling attraction to another member of that sex – again a case of potentially opposing tendencies combined in the same breast. The correct question to ask is whether or not the balancing of the two capacities in most men and women is such that men are less monogamous than women, on average.

Kinsey's judgement in 1953 was quite definite:

The male's greater inclination to be promiscuous shows up in the record of his petting experience, his experience in premarital coitus, in extra-marital coitus, and in homosexual relations. In all of these types of relationships, few females have anywhere near the number of partners that many a promiscuous male may have.

To cite one of the many statistics supporting that general statement, Kinsey found that by the age of 40 about 50 percent of all married men in the United States had 'engaged in extra-marital coitus,' whereas in married women of the same age the proportion was 26 percent. (About half of the errant husbands must have found their way either to unmarried women or to married women who individually were superactive.) Cultural factors certainly accounted for part of this great difference, because there is clear evidence that since the sexual revolution in Western societies a higher percentage of married women than before have engaged in extramarital affairs; but some significant difference between men and women undoubtedly remains.

In the 1930s, Terman put to his sample of nearly 800 middle-class and upper-class Californian couples, averaging about 39 years of age, the question, 'Do you frequently experience desire for intercourse with some one else?' The numbers replying 'Never' represented 28 percent of the men and 73 percent of the women.

As an interesting coincidence, the Schofield study of free-ranging teenagers in England in 1965 (in this case a total of 234 who had engaged in sexual intercourse in the preceding 12 months) showed that those who had gone to bed with only one partner during the year represented 31 percent of the boys and 73 percent of the girls. Meanwhile 19 percent of the boys but only 5 percent of the girls had had more than 6 partners each. Moreover 8 percent of the boys had succeeded in bedding more than 20 girls each during the year: whether true or not, this suggests more than a trace of promiscuous ambitions, which presumably were due to a combination of inherited genes and societal influences.

Clifford Kirkpatrick, a sociologist studying young people in the United States a little earlier, epitomized his findings with the following round sonority in 1959: 'In our culture, at least, males on the average have an earlier, a more intense, more uniform, more genital, more rhythmic, more continous, and more promiscuous sex drive than females.'

This is one of the many areas where more recent data of a reliable quantitative nature are needed, not only concerning our own society but cross-culturally. Nevertheless, if it is granted provisionally that polygamous tendencies probably occur more frequently among men than among women, and that some significant minority of men probably have rather promiscuous tendencies, especially in youth, it will be agreed that this difference between the sexes has in our time given rise in one way or another to a vast amount of unhappiness. This is partly because the difference has not been understood and partly because it is grossly unfair. Unfortunately, the love of fairness which has evolved in human cultures does not exist elsewhere in nature. For the future, our hopes must ride on a combination of human understanding and the human sense of fairness, and always on human love.

## Differences in curves of reproductive activity

This next difference between the sexes is even more unfair, and is the cause of even more unhappiness. At the same time, it is of fundamental importance in the relations between men and women. It needs to be recognized, with both compassion and tolerance, for when distress exists in the world the first necessity is to understand it; our natural tendency may be to avert our eyes, but effective remedies or offsetting measures are not likely to be found that way.

In the human male, sexual activity sets in rather abruptly at the beginning of adolescence, along with change of voice, pimples, and other messy pubertal events. Kinsey's graph shows the curve of male sexual activity rising immediately and very steeply, reaching its precipitous lifetime peak well before the age of 20, on average. Then it starts right away on a long, continuous, very gradual downward slide to zero, which in most men is reached well after the age of 70.

The female curve of sexual activity is different in several ways and more complicated. Ignoring the even greater range of individual variation, the overall average frequency of total outlet of females is lower than that of males at all ages. From the beginning of adolescence (according to Kinsey's American data, always) the average frequency of sexual activity rises very slowly and does not reach its maximum until nearly the age of 30, or even later in the case of women who remain unmarried. In married women the frequency of activity then declines slowly, evidently following the husbands' trend. But in single women and in previously married women who are active sexually, the average frequency of activity stays more or less unchanged until the age of 45, declining only a little. After the age of 45 the average rate of sexual activity declines significantly, but unfortunately Kinsey's data for women are very thin after the age of 50. Obviously, a woman's childbearing activity, as distinct from her sexual activity, comes to a complete stop at the menopause, so that roughly speaking a line representing the average American woman's natural or potential rate of childbearing activity rises slowly from puberty to the late 20s, then levels off and remains nearly flat until menopause, and at that stage falls to zero. The contrast between this female curve and the male curve, it will be suggested below, has many far-reaching effects in the lives of men and women.

First, however, it will be useful to try to understand the evolutionary reasons for the shapes of the two curves. In the case of the males it is not very difficult, for all aspects of reproduction are relatively simple in males. It would seem to be a good guess that in an early hunting environment protohuman males born with a tendency to engage in reproductive activity at very high rates in youth and at progressively lower rates with advancing years would have left more surviving children than would males tending to maintain a constant intermediate rate throughout their lives – especially since some of them would have been lost on hunting expeditions while still relatively young. At the same time, if some males had dominance or leadership qualities enabling them to maintain a privileged position for access to females until late in life, there would have been some important value in a normal male capacity to continue sexual activity, at least on a reduced or declining scale, until old age. And a fair proportion of the surviving children would have passed such tendencies and capacities on to males of following generations.

On the side of the females it will be necessary to look more closely, but some speculations are nevertheless possible. The slow rise in their natural rate of activity in adolescence and until the late 20s would have accentuated their general tendency to hold back somewhat in relations with males and to wait for emotional bonds to form; given the coinciding period of maximum sexual pressure from their male contemporaries there would have been little risk of failure to reproduce altogether, and there would have been the important biological advantages suggested on page 188. The females' subsequent capacity for maintaining and enjoying their sexual activity for a good many years at close to their maximum level could have served to counterbalance any tendency on their part to withdraw from reproductive activity as the burdens of motherhood increased, or could have served in a few cases to offset a flagging interest on the part of aging males.

But the extraordinary phenomenon of the menopause calls for particular inquiry. A suggestion has been made that the menopause is not really a biological adaptation but just an incidental result of the long life-span of modern humans. There are, however, several compelling indications that it is in fact a biological adaptation, genetically controlled. First, the menopause is an abrupt change of life which occurs regularly in all normal women during a particular range of ages; it is categorically different from the very gradual and variable decline of fertility that takes place in aging men. Furthermore, as noted in Chapter 6, demographic estimates by Acsádi and Nemeskéri indicate that old age is not, in fact, a modern invention; indeed those authorities pointed out that even among *Homo erectus* populations of China and Java some individuals were living to ages of 60 or so, notwithstanding that their life expectancy at birth, owing to extremely high infant and child mortality rates, had been only about 15 years. This proposition is corroborated by a pair of contemporary demographic studies of San hunter–gatherers of the Kalahari Desert in Africa, in which Nancy Howell and Henry Harpending have established that among those people the menopause occurs regularly in older women, even though their general life expectancy at birth is still only about 30 years.

But then how could natural selection have allowed, even required, females' childbearing activity to stop while they were still alive and able-bodied? The answer, already glimpsed by Bernard Campbell and one or two other scientists, is to be sought mainly, I think, in the very long period of dependence of the protohuman young – that basic fact which accounts for so many of the human female's physical characteristics and behavioral tendencies. The point becomes clearer if one attempts to visualize the child-rearing problems in a small group of Plio–Pleistocene hunter–gatherers. Chapters 5 and 6 have shown that for them life was often arduous, and speculated that a normally healthy female of that time, if she did not die prematurely, probably gave birth to six to eight children, that she nursed each one for three years or more, that if she left a home base with her young she had to carry in her arms the smallest one and in many cases a second as well, and that all children had to be cared for until they were six or seven years old. In that situation, a female who continued having babies right up to the end of her life would have been dead before she had finished providing the care and attention critically needed by her youngest children, not only the last-born but usually the next youngest also and occasionally a third one. Consequently those orphaned children would often have been lost – even if other females tried to take care of them, because as a rule all grown females were already burdened to the limit with their own young, while juvenile and adolescent females would only rarely have been equal to the task. It therefore seems to be a reasonable supposition that when genetic accidents produced some females whose ability to bear children came to an end while they still had several years of able-bodied life ahead of them, there was on average no loss in the number of their children reaching reproductive age, but on the contrary a slight net again. There would also have been an additional gain through assistance in the care of closely related small children, including grandchildren. On these suppositions, I suggest that natural selection allowed such lines to continue, and even favored them.

It is surely significant that the menopause is not found in other primates or in any other mammals, in their natural environments, and that in other mammals generally the young are tolerably well able to fend for themselves at early ages. Even in the higher primates the period of great dependency is much shorter than in humans; and in chimpanzees, although they are close to humans in this respect as in many others, the young develop fast enough so that in the wild a female's last-born begins to take care of itself before she is ready to conceive again. In all of these other species a menopause would have caused a net waste of reproductive potential – and it does not occur in the wild.

(It has kindly been brought to my attention that in one population of elephants in eastern Africa, a decline in reproductive activity in aging females, 'similar to the menopause,' has been observed. The zoologist reporting it considered it a 'density-dependent or habitat-dependent' phenomenon; and a particularly searching independent study of another elephant population in eastern Africa looked for this phenomenon but could find no sign of it. It is probably significant that in elephants the period of growth and maturing of the young is a conspicuously long one, intermediate between that of humans and that of chimpanzees, in relation to the minimum birth interval; puberty occurs in females at between 13 and 17 years of age, and in males at between 11 and 20).

The suggested workings of natural selection would have taken place primarily in situations where the beneficiaries were the children and other close relatives of the retired older females, with the result that the latter's genes were preserved in succeeding generations. Genes for the menopause in females can undoubtedly be transmitted through sons as well as daughters, just as genes for abundant milk-production in cows can be transmitted through bulls; the explanation is that all the chromosomes of mammalian females occur in males too, even though many of the genes located on them find phenotypic expression in females only.

At the same time one can venture a little further. Perhaps a widespread occurrence of the menopause trait would in addition have had some value to small protohuman groups, and still more value to large groups, because it would have resulted in a situation where one or more experienced and still able-bodied females were available, once their own children were big, to act as foster-mothers for unrelated children – numerous in larger groups – whose mothers had died prematurely or were temporarily immobilized. Those retired older females could have performed other valuable services also, such as caring for the sick or injured or sharing the fruits of their considerable experience in bearing and raising children. Consequently natural selection could have very slowly extended the menopause adaptation for reasons of group advantage also.

Although there is much speculation in all this, it is enough for the immediate purposes that the menopause exists universally in normal human females and that its evolutionary origin is in all probability linked with the long period of dependency of human children. The adaptation seems to represent part of the vast and ill-rewarded contribution which protohuman and human females have made, consciously or not, towards their children's survival and reproduction.

I now set out on some rather adventurous further flights of speculation, hoping to throw a little new light on the relationships between modern men and women. I start with a complex of psychological tendencies and behavioral traits in *men* which may have evolved as a response to the fact of the menopause in females. Given the conditions of existence in the Plio–Pleistocene, with mortality rates among infants and children approaching the extinction level, and with many breeding populations dying out altogether unless birth-rates were very high, I suggest that natural selection must have favored a tendency in males to turn away from females in the shadow of the menopause and towards younger ones. Males who devoted an important part of their mating attentions to females in or near the post-menopausal stage of life would have fathered fewer children than males who had a strong tendency to concentrate on younger females. Generation after generation, very likely for all of our 3,000,000 years, natural selection must have been persistently building up a new tendency of this kind in males, until finally the world came to be rather full of men whose chromosomes carried certain invidious genes for preferring young women. At the same time and for the same basic reason, cultural evolution was probably often working in the same direction, both on this tendency and on most of the others suggested on the pages now following.

This suggestion gains helpful support from the fact that no distinct preference for young females as a class is found in the males of other mammalian species, even in the other higher primates. Paul Simonds in *The Social Primates* remarks that 'unlike some well-known human societies, subhuman primates put no premium on youth for youth's sake. An old female is as likely as a young female to be supported by a young dominant male . . .' In free-ranging chimpanzees in particular, the males of all ages show no trace of preferring young females to older ones; on the contrary, as mentioned in Chapter 3, they have been observed to have a decided preference for older ones. And in those species there is no menopause.

The evolution suggested here for humans can render intelligible an assortment of present-day phenomena in Western societies which otherwise make no sense at all, culturally or in any other way, phenomena which are familiar enough but not always edifying. It can explain, to begin with, why it is not only young men who fall in love with young women. Middle-aged men are at least as susceptible to them, are in fact more avidly aware of their springtime loveliness; and if a comfortably married middle-aged man happens to fall into close contact with an attractive woman of 30 (or 25 or in hopeless cases 18), something very much like a polygynous tendency is apt to manifest itself, sometimes with painful results for several people, perhaps for himself. In most women the corresponding tendencies do not seem to have been developed to such an exaggerated extent, and the biological reason, I submit, is that most men remain able to father children until they are much older: natural selection has allowed women to be less exacting with regard to the age of their partners. These matters will later be considered a little further, in conjunction with pursuit of the 'May-and-December' phenomenon in which a young woman is paired with a much older man.

Again, while the early males were acquiring a pertinacious preference for young females, they must necessarily have been acquiring also a tendency to pay very close attention to females' looks. This is the fundamental reason, I suggest, why today most men take such extravagant interest in a woman's physical beauty. (An embarrassing analogy can be seen, perhaps, in the intense interest which the males of dogs and many other non-human mammals take in the changing odors of potential mates.) It is quite true that widely varying conceptions of women's beauty have developed in different cultures – long willowy lines or opulent lines, small firm breasts or large swelling breasts, extraordinary built-up behinds or small behinds or none at all – and that even in a single culture the standards of feminine beauty can change considerably in the course of a generation or two. On analysis, however, the component elements of feminine beauty are always found to consist mainly of characteristics of youth, including freshness of skin and youthful contours; certain types of bone structure in a woman's face may be especially prized in a particular time and place, but in any culture a dewy complexion and a shy smile will go far to offset any deficiencies in other features. In the varying conceptions of female beauty, the essential biological factors are these two: that men respond very strongly to whatever features happen to be considered important in a particular culture, and that those features always include a test of a woman's youthfulness.

The same phenomenon shows up well in the purely erotic domain. Kinsey and others have produced a good deal of persuasive evidence that men are considerably more aroused by the sight of a woman's body, preferably exposed or generously suggested, than women are by the sight of a man's body. For a single example, 54 percent of the males in Kinsey's large sample had been erotically aroused by pictures of nude females, but only 12 percent of his females had ever been aroused by pictures of nude males. Proprietors of night clubs and purveyors of pornographic magazines and films give commercial confirmation of the point, and while some of them have been tempted by the sexual revolution to undress some bronzed young men, the experiment has not proved profitable enough to be generally adopted. Girl-watching has far more adherents than bird-watching, and boy-watching has not caught on. Girls and women may be carried away, more or less *en masse*, by a male singer, for example, but unmistakably his fascination for them resides more in his charm, his emotional fire, or even his voice, than in the lines of his body or the beauty of his face.

I now dare to speculate on what all this may have done to modern women. I have proposed that the menopause arose in the protohuman past in connection with the exceptionally long dependency of the children. And in the reasoning offered here it was this uniquely protohuman adaptation which gave rise to a pronounced tendency in most men to turn their mating attentions decisively away from older women and towards young ones, helped by a tendency to attach inordinate importance to women's physical appearance.

But is it surprising that the persistence of these male traits in our world today should result in traumatic injury to many middle-aged women? There would be less trauma if women's sexual life were predominantly physical or erotic, calming down in middle age; but instead of that, natural selection was at the same time cultivating a tendency in females to place their highest value on emotional attachments, slower-forming and longer-lasting. In the Plio–Pleistocene, even this inauspicious combination of tendencies would not have been so bad, because at that time, it is thought by many, polygyny was already widespread for other reasons and in all probability simply became more so on this account, while older females still had functions to perform which were satisfying to them and vitally important and doubtless honored in the groups to which they belonged. Modern women in our Western culture, on the other hand, have special sources of anguish: their institution of marriage is officially and ostensibly monogamous, and until recently they have been brought up to expect it to last throughout life, if not throughout eternity; if things turned out differently it was a sign of failure on their part or else of baseness on the part of the men they loved. Surely a formula for despair!

Poignant evidence of the anguish which modern women can go through in middle life is provided by the occasional suicides or attempted suicides of women who have been celebrated beauties in their youth but have begun to fade, and less theatrically but in much greater numbers by the nervous breakdowns and serious neuroses of women in or near the same stage of transition. It is supposed that the hormonal changes with which ovulation comes to an end may directly cause some psychological disturbances in middle-aged women, but if so those disturbances are aggravated by anxiety and emotional distress. The distress hardly arises from the loss of fertility; most women of 45 or 50 have had all the children they want to have, and many are glad to be relieved of the risk. An average woman's distress is due rather to her feeling that her attractiveness to men, or to a particular man, is on the wane.

Although many gallant or lucky women succeed in making the necessary psychological adjustments without giving outward signs of distress, the transition is surely very difficult for most of them: in youth they have opened out as the loveliest of blind nature's flowers; they have been loved and courted and pursued by men of every age, waiting to give their love to a man and to bear and love his children; but after they have performed the tasks imposed on them by nature and begun to show signs of age they must confront the fact, perhaps foreseen but not understood, that men are more attracted to women younger than themselves. This is perhaps the supreme example of the absence of justice and compassion in nature.

A few statistics exist concerning the general state of happiness of modern women at different ages. An interesting Gallup Poll was carried out in Europe in 1975 for the European Communities. It produced data on adequate samples of women in eight countries, showing that a general state of happiness was much more common among women under 25 than among women of 55 and over, as follows:

| Country | Percentage of women describing themselves as 'very happy' | |
| | *Aged under 25* | *Aged 55 and over* |
| --- | --- | --- |
| Denmark | 41 | 31 |
| Belgium | 46 | 31 |
| Netherlands | 35 | 21 |
| United Kingdom | 26 | 25 |
| Ireland | 27 | 15 |
| France | 25 | 13 |
| Germany | 15 | 6 |
| Italy | 11 | 6 |

Doubtless language or semantic discrepancies account mainly for the great differences among countries, but within each country the figures by age should be fully comparable. And the marked drop associated with age may well be due in part to indirect effects of the menopause.

The results obtained on men of different ages in the same countries showed no consistent pattern; in the Netherlands and Germany the proportions 'very happy' were higher in men of 55 and over than in men under 25, and in France and Italy there was no significant difference.

## The selection of partners

It has been proposed that in the protohuman past males and females applied various criteria, consciously or unconsciously, when selecting their mates, and that there were great differences between the two sexes in the criteria used. Those differences can now be seen as having made a contribution to the evolution of highly important human characteristics, and also as having been largely responsible for certain secondary aspects of the behavior of modern men and women, some of which would seem absurd if they were not so familiar.

But at this point it is no longer possible to avoid a short comment on sexual selection, a subject which engaged Darwin's genius more than a century ago and which is still under debate. The animal world contains spectacular examples of characteristics – the gorgeous spreading wing-feathers of the male argus pheasant or the great panoply of antlers of the extinct Irish elk –

which are either a useless encumbrance or a real handicap for the animal. (The elk's antlers, which sometimes measured four meters across, had to be renewed every year, at a substantial and perhaps ultimately fatal cost in vital energy.) Nevertheless they evolved because of one thing: they contributed in some important way to the animal's success in mating. The argus feathers proved irresistible to the female in courtship displays, and the elk's antlers proved useful for contests in which one male could establish dominance over his rivals and thereby his right of access to females. These are classic examples of sexual selection. Most morphological differences between the sexes, such as difference in size, may result partly from sexual selection but they can largely be accounted for in terms of natural selection. Meanwhile some difficult questions about sexual selection await generally agreed answers – for example, exactly how it should be defined, under what conditions it can operate, how its effects can be distinguished from those of natural selection, whether in human evolution it has operated through female choice or male choice or both.

A significant point is that sexual selection could not operate in a strictly monogamous population where every male and every female mated: there must be rivalry, with success for some and failure for others. It could and almost certainly did operate in polygynous protohuman populations in the past, where some males were able to obtain access to more females than others. There, sexual selection must have reinforced the action of natural selection in developing characteristics in males which were reproductively valuable. It is not quite so easy to see that sexual selection operated on protohuman females, because it is almost certain that practically every normal female was mated. But even then, as individual females advanced in their reproductive years, it is likely that some of them retained male attentions longer than others, and this would have left a margin of undetermined size for the operation of sexual selection on females. In more recent and less harsh periods of our evolutionary past, when some females could be left unmated without causing the extinction of their populations, males' preferences would have been exercised even among younger females, with genetic results passing to following generations.

To conclude the comment on sexual selection, it seems justifiable to suppose that this auxiliary force in evolution was in fact acting on protohumans, to a marked extent on the males and to some limited extent on the females.

Taking first the effects on males, what early females needed most in their mates was that they should be good protectors and providers, and sexual selection must have been favoring an increase in the numbers of such males. The best protectors and providers were doubtless of two main types: the protomen exhibiting the complex traits of dominance or leadership (generally resulting in positions of rank or authority and in somewhat later times material possessions as well), and the protomen with tendencies to form emotional bonds with females and children. Sexual selection was probably operating to increase the proportions of both types of males in early populations, and whenever both sets of traits happened to occur in the same males the selection must have been intensified. Males with the strongest dominance qualities would often have been able to command the favors of the females they wanted, somewhat in the style of the Irish elk, and males with the bonding tendencies would often have had a special appeal for the females.

At the same time, another important thing would have been happening: some females would have been more disposed than others to select or accept their mates on these bases, or more successful than others in securing such mates; and those females would on average have done comparatively well for themselves and their children. Under the force of natural selection, they would have left greater than average numbers of children who survived to reproduce in turn, including daughters who often inherited the same traits.

Sexual selection and natural selection would have supplemented and reinforced each other, then, in the promotion of important sets of characteristics in both sexes. In the males, these would have been the qualities of dominance and the competitive drive, and in addition tendencies to form emotional bonds with females and children. Meanwhile natural selection was promoting in males a tendency to take immoderate interest in the physical charms of females and an immoderate preference for young ones. Consequently sexual selection, when operating on females, must have been helping to produce what artists and others know today as the ravishing loveliness of most young women, whatever the idiosyncrasies of particular cultures.

If still more flighty speculation can be allowed for a moment, it may help to account for some familiar absurdities of our world. Most protohuman females must always have been glad to attract males, or we would not be here. There must have been some of them who were more concerned than others to attract a male, to indulge a male's concentrated interest in their physical appearance, including an appearance of youth. Such females would have had more success with capable males than their more careless contemporaries, and would have tended to leave more descendants. Little by little, then, females may have been selected not only for their physical charms but also for a behavioral propensity to enhance them so as to attract male attention. If so, it may have provided an underlying predisposition for modern women's preoccupation with their appearance, and for their singular susceptibility, in our own dizzy society, to the enticements of suppliers and advertisers intent on selling clothes, jewelry, scents, lotions, creams, oils, nutrients, vitalizers, refreshers, pastes, cakes, and muds, all promising to preserve, restore, or simulate the bloom of youth, new and more lustrous hair, new and longer eyelashes, whiter teeth, and ultimately plastic surgery, not so often to straighten noses as to erase wrinkles. Also a glossy array of fashion magazines, endlessly selling women new fashions for the coming season or the coming weekend.

Women know perfectly well that in all of this nonsense the central point is youth, and most of them probably feel that their fundamental motive in staying young is to be attractive to a man. What still waits to be understood is that their behavior is not simply a sign of light-headedness on their part or on the part of men, but may rather be the latest and most absurd of a reciprocating series of responses to biological factors which had been operating during our 3,000,000 years.

Many women have another characteristic which can be seen as proceeding partly from sexual selection. This is a certain degree of amenability to a man's demands or entreaties. It was mentioned above that protohuman males occupying positions of rank or authority would often have been able to command the favors of females they wanted. This form of sexual selection among males, which despite its repugnant aspects helped to propagate the traits of dominance or leadership in males, would have worked best with females who were somewhat amenable, even though hesitant. And some such predisposition in females would have been needed in another situation, one of more frequent occurrence: the case where a particular female failed to attract the interest of the highest-ranking male but where, if her precious reproductive capacities were not to be wasted, she would have to content herself with a less desirable mate.

A resulting amenability is perhaps one of the reasons for the discredited notion that women in general are passive. In any case it can help to account for a better authenticated fact: that many women can be won by men (most men are of course extremely easy to seduce, for different reasons), that even women of the most impeccable virtue can sometimes fall prey to a second man – for example, Madame de Rênal in *Le Rouge et le Noir*, or Fiordiligi and Dorabella in the tender fable of *Cosi Fan Tutte*. Cynics like Don Alfonso can declaim about the inconstancy of women, but Stendhal and Mozart, even da Ponte, understood well that a woman is preculiarly vulnerable to a man's love and a man's need, that sometimes a woman will give her love to a man, even at the cost of infidelity to another, if he can once break through her defenses far enough to make her feel that he loves and needs her desperately.

Going further, juxtaposing two traits – the average man's susceptibility to physical charms and youth in women, and many women's susceptibility to the trappings of leadership in men – some other familiar phenomena fall into place, starting with that sociologists are prone to call 'the upward social mobility of physically attractive young women,' or in more homely language the ability to pretty girls to get into a higher social class, the theme of innumerable well-loved tales from *Cinderella* to *My Fair Lady*.

The same juxtaposition can perhaps also throw some light on women's use of their charms and their favors to obtain prizes of many kinds, from a fur coat to a lifetime of high luxury. The art is practiced by women of all kinds, from starlets to the most esteemed of wives. One hears that for feminists women's beauty is power in the politics of sex. Nor should any man allow himself a sensation of moral superiority or a complacent banality about old professions. To these tendencies in human females, we all, men and women alike, owe much of our material progress, possibly our existence.

Finally, one can now have a fuller view of the May-and-December phenomenon, that everyday spectacle already mentioned, in which a young and attractive woman is paired with a much older man of wealth or position, the relationship being either solemnized in marriage or limited to the lively but less encumbering pleasures of a liaison. In aging men who lose their eyes, and sometimes their hearts, to younger and younger women it is possible to see the Plio–Pleistocene male driven willy-nilly towards females with a good childbearing future. And the young woman's participation in the spectacle may sometimes be assisted by an inborn weakness for men of authority or status: because of the great adaptive value of the dominance traits, there may have evolved in some females a special responsiveness while young to the decaying charms of older males with leadership attainments.

This is one of many topics where some readers will protest that I emphasize too much the genetic as opposed to environmental causes. In reply, I must first agree that cultural factors have been very important in this phenomenon. In particular, in Western societies for many centuries there have been very limited opportunities for young women to acquire wealth and privilege by their own efforts, and our culture has accumulated a formidable tradition of women's economic dependence. It has also imposed differentiated precepts concerning women's sexual behavior. In the past such cultural factors may well have been predominant. Today they are rapidly changing, and as a reaction to archaic conventions some women are angrily rejecting the idea of contenting themselves with older lovers. For, on the whole, women also prefer young partners to old ones: a man's power and possessions may seem to exert an aphrodisiac effect on some women (it used to be said in Berlin that *Geld macht sinnlich*), but it will doubtless be established scientifically someday that most women enjoy young lovers, both esthetically and erotically, a good deal more than they enjoy old ones. (Incidentally there is a perfectly good biological reason why they should: on average, young mature males of the Plio–Pleistocene had an expectancy of more years of vigorous protective capabilities than old ones had; older males were serviceable reproductively, but in most cases young ones were still more so.) In modern times some very attractive or fascinating women have had lovers much younger than themselves, sometimes a succession of younger lovers. With cultural factors now changing rapidly, this pattern may well be seen more often.

Cultural factors, however, could not be mainly responsible for the fact that this last pattern is so much less common than the primary one mentioned above, or for the fact that mere wealth or social position possessed by older women has very rarely produced the corresponding phenomenon of a December-and-May pairing (even though in the United States at present a disproportionate amount of private wealth is in the hands of aging women, including widows). Gigolos do exist in our societies, but they are far less numerous than obliging young women.

In the perspective of this book, the May-and-December phenomenon, like many others treated, is due to a complex of causes. The primary cause here, it is submitted, is that in our evolutionary past the biological importance of having a young partner was more universal and compelling for males than it was for females: natural selection planted strong youth-seeking tendencies in males with a greater frequency than in females for the crucial reason that fertility ended earlier in females than in males. And several other biological factors have been operative also. Thus we know today that the average woman's need for purely physical sexual relief is a good deal less compelling than the average man's. We believe that the average woman places a higher value on the emotional attachment, and is also more sensitive in perception: having both of these qualities she would rarely want to command or buy the attentions of a young man. There is evidence that most women are relatively free of the dominance-seeking impulse that goads so many men; and there is much evidence that the average woman's preoccupation with a potential partner's physical beauty is less exaggerated than the average man's. Meanwhile most young men, for their part, are too aggressive, too little amenable, too competitive, to accept the role of gigolo. It is on top of all such biological factors, and facilitated by them, I submit, that the very important cultural factor of women's economic dependence, normative social pressures connected with it, and differentiated moral precepts have been at work in our societies.

# 11

## *The Enigma of Homosexual Love*

It may be partly because of homosexuality that nobody has written this book before. Since 1965, bits of reliable evidence have been accumulating to indicate that the complex causes of this extraordinary phenomenon must include some inborn factors, and yet it occurs much too frequently to be accounted for by recurrent chance mutations. How can a biologist reconcile such evidence with the inexorable laws of natural selection? How could genes predisposing men and women to non-reproductive or even anti-reproductive behavior have become established in the human gene pool? These are daunting questions, certainly, but this chapter will attempt to show that answers are possible. With the published scientific information available in 1979 precise answers are not yet obtainable, and perhaps complete answers will never be obtained, but it is becoming possible to anticipate the general nature of the answers that are likely to be found.

True homosexuality, in the sense of a lasting erotic and emotional preference for members of the same sex, has been firmly verified only in humans. In a number of other mammalian species behaviors are known where animals of one sex adopt at times certain mating postures or actions typical of the other sex, but on analysis it is found that those behaviors usually arise from factors such as dominance-and-submission relationships, crowding, captivity, or the absence of partners of the opposite sex. Pairs of male monkeys, apes, and dolphins have occasionally, under exceptional conditions or in captivity, manifested affectionate attachments, including in one or two cases behavior that looked like erotic behavior, but in nearly all of the cases observed the animals resumed normal heterosexual activity when females were available. In the wild, juvenile monkeys have been seen to engage in sex play on both a heterosexual and a homosexual basis, but among mature free-ranging chimpanzees van Lawick–Goodall's searching study over more than a decade yielded no evidence whatever of 'anything that could be regarded as homosexuality.'

On the other hand homosexuality probably does occur in most human societies, sometimes without the sort of disapproval which has been attached to it in our own culture. A compilation by C. S. Ford and Frank A. Beach in 1951 based on ethnographic reports available to them indicated that homosexual behavior had been reported in 76 basically preliterate societies; a majority of these societies regarded it as permissible, at least for children and certain special adults, while others condemned or prohibited it with varying degrees of severity. Kinsey in 1953 thought it 'probable that in some Moslem, Buddhist, and other areas male homosexual contacts occur more frequently than they do in our European or American cultures.' The case of classical Greece is renowned, though it may be noted that the practice idealized for free-born Greek men was a variable and reportedly joyous 'bisexuality' rather than compulsive homosexuality, and also that in that particular period of Greek history women had few opportunities for enough cultural development to make them interesting companions for men.

## Incidence

The rates of incidence of homosexual experiences in men and women are a point of crucial importance, and will need to be stated carefully. The Kinsey reports of 1948 and 1953 are still, despite weaknesses, the best available sources on incidences in the United States in modern times. They contain the vital concept that there is a continuous gradation of individuals in terms of their sexual experiences. To measure it approximately, Kinsey developed a 7-point scale, ranging, for any stated period, from 0 (exclusively heterosexual) and 1 (predominantly heterosexual but with one or more incidental occurrences of homosexual response or behavior), all the way to 5 (predominantly homosexual but with one or more incidental occurrences of heterosexual response or behavior and 6 (exclusively homosexual). Although subsequent study and analysis have invalidated some very high figures on the total percentages of men who have one or more incidental homosexual experiences, Kinsey's figures on the incidence of homosexual experiences at the 5 and 6 levels combined (predominantly or exclusively homosexual) have not been seriously challenged and tend to be generally accepted. For the purposes of this book, men and women whose sexual experiences are at the 5 or 6 level for at least three years are regarded as 'true homosexuals,' and attention will be focused on them.

Kinsey's key figures for males are as follows: of all the 4275 males covered by the 1948 report, single and married and of all ages and educational levels, with statistical adjustments to make the percentages representative of the total US population of that time, 6.2 percent were at level 6 for a continuous period of at least three years between the ages of 16 and 55, whereas exactly 8.0 percent were at either level 6 or level 5 for at least three years during the same ages. A little more narrowly (and limited to white males for technical statistical reasons), 4 percent of all males were exclusively homosexual throughout their lives from the onset of adolescence. Simplifying, one can say that true homosexual males represented at least 4 percent of the total male population, and possibly as much as 8 percent. These last figures will be taken as basic.

The 1953 Kinsey report unfortunately supplied no precisely comparable figures for females, but it is certain that they would have been much lower, to judge from the incidences of homosexuality among single men and single women, on which the report did furnish a few comparable figures. It gave the following comparison of homosexual experiences of unmarried men and women during a period of one year at ages 20, 25, 30, and 35:

|  | Men (%) | Women (%) |
|---|---|---|
| Levels 5 and 6 combined | 5–22 | 2–6 |
| Level 6 only | 3–16 | 1–3 |

Allowing for some possible overstatement at the top of the range for men (owing to the small size of one sample), it can be said for simplicity that true homosexuality in single males appeared to be 2 to 4 times as high as in single females. Applying these ratios to the range of 4 to 8 percent just derived for male homosexuals, it would appear that on the female side the true homosexuals represented at least 1 or 2 percent of all women, and possibly as much as 4 percent. Although there is no comparable wealth of statistics for any country other than the United States, some qualitative confirmation of this range is afforded by the judgement of F. E. Kenyon in 1970 that in England lesbians represented a little over 2 percent of all women.

The comparatively low range of incidence of homosexuality indicated for women gains additional meaning when placed beside the figure for women without any sexual response at all – the 'X' level to which Kinsey assigned individuals who do not respond erotically to either heterosexual or homosexual stimuli of any kind and do not have physical contact with individuals of either sex. The 1953 report gave the following average figures for women rated X for a period of one year at ages 20, 25, 30, and 35:

|                      | (%)   |
|----------------------|-------|
| Single               | 14–19 |
| Married              | 1–3   |
| Previously married   | 5–8   |

In other words, the proportion of single women at the X level was much higher than the proportion at the 5 and 6 levels combined. (As one should expect, the corresponding figures for men at the X level were far lower, o percent for married men and 3–4 percent for single men.)

The simple meaning of these figures extracted from Kinsey's statistics seems to be this: that true homosexuality occurs in somewhere between 4 and 8 percent of the men of our culture; but that in women the incidence is much lower, somewhere between 1 and 4 percent, and also much below the incidence of complete sexual unresponsiveness. Thus, there is an important difference between men and women in the incidence of homosexuality, and it is especially in men that the phenomenon calls for explanation. Accordingly, in the discussion which follows, attention will be focused on homosexuality in men; homosexuality in women will be very briefly dealt with.

*Evidence of both genetic and environmental causes*

There are many different types of male homosexual, in personality, temperament, and behavior. In strictly sexual behavior, as Kinsey emphasized, there is a continuous gradation all the way from exclusively heterosexual to exclusively homosexual.

These facts alone are a good indication that there are many different possible causes, any combination of which may be operative in a particular case. They could even suggest to a geneticist that the possible genetic causes alone may consist of several different genes rather than simply one or two particular genes, and that in a person rated 5 or 6 on the Kinsey scale throughout adult life a number of such genes may be present, with additive effects.

There are at present two principal kinds of evidence that genetic factors operate: twin studies and extended family pedigrees. While neither kind of evidence by itself is altogether conclusive, the two of them together are strongly indicative. As to the first, a study published about a generation ago by F. J. Kallmann presented some astonishing figures purporting to show 100 percent concordance for homosexuality in 37 pairs of male monozygotic or MZ twins (twins developed from a single zygote and therefore substantially identical genetically), compared with less than 12 percent concordance (at the 5 and 6 levels) in 26 pairs of dizygotic or DZ twins (developed from two separate and non-identical zygotes). A few of the MZ twins had been separated during their youth. Kallmann's apparently definite proof that homosexuality is genetically determined met with a good deal of reserve – including reserve on the part of some geneticists, who saw reason to doubt whether 100 percent phenotypic expression of the genetic factors was likely in a case like this. A few reports were then published giving particulars on one or two pairs of male MZ twins that were *non*-concordant for homosexuality. In the end Kallmann himself published an article conceding that the 100 percent concordance could be 'regarded as a statistical artifact'; but even if the figure is heavily discounted, for example to 50 percent, it will still remain suggestive of important factors in male homosexuality.

Support for that possibility has been forthcoming from several unquestioned reports on isolated twin pairs, and in 1968 L. L. Heston (US) and J. Shields (UK) published an authoritative review of all the then-existing scientific literature on the point, together with carefully scrutinized data of their own on 14 new pairs of male twins. These latter consisted of 7 MZ and 7 DZ pairs (including 2 pairs of MZ twins belonging to a single extraordinary family described below), in which concordance for homosexuality was definitely established in 4 of the 7 MZ pairs but in only 1 of the DZ pairs. These 14 twin pairs constituted all of the male twin pairs in which at least one member was homosexual, out of a total of about 180 male twin pairs on which records had been kept over a period of years by the Maudsley Hospital psychiatric clinic in London; thus the 14 pairs were a very small but genuinely random sample of male twin pairs. The scrupulously careful conclusion of Heston and Shields, based on all this material, including their own 14 twin pairs, was as follows: 'The tendency is for concordance to be incomplete in series of MZ twins but to be higher than in corresponding DZ pairs, a finding which ... points to the importance of both genetic and environmental causes.' Most other workers who are in possession of the twin-pair evidence now share this judgement. In a widely respected article published in England in 1970, the psychiatrist J. H. J. Bancroft wrote, 'It is clear that the concordance rate is significantly higher in MZ pairs.'

The Heston and Shields study incidentally disposed of two possible doubts, by showing statistically that 'the ratio of twins to non-twins is about the same ... in the Maudsley clinic register ... as in the general population,' and that there 'appears to be no good evidence from the present material or from other work for supposing that twins have a high risk of being homosexual.' (All of the information on twin pairs referred to above related to homosexuality among males only. On female homosexuality there is at present not enough twin-pair evidence to warrant generalizations.)

The provisional conclusion that there is a significant genetic element in male homosexuality is supported by some data on family pedigrees, or the occurrence of homosexuality in relatives other than twins. The data are unfortunately still fragmentary at present and must remain incomplete until three or four generations after general social attitudes have ceased to cause concealment of homosexuality. One particularly valuable fragment is found in a 1973 endocrinological study by Sydney Margolese and Oscar Janiger in California. The primary purpose of that study, referred to in the next section, was a refined comparison of sex-hormone levels in a group of homosexual men and a control group of heterosexuals, but biographical data obtained in the study brought to light at the same time the following striking particulars: of the 24 heterosexual controls included in the study, rated 0 to 2 on the Kinsey scale, 2 (about 8 percent) reported having consanguineous relatives who were homosexual, but of the 28 homosexuals rated 4 to 6 on the Kinsey scale, 17 (about 61 percent) reported having consanguineous homosexual relatives, including 5 who had 2 each. The difference is highly significant in terms of statistical probabilities. (According to the chi-square test with the Yates correction, P = less than 0.001. What this means is that in a random sample, with an adjustment for the small size of the classes, there would be a probability of less than 1 in 1000 that a difference of this magnitude would occur by chance.) Supplementary details kindly furnished by Dr. Margolese in personal correspondence reveal that three-quarters of the reportedly homosexual relatives were males and 5 of them actually brothers of the homosexual subjects. The latter themselves included 2 pairs of fully concordant MZ twins. All this points very strongly indeed to an inherited factor of some kind.

A smaller fragment of evidence of this kind is found in a comprehensive survey of homosexuality by M. T. Saghir and E. Robins, Saint Louis psychiatrists, also published in 1973. The primary findings of this broad survey will be discussed in a later section, but what is pertinent here is that among the 89 male homosexuals covered, 16 percent 'mentioned that they knew or suspected that a member of their parental home or a relative was a homosexual,' whereas none of the 35 heterosexual controls reported having relatives known or suspected to be homosexuals.

Finally, the Heston and Shields study summarized above

included detailed information on a single extraordinary family in which there were actually 2 pairs of MZ twins concordant for homosexuality (included above in the 4 Heston and Shields cases of MZ twin pairs concordant for homosexuality) and also a pair of MZ male twins who were concordantly heterosexual. There is thus in this family striking evidence of a genetic factor in male homosexuality. But this family had other striking features as well: there were a total of 14 children, 11 boys and 3 girls; it was a working-class family in the slums of a large British city, and the father, a dock worker, was a heavy drinker who brutalized his wife and inspired great fear in the children. The mother appears to have been of limited capacities but warm and loving with all her children. A thread of depression was found to run through the histories of the 4 homosexual sons and also that of 1 of the sisters; but this 'contrasts strongly with the social effectiveness and apparent psychological health of the other 9 siblings.' Consequently this unlucky family was a nature–nurtural microcosm for the study of homosexuality, among other problems. Both pairs of homosexual twins were evidently born with at least a susceptibility to homosexuality, but not the 9 well-adjusted brothers and sisters – some of whom may have been of the type which psychologists have called 'invulnerables,' able to withstand almost any environmental insults. It would be very hard to argue that either genetic factors alone or environmental factors alone were responsible for the homosexuality found in this family. As Heston and Shields concluded, 'An etiology based on the interaction of these factors is required.'

Attempts have been made to establish a causal connection between homosexuality and factors such as the ages of the parents, the birth order of homosexuals in relation to their brothers and sisters, and the male–female sex ratios in their families, but the results are not very helpful.

To turn, then, to the question of major environmental or experiential causes, a full treatment of these is not attempted in this book, but some of the principal ones which have been proposed by psychiatrists and others may be briefly noted. There can be no doubt that there are non-genetic as well as genetic elements in the causation of homosexuality. Since even standard reflex responses of lower animals can be conditioned by training, the eminently plastic behavior of humans can surely be modified by recurrent experiences. The real problem is to find out what the non-genetic elements are.

To psychoanalysts from Freud on down, working with the troubled people who came to them for treatment, we are indebted for many individual accounts indicating a correlation between male homosexuality and childhood exposure to 'close-binding-intimate' mothers and 'detached or hostile' fathers. Our debt is less onerous for some of the theoretical or doctrinal teachings of psychoanalysis, such as those concerning Oedipal conflicts, castration fears, narcissism, repressed anal interests, and human constitutional 'bisexuality.'

Within the past generation, some psychiatrists and others have prepared a few statistical studies comparing life histories of selected groups of 30 to 100 homosexuals with those of control groups of heterosexuals, obtaining in this way at least a little quantitatively significant information on differences between them; D. J. West summarized several such studies in his widely-read *Homosexuality* (1968 edition). Most of these studies have found more frequently in male homosexuals than in male heterosexuals a close attachment with mothers during childhood, combined with unsatisfactory relations with fathers; the homosexuals' mothers were sometimes soft and overprotective, in other cases domineering, while the fathers were sometimes hostile, sometimes weak, and sometimes simply absent.

Since most of these homosexual samples were composed of psychiatric patients, particular interest attaches to the Saghir and Robins survey previously mentioned, which deliberately excluded from consideration any homosexuals with a past history of psychiatric illness (and wisely also any with a prison record). At the same time that survey contained its own psychiatric investigation of the personality and family experiences of each homosexual subject. The homosexual samples consisted of 89 male and 57 female volunteers recruited from homophile organizations in Chicago and San Francisco, aged mainly in their early 30s but ranging from 19 to 70, essentially 'hard core homosexuals who have made some adjustments to their homosexuality and to the world at large'; they were functioning members of the communities where they lived, often in upper occupational situations. They doubtless belonged at the 5 and 6 levels of the Kinsey scale, and in the case of the males the statistics of their signally active sexual lives indicate that many of them ranked well up towards the high end of the frequency-of-outlet ranges established in Kinsey's comprehensive sample of all males. Practically all of the male and female homosexuals were single, divorced, or separated, and all were white. Thus, these small self-selected samples were not random samples, and they were not proposed as representative of the entire homosexual population, being considerably more successful in several ways than the average. The 35 and 42 male and female matched heterosexual controls were all unmarried; consequently they were comparable in this respect with the homosexuals, but at the same time not representative of heterosexual men and women in general.

Despite the qualifications just mentioned, and the regrettably small size of the samples, the study provides valuable information about the experiential backgrounds of quite a number of well-adjusted overt homosexuals. To start with, 67 percent of the male homosexuals described themselves as having been girl-like during childhood (as compared with only 3 percent of the heterosexual male controls); they had been called 'sissy' or effeminate, and most of them had played mainly with girls and avoided boys' games, in many cases wishing they were girls. As adults, 40 percent of the homosexual men (compared with 3 percent of the controls) did not consider themselves adequately or appropriately masculine, though only 16 percent of them were observed to be obviously effeminate in manner. (Childhood histories of girlishness are often, though not invariably, reported for homosexual men. For example, I. Bieber and others reported in 1962 that studies of about 100 male homosexuals and about 100 heterosexuals, all of them undergoing psychoanalysis, had found that one-third of the homosexuals recalled having preferred girls as playmates when they were children, as compared with only 10 percent of the heterosexuals.) Saghir and Robins searched the conditions of family life of their homosexual men to see whether there had been any difference which would explain why two-thirds of them had been girl-like in childhood and one-third of them boy-like. No significant differences were found, however, in the family constellations of the two homosexual sub-groups.

Taking all of the homosexual men together, the Saghir and Robins survey made a number of valuable findings concerning the family environments during childhood. A slightly higher proportion of the homosexuals than of the controls – but in both cases a minority – had lost their fathers by death or divorce before they reached the age of ten. There was a much more significant correlation with discord between the parents: 52 percent of the homosexual men but only 17 percent of the controls (P = less than 0.001) reported that during their childhood their parents had engaged in frequent fighting which interfered with the emotional and physical well-being of the family.

The study provided scant support for the Oedipal interpretation still so dear to many psychoanalysts: in mother–son relationships during childhood, there was no difference of statistical significance between the homosexual men and the controls, though the figures were slightly tilted towards possessive or overbearing mothers in the case of the homosexuals; and only 3 percent of the homosexual men reported that at some point in their childhood their mothers had approached them sexually, while 97 percent made no report of 'any attempts at undue physical closeness' – a vindication of all those unhappy Jocastas.

On the other hand the overall relationships of the homosexual males with their fathers during childhood had been unsatisfactory in a very large majority of the cases – in 82 percent of the families, as compared with 12 percent in the controls (P = less than 0.001). Only 13 percent of the homosexual males had 'identified' with their fathers during childhood, as compared with 66 percent of the controls (P = less than 0.001); the fathers had played the dominant role in the family somewhat less often in the case of the homosexual men than in the case of the controls; two-thirds of the homosexual men, but only one-third of the controls, had identified primarily with their mothers (P = less than 0.01).

Thus the Saghir and Robins survey indicates that male

homosexuality was strongly correlated in that sample with a bad family atmosphere in childhood, and especially with a father whose attitude or role was unsatisfactory in some way. Yet the minorities should not be overlooked: in 48 percent of the cases there had not been unusual discord between the parents, and in 18 percent the homosexual men had had satisfactory relationships with both of their parents.

Regarding the unsatisfactory father–son relationship in particular, two points may be noted in passing. Where the difficulty was one of hostility or lack of interest on the part of the father, this may in certain cases have been the *result* of the girlish ways of a pre-homosexual boy. On the other hand, where the difficulty was one of insufficient masculine authority on the father's part, there is a possibility that in certain cases this was due to the presence of some slight or concealed homosexual characteristics in the father himself – as there could have been if there were genetic factors for male homosexuality transmitted from father to son.

A different note of caution comes from another study of homosexual men, reported in 1971 by R. C. Kolodny, W. H. Masters, and others, which focused primarily on some hormone tests which will be referred to in the next section. In this case the sample was very small indeed, and in terms of environmental influences even less representative, consisting of 30 white homosexual university students, three-quarters of them from middle-class or upper-class families, compared with a control group of 50 heterosexual students. In this very small and notably advantaged sample, 60 percent of the homosexuals recalled the family constellation of their childhood as having been 'very happy' and a further 23 percent recalled it as 'moderately happy.' Moreover, the father had been the dominant parent in 67 percent of the cases, and weak or ineffective in only 10 percent.

On the whole, as the psychologist Evelyn Hooker at the University of California, Los Angeles, had concluded with considerable prescience in 1968, the evidence does not support an assumption that pathological parent–child relationships are by themselves either necessary antecedents or sufficient determinants of adult homosexuality, but rather 'the evidence does indicate . . . that some forms of familial pathology appear to be associated with increased vulnerability of some individuals to homosexual development.' Saghir and Robins, while as psychiatrists they were strongly impressed by the potential importance of the parental constellation during childhood, came to the following conclusion: 'We believe that the association of a poor parental relationship and male homosexuality is not necessarily a causative association although it might have been an important contributing factor.'

There may well be factors of an experiential kind which have not yet been identified. Ironically, the clearest evidence that there are in fact important experiential factors is the evidence concerning the genetic factors: it shows that the latter are unmistakably present and important themselves, but that they cannot alone account for all the known facts about the occurrence and non-occurrence of homosexuality.

Parenthetically, it must be acknowledged that there is a great deal of homosexual *behavior* which obviously takes place because of environmental situations. Notably, homosexual activity is known to be extremely widespread in men's prisons (and is also fairly common in women's prisons), but in the great majority of cases it comes to an end as soon as the prisoners get out and find heterosexual partners. It also occurs sometimes in other situations where heterosexual opportunities are absent; for example it has had a traditional place in English boarding schools for boys, from which the overwhelming majority of the imprisoned boys later emerge securely heterosexual, some of them rampantly heterosexual. This is called situational homosexuality or sometimes facultative homosexuality. It obviously has little in common with a settled emotional and erotic preference for members of the same sex, predominant and compelling even when members of the opposite sex are available, which is sometimes called obligatory or compulsive homosexuality – the 'true' homosexuality which is the main subject of this chapter.

While much remains to be learned about environmental or experiential causes, it is already possible with the information now on hand to scale down the importance which has often been assigned to certain causes of that kind. Thus seduction of children by adult homosexuals is found on examination of the facts to be fairly minor as a cause. The pathological case of adults who are subject to strong erotic attraction to children, pedophilia, is rare in men and practically unknown in women, and moreover the attraction is sometimes felt for children of either sex; it is a painful problem when it occurs, but not necessarily a homosexual problem.

On the other hand it does appear that adolescent boys are especially attractive to some significant minority of homosexual men – as adolescent girls are poignantly attractive to certain heterosexual men. But half a dozen investigations carried out in England, the United States, and the Netherlands indicate that adolescent boys who have had homosexual experience with such men are rarely influenced by them to any significant degree. D. J. West's conclusion from his review of these investigations was vehement: 'It cannot be emphasized too often or too strongly that a positive aversion to heterosexuality is the crux of the chronic deviant's difficulties, and this has nothing to do with a history of seduction.'

Again, it would be premature now to assume that traumatic heterosexual experiences are a major cause of homosexuality. Saghir and Robins drew the following conclusion from their psychiatric investigation:

It is possible and likely that a small proportion of women and men who become involved homosexually as adults are experiencing a deep-seated avoidance fear of heterosexuality. However, we believe this is only a small minority of those homosexually involved and such a group would conceivably respond relatively well to psychotherapeutic intervention or to deconditioning techniques . . . The majority give very little evidence of early sexual trauma or later fear of heterosexuality.

Saghir and Robins did note that a different kind of fear of heterosexuality occurs in some homosexual men: the fear that in a heterosexual encounter they might not be able to perform. But in particular cases this could be a result rather than a cause of homosexuality.

In the Saghir and Robins samples the homosexual men were not found to be more susceptible to psychopathology than the controls were. Psychiatric disorders (not previously treated) were found to occur about equally in the two groups, most commonly alcoholism and depression. The immediate cause of depression in both groups was usually a broken love affair; nearly all homosexual men at times form homosexual relationships involving deep or intense emotional attachments, even though casual physical encounters are exceedingly prevalent, known as 'one-night stands.'

In the context of psychiatric observations, it must regretfully be mentioned that there are extremely few records of verified psychiatric 'cures' in which a true homosexual has been established securely in a heterosexual orientation. Indeed, psychiatrists have often wisely concentrated their efforts on helping their patients to acquire a satisfactory adjustment as homosexuals. And of course the great majority of homosexuals never seek or obtain psychiatric treatment of any kind. These circumstances appear to mean either that the experiential causes of homosexuality can very rarely be neutralized retrospectively by psychiatric treatment or else that the experiential causes have not yet been accurately identified.

Even the rather special techniques developed by W. H. Masters and V. E. Johnson for helping homosexual clients to convert or revert to heterosexuality have yielded only mediocre results. Those hard-working therapists collaborate as a male–female team in treating a client who has a strong desire to make such a change, guiding him or her through a course of varied erotic experiences with an interesting and actively cooperating partner of the other sex. Although this persuasive treatment leads a good many more or less convinced homosexuals to convert or revert to effective heterosexual functioning, the long-run failure rate is still high. As Masters and Johnson put it, this 'represents the "disaster area" in the Institute's treatment program for sexually distressed homosexuals. The overall combined (male and female) failure rate was estimated at approximately 35 percent.' And this 35 percent itself can be considered an understatement, because Masters and Johnson adopted 'rigorous selection procedures' in accepting such clients for treatment, declining to treat 22 percent of the homosexuals who applied to them for help in a change to heterosexuality. Moreover, among the clients accepted, some of the illustrative and 'representative' cases described individually by Masters and Johnson would seem to fit rather neatly into the small minority of traumatized subjects mentioned by Saghir and Robins above, who 'would conceivably respond relatively well to psychotherapeutic intervention or to deconditioning techniques.'

Masters and Johnson nevertheless remain optimistic that in the future, with increasing public confidence in their methods and with improved efforts on their part, better results should be obtained. And surely a better identification of the experiential causes of homosexuality is within the capabilities of modern scientific research, though this will certainly be difficult, considering that only small and unrepresentative minorities of homosexuals are today accessible for study, and that there are a great variety of homosexual behaviors and tendencies and a large area of overlap between homosexuality and hetero-sexuality. What seems most likely is that both among experiential factors and also among genetic factors there can be a number of causes.

## Possible genetic mechanisms

The primary objective of this chapter is to suggest genetic factors that might underlie and homosexuality – factors which could establish in some men an inherited predisposition, bias, or susceptibility in that direction, as a substrate upon which environmental influences and personal experiences could operate, resulting sometimes in actual homosexuality.

For a generation or so preceding the 1960s the dominant trend of Western thought on homosexuality was to the effect that the genetic factors, if any, were relatively unimportant. In part this was due to the wave of psychoanalysis which was then rolling forward, especially in the United States: people tended to interpret all kinds of psychological tendencies in terms of individual experiences in infancy or early childhood. And in part it was due to ignorance or mistrust of the then-available evidence from twin studies. But there were also two scientific discoveries which seemed to mean that neither inborn hormonal factors nor chromosomal constitution could have much to do with homosexuality: the first was that when male or female sex hormones are administered to adult humans, homosexual or heterosexual, no change occurs in the emotional and erotic orientation which has already been established; the second was that so far as chromosomal structure is concerned homosexuals are exactly like heterosexuals in the sense of having in males the normal complement of an XY pair of sex chromosomes and 22 pairs of autosomal or non-sex chromosomes, and in females an XX pair of sex chromosomes and 22 autosomal pairs, all visible microscopically.

More recently, with the wave of psychoanalysis receding at last and with small waves of quantitative scientific research advancing, a more balanced assessment has been possible. Several studies in the late 1960s and the 1970s, employing refined techniques for measuring hormone concentrations in humans, have shown a very significant correlation between male homosexuality and hormonal irregularities of one kind or another. For example, in the study by Kolodny, Masters, and others in 1971, it was found that concentrations of testosterone (the principal male sex hormone) in the blood plasma of 15 male homosexual university students rated 5 and 6 on the Kinsey scale were significantly lower than in the heterosexual controls (P = less than 0.01). Similarly, the 1973 study by Margolese and Janiger showed that the ratio between two metabolic derivatives of testosterone was different in a highly significant degree in urine samples of 15 male homosexuals rated 6 on the Kinsey scale as compared with corresponding values for 24 heterosexual controls (P = less than 0.001). A group of advanced endocrinologists working in East Berlin discovered in the 1970s yet another statistically significant irregularity of hormonal functioning in 21 homosexual men; their particularly interesting findings will be discussed in some detail later in this section.

Some other studies in recent years have failed to show a definite association between homosexuality and hormonal irregularities, but it appears that this could be accounted for by a lack of precision of focus in the studies. On the whole, there now seems to be enough scientific evidence to support a provisional conclusion that abnormal hormonal conditions do indeed have something to do with homosexuality, though exactly what and in what way is still under study.

In addition it has been well established in experiments on animals that it is during a critical period of fetal or perinatal development that the sex hormones exert their major influence in turning the animals' sexual organs and sexual behavior in a male or female direction. (Some of the important findings in these experiments will be summarized in a moment.) This could explain why the administration of sex hormones to human adults had no effect on erotic orientation: it is probably then much too late, as it is known to be in the case of the experimental animals.

As for the second of the negative discoveries mentioned above, concerning chromosomal structure, it is still perfectly true that homosexuals in general exhibit no gross chromosomal abnormalities such as the XXY or the XYY condition, in which a supernumerary X or Y chromosome is received from one of the parents. But neither do people affected with hemophilia, dwarfism, albinism, the Hapsburg jaw, and many other striking conditions that are known to be inherited. It will never be possible to have *visual* proof or disproof of a genetic element in homosexuality (or in any other phenotypic trait) unless technology can contrive a means of seeing and identifying each existing form of each of the myriads of human genes.

Consequently there is no longer any good reason to hold that genetic factors could have little to do with homosexuality. On the contrary, it will be suggested here that genetically-controlled mechanisms can well be imagined which could occasionally have given rise to a homosexual susceptibility, and that such mechanisms could have arisen and persisted in our species and even increased in frequency under certain environmental conditions.

For those readers prepared to brave the complexities of the suggested mechanisms, it will be best to start by looking into a few of the many intricate processes of sexual differentiation in the fetal development of humans and other mammals, those marvelous processes in which an apparently neutral or bipotential embryo, originally containing undifferentiated sex glands and other rudimentary structures, acquires little by little a definitely male or female character. In recent years scientific research has begun to penetrate these mysteries. Hundreds of ingenious studies have been carried out, mostly since the mid-1960s – experiments on newborn rats and on fetal rhesus monkeys and other animals, together with searching study of abnormal human subjects – from all of which it is becoming possible to sketch out, partially and provisionally, the complex developmental factors and stages which normally lead to the formation of a definitely male or female infant at birth. The biochemical–neural processes of sexual differentiation can be probed much more searchingly in experimental animals than in humans; consequently the next few pages will give a good deal of attention to them, and especially to the laboratory rat, which helpfully completes its sexual differentiation in the four or five days after it is born. Since the recent studies in this area are little known except to specialists, an attempt will be made here to outline some of the principal findings. The outline will necessarily be greatly simplified, omitting not only complexities of detail but also unresolved problems and incongruities; more complete information can be obtained from reports listed in the Bibliography and referred to in the Index. (If some readers find that even the outline requires too heavy an exertion, they are advised to skip to page 240.

One of the first of the modern discoveries, by now quite well established, is that the underlying trend of a mammal's body is towards femaleness, that if a male is to be formed a male differentiation has to be imposed on the system at an early stage. In other words, female patterns of development tend to emerge unless there is active intervention by a masculinizing influence at a critical early stage. One may guess that natural selection settled on an arbitrary scheme of development of this kind in mammals – the reverse seems to work fairly well in birds – because it happened to provide a maximum probability that each individual animal would end up either as a female or as a male, and able to function reproductively in that capacity.

Next in the sequence of logic, it has been known for a good many years that the principal masculinizing influence which either appears or does not appear in the embryonic development of a mammal depends primarily on the presence of a gene, or more likely a combination of genes, located on the Y chromosome, in most humans a very small chromosome; the X chromosome paired with it is much larger. (In mammals, it will always be remembered, the normal female has in every cell of the body an XX pair of sex chromosomes and the normal male an XY pair.) There is rather good evidence that in humans the gene or genes which initiate the development of a male sex are located on the very small 'short arm' of the Y chromosome.

Although a great deal remains to be learned, it is believed that in all normal cases the major effect of the masculinizing genes on the Y chromosome is that of influencing the bipotential sex glands of the embryo to develop as testes instead of as ovaries. Whatever may finally prove to be the particular mechanism by which that is accomplished, the ensuing developmental events are now reasonably well known in broad outline. Starting at a very early fetal stage, the testes secrete predominant quantities of male sex hormones (androgens, mainly testosterone), which initiate a long succession of interlocking biochemical processes; these processes normally cause the growth and development of the internal and external sex organs, and other physical features of the body, on the male pattern. (Males also secrete small quantities of estrogens, female sex hormones, and in both sexes the adrenal glands secrete some androgens and also the female hormone progesterone. Normally androgens predominate in males, and estrogens and progesterone in females.) Thus the male-determining genes on the Y chromosome exert their influence on the growing fetus through the chemical medium of androgens, primarily testosterone.

At a later fetal stage, after the gross bodily structures of sexuality have been differentiated, testosterone is carried by the bloodstream from the testes to parts of the brain, and there is evidence that this normally causes a male pattern to be established there also, with effects on behavior as well as on certain bodily processes. By means of experiments on animals, especially the rat, it has been possible to identify some of the many intricate biochemical processes by which this may be accomplished, and to infer others. For example, by incorporating a radioactive isotope of hydrogen (tritium) in molecules of testosterone and injecting this labeled testosterone into a newborn male rat, after the rat's own testes have been removed, and by later auto-radiographing specimens of tissue taken from the rat's brain, it has been determined that the testosterone has reached parts of the hypothalamus, the preoptic area, and the amygdala in high concentrations, and certain other areas of the brain in lower concentrations. (Meanwhile, although the brain normally works as an integrated whole, it is known that certain particular areas of it are critically important for certain functions. Mapping of the brain is proceeding actively.) Moreover it has been found by other experiments on rats that when the testosterone reaches and enters cells of a rat's brain it is changed metabolically, under the catalytic influence of enzymes present in the cytoplasm of those cells, into two derivatives, both rather similar to testosterone in chemical structure. In fact it has been possible to follow radioactive tracers all the way from the original testosterone to these two chemical derivatives in their final resting-places in the nuclei of nerve cells in the preoptic area, the hypothalamus, and the amygdala of the rat's brain.

Paradoxically, and making things still more complicated, it appears that the derivative most important for masculinizing the rat's brain is estradiol, an estrogen, a female sex hormone which in an adult female rat induces female mating behavior. In this curious caprice of nature, according to some good experimental evidence, a female hormone performs in the critical perinatal stage of development the function of imposing permanent male patterns of behavior on the brain of rats whose reproductive organs have already been established in the male pattern.

Next, it has been found that the brain cells primarily concerned with sexual differentiation of the rat's brain contain normally in their cytoplasm not only the critically needed enzymes but also certain other critical chemical substances, which are called 'receptors.' (Receptors for various hormones are known to be present in the cells of target tissues located in many different parts of an animal's body.) The testosterone derivatives combine tightly with these receptors and are thereby enabled to penetrate into the nucleus of each cell, where at last they come into contact with the chromosomes and then activate certain target genes. These genes, it is believed, then start up a whole new series of biochemical processes; the result is the establishment of a male pattern in the rat's brain, which will give rise to male types of behavior throughout life (and also to certain brain-dependent developments in the rat's body).

The preceding account – which a non-specialist may find rather complicated and an endocrinologist will certainly find highly simplified – relates mainly to sexual differentiation in the male direction. A contrasting succession of events is started up if the newly formed rat embryo does not possess a Y chromosome, that is, if the father's divided sperm cell which succeeds in fertilizing the mother's divided egg cell happens to be a sperm cell containing an X chromosome instead of a Y. In that case, with the mother always supplying an X chromosome, the fertilized egg cell receives an XX pair of sex chromosomes. Then the bipotential sex glands develop into ovaries, and the ovaries secrete no testosterone but instead female sex hormones – estrogens from an early age and progesterone much later.

Thereupon, in the absence of testosterone in the critical early period, the rat's reproductive organs tend to develop and grow on the female pattern, and the brain also takes a female direction. Conceivably progesterone from the adrenal gland contributes to the organization of female patterns in that early period, on the condition that testosterone is not present. The hypothalamus acquires the pronounced cyclical rhythms which are characteristic of females at later stages of life, and it passes its commands in those rhythms to the subjoined pituitary gland. The latter secretes several pituitary hormones in both sexes, but the developing female body responds differently from a very early age: in the female a complex interaction is set up, starting at a fetal or perinatal stage, between the ovaries and the hypothalamus–pituitary axis, perhaps aided by the adrenal gland, and it dominates the differentiation and development of a female sex, first physical and later behavioral.

There are at present two types of experimental evidence, involving several species of mammals but most conveniently rats, that male or female patterns are indeed established in an animal's brain before or just after birth. The first type of evidence has to do with sexual behavior at the adult stage. If a male rat is castrated as an adult, it will nevertheless continue to show characteristically male sexual behavior thereafter; but if the testes are removed from a newborn male rat, the rat will display in maturity a female pattern of behavior; it will display weak male sexual behavior if testosterone is then administered, and strong female sexual behavior if estradiol is administered instead. (In this context male behavior refers to mounting, and female behavior to lordosis – presenting the rear-end in an enticing manner – in either case performed in certain controlled test conditions.) Conversely, if a tiny amount of testosterone is implanted in the preoptic area and the hypothalamus of newborn female rats, they will perform in maturity like normal males in tests for male and female sexual behavior.

The second type of evidence concerns the actual physical organization of nerve cells in parts of the brain. Experiments have shown that in adult rats (among other animals) there is a difference between males and females in the physical patterns of synaptic contacts established between nerve cells in parts of the brain. And it appears that castration of newborn male rats during the critical period, but not later, will prevent the male patterns from emerging; while if newborn females are treated with testosterone they will develop the male patterns of synaptic contacts.

The provisional conclusion which endocrinologists draw from these experiments is that during the critical period of early development in rats, just after birth, the continuing secretion of testosterone by the testes in males initiates a secondary series of mechanical, biochemical, and neural events which ends with the establishment of male synaptic patterns in parts of the brain, while in females, lacking testosterone, the nerve cells in the same parts of the brain develop synaptic contacts on the female pattern. It is believed that these synaptic patterns cause nerve circuits to be organized in parts of the brain in the critical perinatal period, and that the nerve circuits normally persist into maturity, controlling sexual behavior; they cannot then be permanently altered by the administration of hormones.

It is true that the two types of evidence just summarized are obtained mainly from the laboratory rat, that unlucky experimental subject which in a sense completes its fetal development in the four or five days after it is born. It would be rash to assume that the processes of sexual development are the same in humans. They are certainly not exactly the same. Yet certain workers have shown that the localization of estradiol-concentrating nerve cells in the brain is remarkably constant in fishes, amphibians, birds, and mammals, and in particular that the brain of at least one primate, the rhesus monkey, has the same localization of estradiol-concentrating nerve cells as the brain of a rat. It therefore seems permissible to suppose provisionally that in humans some homologous processes of sexual differentiation – meaning processes which are similar because of common evolutionary origins – take place during fetal development. They are in all probability different in some important ways from those in the rat, and they are certainly more complicated, since the human brain is much more elaborated.

As it happens, there is persuasive evidence that homologous processes of sexual differentiation do in fact take place in humans before birth. Three examples involving humans will be mentioned here, all of them rare but well-known and well-studied conditions of partial hermaphroditism.

The first is called progestin-induced hermaphroditism in human females. During the 1950s certain synthetic hormones named progestins were given to some expectant mothers as a protection against miscarriage. But the progestins were similar in chemical structure to androgens. And occasionally, until their use was discontinued, they had the side-effect of masculinizing in some degree the external sexual organs of a female fetus.

The second clinical condition in human females, known as the adrenogenital syndrome, occurs naturally as a rare inherited abnormality. In this case the adrenal gland, which normally produces a small quantity of androgens, functions defectively in an affected female fetus: what happens is that a normal shut-off mechanism fails to operate and the adrenal gland keeps on producing androgens indefinitely unless an artificial shut-off is administered medically. The baby girl is born with partially masculinized genitalia.

In childhood and adolescence, both of these conditions are accompanied, in a significant percentage of the cases studied, by some masculinization of behavior also, including a preference for boyish play, boyish clothes, and boy companions, a lack of interest in later becoming a housewife and mother, and in the adrenogenital cases a lack of fantasies and daydreams about pregnancy and having children. (Some cases of both types have been successfully treated medically by Dr. John Money and others, with the administration of hormones and sometimes with corrective surgery, and always with parental guidance of the child.)

The third example of homologous processes of sexual differentiation in humans is provided by testicular feminization of males. In this strange phenomenon – also a rare inherited condition – a male embryo, possessing the XY chromosomal constitution of all normal males, possesses also a genetically-determined defect, most probably the lack of a critical receptor or enzyme, as a result of which all cells of the male embryo, and later the male person, are at all stages insensitive to the testosterone produced by the testes, i.e. unable to take up and utilize the testosterone. The condition is known also by the more descriptive name of androgen insensitivity. In the developing fetus, some unidentified agent blocks (as it does in all normal males) the development of ovaries, uterus, and other female internal structures, but the cells of the body are unable to respond to the testosterone produced by the testes, and the testes themselves never descend. Instead, the body develops in the female direction, aided by the small quantities of female hormones, estrogens, which are also produced by the testes, and the external sexual organs develop generally on the female pattern. At birth, many of the male babies affected look like normal baby girls. Thereafter, the testes secrete androgen into the bloodstream in normal quantities, but it has no effect; the child develops as a normal little girl. At puberty, the rising levels of testosterone still have no effect, but increased quantities of estrogen are also produced then by the testes, and these are sufficient to bring about complete feminization of the bone structure and outer contours of the body, including the development of normal female breasts. These young 'women' are sometimes very attractive. In psychological orientation and behavior, they are generally speaking perfectly normal females, predisposed to fall in love with a man, to marry and raise a family; indeed many of them do so quite successfully, adopting children since they lack the internal apparatus needed for having their own.

A significant detail concerning testicular feminization, or androgen insensitivity, is that the condition has occasionally been discovered in laboratory rats and mice also. And certain advanced genetic studies reported in the 1970s have added a further detail which would be sensational if it were not so highly technical: it is that the condition apparently arises, both in the mouse and in humans, from a recessive gene located on the X chromosome. If confirmed, this will be pretty nearly conclusive evidence that there are indeed some homologous processes of sex differentiation in mice and humans.

These three rare phenomena, then, two of them being nature's own experiments on humans, comparable with the experiments which human scientists practice on a great many unsuspecting perinatal rats, provide part of the evidence that the early processes of sexual differentiation in humans do possess some features similar to those in rats and that the similarity is due to common evolutionary origins. And it is known that in humans as in other mammals studied the hypothalamus at the base of the brain has normally acquired by the perinatal stage a demonstrable male or female character; from then on it delivers hormonal stimuli, cyclically in the case of females, to the pituitary gland just below it. The latter responds by secreting into the bloodstream several kinds of pituitary hormones which strongly influence the growth and development of the whole body, in humans and other mammals. In males the pituitary hormones travel to the testes as well as to other target areas, and some of them cause the testes to secrete additional androgens; an extremely complex interaction is thus set up between testes and brain at a fetal stage, and it starts the development of a differentiated male sex. In the females of humans and other mammals a corresponding interaction is set up at a very early stage; pituitary hormones travel in the bloodstream to the ovaries and other target areas, and these respond by assisting prenatal development in the female direction.

In humans the process of sexual differentiation of the body is far from complete at birth. It continues gradually throughout childhood and very rapidly during adolescence; in certain features it continues still longer. There are differences between male and female children in rates of physical growth at various stages; and their bones, muscles, and other structures assume progressively different characteristics. In adolescence, when the human primate is being hurriedly prepared for reproductive activity, those differentiations are greatly accelerated, and the striking differences in secondary sexual characters make their appearance in a disconcerting rush, not to mention the equally striking physiological events. The *speed or intensity* of differentiation of the human body at the stage of adolescence is evidently due to accelerated secretion of sex hormones – a 20-fold surge in the quantity of testosterone circulating in the blood has been observed in a good-sized sample of healthy pubertal boys – but there is convincing evidence that the *direction* of the physical differentiation has already been determined by the interaction between sex glands and brain in the period preceding birth and normally cannot be reversed later in life.

All this is believed to be true in some considerable degree of behavioral characteristics too – tendencies, capabilities, susceptibilities – even though these are far more plastic in higher animals and above all in humans. No doubt, the influences contributed by the environment through the central nervous system and human consciousness are much more important in determining behavior than they are in anatomy or physiology; and hormonal influences are less rigidly compelling in behavior than they are in anatomy or physiology. Yet in behavior also both types of influence are present and important. The genetic element in human psychosexual tendencies – including the genetic element in the differences between the sexes noted in the two preceding chapters – is inherent in the male or female determination normally established in infants before birth, through interaction between fetal sex glands and brain.

And the differences in behavioral characteristics, like the differences in anatomy and physiology, become progressively more evident in the course of childhood and especially adolescence. They include the radically differentiated behavioral traits of aggressiveness and nurturance. In infancy neither of these traits is evident; babies of both sexes are sufficiently occupied with clinging to their mothers, feeding, sleeping, and growing. In early childhood, however, signs of future aggressiveness, notably the 'rough-and-tumble play' so easily and so frequently measured by students of pediatrics, begin to appear in most boys – as in most juvenile male rhesus monkeys – and those signs increase gradually until adolescence, when there is a surge of aggressive tendencies in many boys; little girls begin to take an interest in dolls when quite young, and as they grow older their mothering and protecting tendencies become gradually more pronounced.

There can be no doubt that the development of these differentiated behavioral tendencies during childhood and adolescence is powerfully reinforced, or sometimes restrained, by environmental influences such as teaching by parents and especially by young companions. Indeed, as previously mentioned, there are certain writers who still insist that 'gender roles' are almost entirely learned by human children, rather than inborn. The trend of expert opinion since the early 1970s is in the direction of according much more substantial importance than before to genetic factors, but a final assessment of the relative strengths of the two sets of influences will not be attempted here. Here it is simply emphasized that the progressive differentiation of behavioral tendencies in children and adolescents proceeds side by side with the progressive differentiation of their physical structures and functions, and that the differentiation of the latter takes place admirably well without parental or other teaching. It looks very much as if natural selection had arranged things in such a way that in all normal cases both physical structures and behavioral tendencies or predispositions develop in parallel and are thus ready for service together at the stages of life when they are most valuable for survival or reproduction. A dual program of this kind under genetic control or influence is extremely probable in principle, once it has been established that it is possible for human behavioral tendencies to be transmitted genetically (as in the cases of mother–infant bonding, mating tendencies of men and women, or incest avoidance).

In particular, the erotic orientation towards the other sex which the overwhelming majority of men and women have in maturity is not present in infancy. Rather, it seems to develop little by little in normal childhood and accelerate in adolescence. In boys, there is strong evidence that in preadolescence a homosexual arousal is about as likely to occur as a heterosexual arousal, or even more so because at that stage (in many different cultures) a boy associates more with other boys than with girls. Thus, in Kinsey's 1948 data, for preadolescent boys who engaged in sex play the play was homosexual about as often as it was heterosexual, and significantly more so between the ages of 9 and 14. Kinsey's data also showed that, at 5 years of age and 10 years of age, 50 to 60 percent of all boys who had any erotic experiences had homosexual experiences at least as often as heterosexual ones (Kinsey levels 3 through 6), whereas at age 15 the corresponding percentage was less than 25 percent, and at age 45 less than 5 percent. At the onset of adolescence, when testosterone surges into the bloodstream, boys undergo an urgent genital restlessness, which can readily find expression in actions or fantasies involving persons of either sex or the boys' own bodies. Emotionally, moreover, preadolescent and early-adolescent boys can worship a male hero almost as readily as they can fall in love with a girl or a young woman; one is reminded of the temporary homosexual experiences common between adolescent and preadolescent boys in English boarding schools for sons of what used to be the ruling class. But by the late stages of adolescence the erotic and emotional orientation towards the other sex has in most cases been decisively fixed. This is when the flood of testosterone is at its maximum and the sexual drive at its most powerful – and it is precisely at this stage that young males of a Plio–Pleistocene population were biologically and culturally best qualified to start reproducing, having reached approximately full growth and strength, having had a long period of learning, but having still a long period of vigorous adult life ahead of them.

We do not yet know how all this is accomplished, what the mechanisms are which can provide such wonderful scheduling. In the light of one important hypothesis of modern genetics, derived originally from experiments with bacteria, it is possible that the timing of successive stages of morphological development in humans – and likewise of the genetic element in their behavioral tendencies – depends on a complex cooperation among certain postulated different types of genes, principally 'structural genes' which, when started up, synthesize enzymes capable of catalyzing biochemically the formation of physical structures or substances, and 'operator genes' which switch the structural genes on and off at determined stages, perhaps with 'regulator genes' in the background. Something of this kind must be responsible for the differentiation of the cells of living organisms: our own DNA is normally of the same unique chemical construction in every cell of a particular body, and yet our cells normally differentiate to form bones, ears, and toenails, in the proper places and not elsewhere; the cells multiply and then stop multiplying; the structures renew and even repair themselves, within limits, for a lifetime. This is one of the marvels that give such extraordinary fascination to the study of cellular biology and genetics.

The relevance of all this to homosexuality may now be discernible. Starting from this point, I will venture to suggest certain possible genetic mechanisms which could be among the multiple causes of homosexuality in men. The first suggestion is offered not as a fact or even as a developed hypothesis, but simply as a heuristic speculation. The existing state of scientific knowledge does not seem sufficient to support much more than that; but a basis does seem to exist today for beginning to descry some of the directions in which valid causes are likely to be found.

The first suggestion is concerned with neoteny, that curious phenomenon in which one or more characteristics of an animal species that normally occur during a juvenile, infantile, larval, or fetal stage are enabled in a mutant line of descendants to persist throughout life.* Neoteny is believed to have occurred many times in the course of animal evolution, occasionally with sensational results: it may have been responsible, half a billion years ago, for the emergence of the vertebrates, including fishes and ultimately humans, out of a primitive ancestral form related to the sea urchins. And much more recently it is perhaps responsible for the rounded shape of the human head (resem-

*The term 'neoteny' is used here in its broad sense, for which some authorities prefer to use 'paedomorphosis.'

bling that of apes at a fetal stage), which has facilitated the development of a large brain. And yet what is needed in order to initiate a neotenic change is nothing more than a tiny error of gene replication, conceivably a mutation in an operator gene as a result of which the operator by mistake switches off the development of an organ or a substance, or switches on the development of another one, at a premature stage.

The suggestion offered is that at various points in proto-human or human evolution there might have occurred neotenic mutations which caused certain terminal stages of male behavioral differentiation to be dropped in some individuals. (It will be remembered that in rats and other experimental animals the differentiation of the brain takes place slightly later in time than the differentiation of gross bodily structures.) One of the results might have been a failure of a few of the individuals in the mutant lines to develop the normal psychosexual orientation in maturity, so that they remained psychologically at a stage where homosexual and heterosexual reponses were more or less equally possible. The next section will suggest conditions in which such a mutation might have become established in a small minority of males in human populations.

Seen through this lens, then, some homosexual men of today could be men whose growth and development have taken place in a standard normal way in the body generally but whose differentiation in the brain as males, including particularly the completion of their erotic and emotional orientation, has been arrested or switched off at a late premature stage; in them a normal developmental coordination between physical struc-tures and behavioral tendencies could have failed to take place. Reverting to the undefined erotic orientation of many pre-adolescent and early-adolescent boys, which psychoanalysts like to call 'bisexuality,' the suggestion is that in some very small proportion of boys this early condition may persist into later life, resulting in a continued capacity for homosexual experiences, a capacity which then is used and developed if external influences happen to work in that direction.

It seems possible to interpret in the same way some other psychological tendencies which are generally thought to be present, one or more of them, in some sizable proportion of homosexual men: a lower-than-average level of aggressiveness, a retention of some degree of preadolescent or early-adolescent sensitivity and tenderness, a tendency in a full-grown man to retain an unusually close and dependent emotional attachment to his mother, or a related tendency in a young man to find special pleasure or reassurance in the company of much older women.

The other genetic mechanisms to be proposed here are fairly close to neoteny, but a little different. With a neotenic change, the development of certain behavioral tendencies would be arrested at a preadolescent or early-adolescent stage; in the mechanisms which will now be proposed the development of certain behavioral characteristics would continue to an adult stage, but in the female direction instead of the male direction.

Concerning these mechanisms some very advanced scientific work has already been done. At the Ciba Foundation's Symposium Number 62, in 1978, an assembly of outstanding endocrinologists, psychiatrists, and other authorities from several countries pooled their resources on 'Sex, Hormones and Behaviour.' The papers and the ensuing discussions were published by the Foundation in 1979 in a book of high quality carrying the title of the symposium. The subject of homosexuality in human males was directly addressed in a paper 'Brain Differentiation and Sexuality' by Günter Dörner, a prominent endocrinologist of East Berlin. That paper reports on a series of increasingly elaborate and sophisticated laboratory studies conducted by Dörner himself and several associates, from the early 1960s to 1977, on rats and humans. Most of the studies had previously been reported only in German periodicals, but the new paper provides a comprehensive review of all of them in English. In the paper and the ensuing discussion, Dörner takes account also of recent work by other workers elsewhere (sometimes in agreement with his own and sometimes not).

Dörner's work and the resulting findings, as reported, include the following particulars:

1. Male rats were castrated on the first day of life, and given injections of replacement androgen when they reached adulthood: in adulthood they were then found to be 'sexually excited preferentially by partners of the same sex.'

2. Male rats were castrated on the first day of life, and later given injections of estrogen: after the estrogen had circulated in the bloodstream, their pituitary glands secreted increased amounts of a certain hormone (luteinizing hormone, LH, which performs important differentiated reproductive functions in the two sexes). This 'positive feedback effect' is similar to that observed in normal female rats when they are given injections of estrogen; but it could not be induced in male rats which had been castrated later than the fourteenth day of life.

3. A group of 21 intact homosexual men were given injections of estrogen: three days later their pituitaries secreted significant amounts of LH – a positive feedback effect similar to that observed in normal women when they are given injections of estrogen. However, 20 heterosexual men and 5 'bisexual' men failed to show this positive feedback effect. As Dörner puts it, 'This finding suggests that homosexual men may possess, at least in part, a predominantly female-differentiated brain.' (A 1975 paper by Dörner and others had added here, 'This may be caused by an absolute or relative androgen deficiency during the critical hypothalamic organizational phase in prenatal life.')

These starkly simplified points, and numerous others, are developed in Dörner's paper with full details of the studies. Nevertheless the findings did not win general acceptance at the symposium. Conceivably some of the participants may have considered them almost 'too good.' In the prolonged discussion which followed, some participants accepted the findings, while others expressed dissatisfaction with them, and still others seemed reserved or hesitant. Studies by other workers were cited which had yielded discrepant findings, though all those other studies had differed from Dörner's as regards the estrogen injected, the size of the dosage, or other details. It is evident that much further study will be needed, employing elaborate and meticulous experimental techniques, before final conclusions can be drawn. But in the meantime Dörner's hypothesis must be accorded serious attention and respect. In the words of his sharpest critic, Anke A. Ehrhardt, psychiatrist and former collaborator of John Money, 'If replicable by other laboratories these findings may have potentially great significance for a neuroendocrine theory of sexual orientation.' What is more, they may even have practical implications for preventive medical treatment. Dörner and others have made comparative studies of the development of the hypothalamus in large numbers of rats and in 84 human fetuses, indicating that 'the critical period of sex-specific brain differentiation occurs in the human between the fourth and the seventh months of fetal life.' Dörner adds that hormone-induced abnormalities during this period can be detected and 'may be accessible to preventive therapy.' In other words, it is possible that hormonal irregularities underlying a susceptibility to homosexuality can someday be corrected before birth.

Findings and conclusions supporting Dörner's hormonal theory of homosexuality had previously been reported by Dr. Robert Goy, a psychologist and primatologist at the University of Wisconsin. In an important essay published in 1968, Goy reviewed earlier experiments exploring the sexual differentiation of guinea pigs, rats, rhesus monkeys, dogs, and hamsters, and reported new experiments which he and fellow workers had performed on rodents and rhesus monkeys, all tending to demonstrate or confirm that 'many physiological and behavioural characteristics of mammals, beyond those which are directly instrumental to reproduction, are established in either masculine or feminine form by the presence or absence of androgens respectively during early developmental periods.'

Goy's conclusions properly acknowledged that 'the importance of early experience to the expression of normal patterns of sexual and sex-related behaviour is well documented,' but he continued as follows, ending with clear implications concerning male homosexuality:

The results from experiments with prenatal hormones suggest that the contributions made by experience act upon a substrate that is already biased either in a masculine or feminine direction. As a result of some action of androgen on the developing nervous system, the individual, whether genetically male or female, is predisposed to the acquisition and expression of behaviours which normally characterize the genetic male . . .
The results suggest that the process of psychosexual differentiation

occurs at a later stage than genital differentiation . . . It no longer seems unlikely that for primates as well as rodents certain psychosexual disorders in the male might result from androgen insufficiency at prenatal stages of neural differentiation which follow in time the stages of normal genital differentiation. In other words, androgen secretion might be sufficient for male genital differentiation at an early stage of development, but later failure of secretion might prevent the proper development of male behavioural characteristics . . . The possibilities, because of their relevance to homosexuality and incongruent gender role, deserve direct experimental attention.

Meanwhile, studies of other kinds have provided material for an extension of Dörner's and Goy's suggestions. Where Dörner and his associates in East Germany have concerned themselves only with 'androgen deficiency during a critical period in men,' and where Goy's suggestion was limited to possible effects of 'androgen insufficiency' during the critical period, a much more comprehensive view of the relevant factors is now possible. Endocrinologists today have reason to believe, as indicated on pages 230–3, that testosterone reaches and enters certain cells in the brain of the newborn male rat, that it is acted upon there by enzymes present in the cytoplasm of the cells and is transformed into estradiol and another derivative, that the estradiol then combines with other chemical substances which act as receptors and, escorted by the latter, enters the nuclei of the cells and activates certain genes located on the chromosomes waiting there, and that the final result is the establishment of permanent synaptic contacts and neural circuits in the rat's brain which are characteristic of males. Thus, where Goy (and similarly the Germans) could only speculate that 'androgen secretion might be sufficient for male genital differentiation' but not sufficient later for 'the proper development of male behavioural character- istics,' recent experiments show that several variables other than the volume of androgen secretion might be responsible for the behavioral effects observed – starting with the presence and the exact chemical structure and normal functioning of enzymes and then receptors.

While this additional evidence concerns only newborn rats, there is reason to believe that homologous processes take place in the developing human fetus also, and that they are probably more complicated still. The essential point is that there are several different points in the long biochemical–neural pathway – testosterone, enzymes, estradiol and another derivative, receptors, genes, other enzymes, synaptic connections in parts of the brain – where something could go wrong (despite a generally very high level of accuracy in these matters) before the influence arising from testosterone is finally reflected in the development of adult behavioral tendencies in the male.

The possibilities for genetic error are actually more numerous, even in the rat, than the foregoing schematic and highly simplified outline would suggest. For example, the conversion of testosterone into estradiol and another derivative appears to depend on the presence of two or more different enzymes in the cytoplasm of target cells in the brain; if any one or more of them happened to be missing or insufficient or defective, the normal processes could be blocked or altered. Next, the estradiol-binding action of the receptors is impaired if certain other available chemical substances, exerting a negative influence, happen to be present in the same brain cells. In addition, there are some differences in the number of estradiol receptors in individual target cells; perhaps those cells which contain fewer receptors are subject to a greater risk than the others of failing to masculinize normally. Finally, the second chemical substance into which testosterone is converted in rats with the aid of enzymes is dihydrotestosterone; it is believed that this second one is in itself relatively ineffective in imposing male patterns on the rat brain, but that it does increase the effectiveness of the estradiol. And receptors for dihydrotestosterone are less plentiful than those for estradiol, and their distribution in the brain is a little different. Consequently irregularities in only the dihydrotestosterone receptors could have some effect, perhaps minor, on the degree of masculinization of the brain.

Without piling up further examples, it is evident that an error at any one of many different points in the biochemical–neural pathway might interrupt or impair the development of a male pattern in some particular behavioral characteristic, and allow a female pattern to develop there instead. And an accumulation of several such errors or breaks in a particular breeding population, whether rat or human, might occasionally result in an individual male carrying more than one of them and consequently having a predisposition or susceptibility to homosexuality. In subhuman animals in the wild, it is evident, natural selection has promptly eliminated all deviants of that kind, but the next section will suggest that in the ancestry of humans a different result was possible in some situations.

It may be noticed that errors or breaks such as those suggested above could arise at a fetal stage of development in two different ways: either through the presence of certain faulty genes in the males affected, or else through accidents or chance events befalling those males in their uterine environments. In the first case the errors or breaks would be under direct genetic control in the males themselves, and in the second case the accidents or chance events might be caused or facilitated by certain irregular genes present in their mothers. In both cases the mechanisms suggested would be under some degree of genetic control, direct or indirect. In both cases the end result would be that certain behavioral characteristics of the affected males would tend to develop in the female direction.

At the human level, there is support for this idea in the evidence previously reported that some considerable proportion of true homosexual men – say between one-third and two-thirds – have a history of girlishness in childhood and of below-normal masculinity in adulthood (including the small number who openly affect coquettish wrists and swishing ways). Meanwhile, the possibilities for many varied biochemical errors as indicated above could help to account for the well-documented diversity of temperaments and behavioral characteristics in homosexual men.

The biochemical–neural hypothesis can also be reconciled with three especially curious behavioral facts, at first glance enigmas within a biological enigma. According to numerous studies, including particularly that of Saghir and Robins, large but doubtless varying proportions of homosexual men display three psychosexual characteristics which are far more typical of men in general than of women: a distinct tendency towards promiscuity, a relatively strong and urgent genital drive in sexual relationships, and a marked preference for youth and physical beauty in their partners – all of which, as suggested at length in the two preceding chapters, seem to have evolved in the human male because of their biological value in reproduction, a matter of sadly little relevance for true homosexuals. The tendency towards promiscuity and the comparatively strong genital drive could result simply from higher-than-female levels of circulating androgens at the adult stage, and might not necessarily have any place in the patterns usually imposed on the male brain at the fetal stage. The preference of many homosexual men for youth and physical beauty in their partners is more puzzling, but it could result from a brain-patterning in which particular brain cells that are important in this widespread heterosexual male characteristic happened to receive their hormonal influences in the ordinary male direction, even though as a result of inborn biochemical errors other target cells in the brain were allowed to develop in the female direction instead.

These three curious facts tend to support a central judgement of this book – that major psychosexual differences between the sexes are in some large part genetically determined. Although exact statistics are lacking, the three characteristics certainly occur too often to be accounted for by chance; and it cannot reasonably be argued that they are caused in both heterosexual and homosexual men by environmental or experiential factors, since everybody agrees that so far as psychosexual development is concerned the two groups of men are probably exposed to very different external influences.

A somewhat similar anomaly turns up in a different context, concerning both male and female homosexuals: there is a little evidence that in both sexes homosexual relationships are extremely rare between close blood relatives. This would seem to be a uniform expression in homosexuals of the tendency of nearly all heterosexual men and women to avoid incestuous relationships. It is another indication that the genetic mechanisms contributing to homosexuality do not affect all areas of the brain. And once again the basic tendency was developed by natural selection for good biological reasons, as set out in Chapter 8, but it is one that obviously has no biological function whatever in homosexual relationships.

In summary, then, two types of genetically-controlled mechanisms are suggested which could produce a susceptibility or predisposition to homosexuality in men: an uncompleted psychosexual development as in the neotenic model, and a development of certain psychosexual tendencies in the female direction, as a result of errors at any point in a long biochemical–neural pathway. No doubt other genetic mechanisms are also possible.

## The operation of natural selection

It remains to explain how any such mechanisms could have been established in humans, how natural selection could have allowed them to reach a high enough frequency so that today at least 4 percent, possibly up to 8 percent, of American men may be homosexual. Most known mutations occur in only a tiny fraction of 1 percent of all live-born babies, and many of them then prove lethal and are promptly eliminated. Unless they turn out to be advantageous in some way, or at least harmless, their frequency in a population very rarely builds up to a level as high as 1 percent.

One is therefore constrained to pose the following question: Is there any way in which, in the course of human evolution, male homosexuality could have arisen as an occasional side-effect or by-product of some adaptation of positive value? Answers to this biological riddle must, in the nature of things, be sought initially by means of inference, reasoned speculation, and guesses, taking account of as much information as is available concerning our evolutionary past. (The essential minimum of relevant information has been given in Chapters 4 to 6.) On that level, then, the following scenario is presented; it is placed provisionally in the Middle Pleistocene, or sometime after about 700,000 BP. It is offered as a speculative hypothesis, for consideration and ultimately testing.

At that date the adult protohuman male, of the species *Homo erectus*, was still decidedly brutish by today's standards. His physique was powerful, his skull thick and rugged. According to the reasoning of earlier chapters he was far more intelligent than any other primate, well capable of love, and able to make handsome stone tools; but most probably he was also highly aggressive and given to harsh struggles for dominance among his male peers. His vocal communication, and therefore his cultural capabilities, were probably inferior to those of very simple hunting–gathering tribes of today. He had quite an evolutionary distance still to travel before arriving at a stage where civilized culture was possible.

On the other hand the preadolescent or early-adolescent males and the adult females of that time may have been significantly closer to a *Homo sapiens* level. The fossil skulls regularly assigned to them on the basis of anatomical knowledge are those with more resemblances to the skulls of modern humans. With youthful tenderness or with mothering and nurturing tendencies well above the level of the adult male, they would have been more disposed to form emotional bonds. They would have been less aggressive, and correspondingly more responsive to others and more sensitive or impressionable in general. They may well have been more given to vocal communication.

Meanwhile by the Middle Pleistocene the ecological predicament of the genus *Homo* is known to have changed greatly from that of around 3,000,000 BP. With successful hunting, mastery over big predators was well developed. The imminent danger from that quarter was reduced so much, and the techniques of hunting and defense had evolved to such a point, that it may well have been of adaptive value for protohuman males to become a little less brutally aggressive, a little more sensitive, a little more responsive to external influences, a little more communicative – all of which would have been possible through the retention of certain psychological traits of early adolescence or through the acquisition of a few particular female traits. I venture to suggest that if a mutant gene appeared which had such an effect, it may have been not merely tolerated by natural selection but actually favored, in fact strongly favored.

Obviously, if homosexuality occurred it had a pretty serious biological disadvantage, in that homosexual males would have had no children or at best fewer children. But the speculation offered is that a few homosexual males could have arisen as only rare and non-adaptive sub-variants of new and adaptive variant types of protohuman male.

Males of the adaptive types would have been distinguished by incomplete development of some behavioral propensities characteristic of most adult males of that time, or by the development of certain propensities of adult females. That is, they would have been firmly heterosexual, but either they would have retained some of the impressionability, sensitivity, and affection of early adolescence, or else they would have possessed a little of the adult female's emotional bonding tendencies, of her sensitivity and perceptual speed, and of her expressiveness. They would thus have had some highly important selective advantages, once a stage was reached where survival depended less on simple prowess in fighting. Such males would have been more receptive to external events; with no loss of reasoning power or physical strength, they would have been capable of quicker and more flexible responses to environmental surprises than the ordinary run of Pleistocene males. They would have been more disposed to form emotional attachments. They might have been more apt to seek their objectives by cunning or persuasion instead of by brute force. They might well have been a little better able to develop or use an early form of language. If they were more receptive to communication from others they would have had improved faculties of understanding, enhanced learning ability, and thus a greater potential for cultural development. Because of advantages like these they would have been better able to protect and support their women and children. Such males would have survived, individually, at least as long as the more rugged Pleistocene types; and (still ignoring for the moment any homosexual sub-variants) they would certainly have enabled more of their children to reach maturity and reproduce in turn. In other words, natural selection would have strongly favored the new variants in propitious environments.

At the same time, some females would surely have preferred such males when they appeared. Their preferences might not have counted for very much 3,000,000 years ago; they might still have been too much at the disposal of the highest ranking males. But in less endangered populations the females' preferences could have had some contributory effect through sexual selection. And since more of those females' children would have survived to maturity, natural selection would have favored an increase in the proportion of such females in protohuman populations. Thus natural selection and sexual selection could have worked together in causing males to become a little less brutally male in certain behavioral tendencies, or a little more like females in certain others, in the course of thousands of generations.

Pursuing this measured fantasy a little further, such a trend could have become progressively stronger as protohuman and ultimately human populations made further advances in dealing with environmental dangers and hardships: qualities of the physical bully and the redneck were perhaps becoming less adaptive, and qualities of the persuader, the lover, and ultimately the poet, more adaptive. An irregular trend of this kind could be one of the few evolutionary developments which have taken place in 'human nature' in the course of the last few thousand generations. Such a trend would certainly have made important contributions to the rise of civilization; thus it may have proceeded a little further after the emergence of *Homo sapiens sapiens*.

A rather special point might also be made, about a few very exceptional individuals. In the civilized world people have long recognized, at least since the time of Julius Caesar and probably longer, that a man who is strongly male in most respects, and intelligent and commanding in a high degree, but who is also endowed with the sensitivity, emotionality, and expressiveness of a woman, is sometimes a human being of extraordinary capabilities. It seems possible that men of that exceptional type have figured more than proportionately among the outstanding military, political, and cultural leaders of history. Precursors of such men must have appeared in the Pleistocene also, and may sometimes have made major contributions to human advances.

The dating of the scenario proposed above can be changed at will. Mutant genes which had the effect of moderating a little the aggressiveness of males, or of enhancing their perceptiveness, their bond-forming tendencies, and perhaps their capacities for communication, could have made a successful appearance at points in prehistory earlier or much later than 700,000 BP – later, for example, in the northern world, during an interglacial phase or perhaps towards the end of the Pleistocene as the extreme rigors of the ice ages were finally drawing to an end. Conceivably they could have contributed to the evolutionary development outlined in Chapter 4, in which the burly forms of *Homo sapiens* were gradually outlived and replaced after about 70,000 BP by less burly and more modern forms, a development which has not yet been fully accounted for in other ways. They could also have arisen during Neolithic times in agricultural populations. And of course one or more mutant genes having some of the effects suggested would have arisen repeatedly in the course of thousands of generations; what cannot be easily determined is the point of time at which they might first have been strongly favored by natural selection.

But to return to homosexuality, the suggestion offered here is as follows: the postulated selection for either or both of the adaptive variant types of protohuman male may have been so intense that it not only reached the optimum point but then continued and went a little further, until at last it produced a few males who began to fall in love with males instead of with females. An over-reaching of the optimum would have been inevitable sooner or later, if there was selection for several different mutational errors such as those suggested, since two or more of them would sometimes have occurred at different points in a single line of descent, and would have occasionally turned up together in certain individuals, with additive effects. Also, the same sort of result – a sub-variant predisposed or susceptible to homosexuality – could conceivably have occurred in a few rare cases where one particular gene contributing to the development of a new adaptive variant type of male happened to turn up in a particular male homozygously, in double dose, from both parents; unless that particular gene was located on the Y chromosome, females as well as males could have been carriers passing it on.

When human mastery of environmental dangers and hardships had attained some critical level, say from Neolithic times on, the suggested non-adaptive sub-variants, the men with a homosexual predisposition or susceptibility, would sometimes have enjoyed enough protection or tolerance in their social groups to escape elimination by natural selection if they left any children at all. But even in the Middle Pleistocene natural selection could have allowed a certain number of such males to continue to appear. If some of them were just masculine enough in erotic orientation so that they would occasionally take an interest in a female also, they and the tender females who liked them could have passed on some genes causing a susceptibility to homosexuality in males. In addition, at that hunting–gathering stage there would sometimes have been an advantage in having an able-bodied young male of undifferentiated or feminized inclinations who preferred to hang around the home base with the females, the children, and the aged, rather than to go off on hunting expeditions as a member of a male team. His physical strength and other abilities would have been useful for protection of the family groups as a supplement to the females' abilities. And even if the resulting opportunities for heterosexual ventures were never taken up, the presence of such a male would have increased the chances of survival of his close relatives, so that his genes could sometimes have been passed on through kin selection.

But there was probably a more important genetic factor tending to prevent rapid elimination of homosexual subvariants: genes underlying the suggested new characteristics of males would have occurred about as often in the mothers as in the fathers (never in mothers in the case of a gene located on the Y chromosome, but all other such genes at least as often). In the mothers, one may suppose, such genes would have had no important effects, or possibly an effect of enhancing certain female traits – indeed they might conceivably result in some 'close-binding-intimate' mothers – or adolescent traits; but when the genes were transmitted to male children they would have resulted in males of the suggested new and highly adaptive variant types, and occasionally the suggested sub-variants predisposed to homosexuality. In these last cases, even though the homosexual males themselves would have left very few children, their mothers and sisters would have had normal numbers, including a small minority of children possessing genotypes contributing to homosexuality in males.

This last factor might provide a moment of entertainment for a sociobiologist fond of calculations concerning the transmission of genes for altruistic behavior: in cases where homosexuality arose in males with the aid of certain irregular genes carried by their mothers, in one of the ways just mentioned or in the way suggested on page 247, the elimination of those genes from a population would have been slowed down for a special reason: these would have been special cases of genes for altruism in somebody else.

Turning at last to the case of female homosexuals, it is easy enough to imagine a genetically-controlled mechanism – an error somewhere along the biochemical–neural pathway – which could actively impose some partial masculinization on the brains of human females. Probably there are a number of such mechanisms. It is not necessary to spell them out here, because homosexuality among women is considerably less difficult to explain.

In the first place, as previously noted, it occurs much less often than in men, perhaps in only 1 percent of all American women and at the maximum not in more than 4 percent. Occasional mutations, even though not passed on through inheritance, could account for a perceptible fraction of homosexual women.

Second, the mothering tendencies which are developed to such a high degree in most human females are undoubtedly accompanied by a large capacity for affection and tenderness in relationships with others of both sexes. Among preadolescent and adolescent girls, some substantial proportion have emotional crushes on other girls or older women, and perhaps it is not rare for a mature woman to feel an emotional attraction to another woman which amounts to something more than friendship (though at present there is no scientifically valid information about how widespread such experiences are or about the extent to which they may include conscious or unconscious elements of physical attraction). Consequently it is much easier, in a society like ours, for a woman to have a homosexual attachment than it is for a man: a tendency in that direction may be so inconspicuous that it causes no social disapproval or occupational disability; it may have relatively few obstacles to overcome.

More fundamentally, while natural selection may have been rather slow in weeding out homosexuality among men, it would have been much slower still in weeding it out among women. There are two plain reasons for this. First there is the easy inference that in most prehistoric times females were critically dependent on males' protection and support (while at the same time themselves very important and necessary to males), and also less powerful physically and less aggressive, so that most of them would have found it natural and advisable to comply with male sexual demands without too much concern for their private inclinations. Second there is the physiological fact that females can conceive children without being erotically interested in the undertaking themselves. Natural selection's very broad toleration of variations in women's erotic inclinations is evident enough in the complete sexual unresponsiveness of a significant minority of women, a minority considerably larger in the Kinsey samples than that of homosexual women. Consequently there is little need to strain for explanations of a heritable susceptibility or predisposition to homosexuality in a very small percentage of women.

In fact, one really ought to ask why the incidence is today so much lower among women than among men. Perhaps the primary answer is this: that the females of Pleistocene populations happened to be in certain respects a little further along than the males were in evolutionary development in the direction of modern humans, at times when development in that direction was proving to have great adaptive value. In other words, it was then advantageous for males to become a little more like females in those respects – but not vice versa.

# 12

## *Other Varieties of Love*

The capacities for love which natural selection developed in mammals, especially in the higher primates, have developed in humans far beyond the primordial mother–infant bond, and have spread in several new directions. Preceding chapters have suggested ways in which the basic mammalian resource of emotion may have been channeled into varieties of love between a woman and a man, of love between a man and the children surrounding him, and even, paradoxically, of homosexual love. But biological evolution and cultural evolution have not stopped there.

### *Ties of affection within small social groups*

In small social groups of protohumans – home-base groups and small breeding populations comprising several such groups – a number of other kinds of affectional ties must have evolved, including attachments among juvenile companions and play-mates, and 'male bonding' among members of hunting teams. These and other affectional ties will be briefly discussed below. All of them would have produced or facilitated cooperative social behavior, which in turn would have proved advantageous both to the individuals concerned and to their social groups. Consequently any genetic tendencies underlying the formation of affectional ties would usually have been favored by natural selection, operating both at the individual level and ultimately, much more slowly, at the group level. This evolution must have been assisted by the fact that many members of each small social group were related to each other by close or distant kinship, because in that situation the process of kin selection could make its significant contribution.

Furthermore cultural evolution must in many cases have

brought its much faster influence to bear, reinforcing and extending the formation of affectional ties in small social groups and thereby helping those groups to prosper as compared with others. It would require some daring to estimate the proportions of the genetic and the cultural factors in these evolutionary developments. It is enough that they were both important.

There are some rather persuasive signs of genetic factors in the attachments formed among siblings and other playmates. Such attachments can be observed in numerous species of higher primates, as mentioned in Chapter 3, and for that matter in some other species of higher mammals – broadly speaking, wherever the periods of infancy and dependent childhood are unusually prolonged. And play among juvenile primates and protohumans through long days, months, and years together may well have been genetically assisted because it afforded the young an especially effective preparation for the pursuits of adult life.

The resulting special ties of intimacy, loyalty, and enduring affection between children raised together have manifestly been developed in humans further than in other primates, reaching enshrinement in our own culture with the name of brotherly love. It is true that in humans there are paradoxical findings of adolescent peer-group solidarity and at the same time sibling rivalries, especially between males. These contradictory phenomena, however, may be merely another instance of the evolution of two opposing tendencies side by side, the peer-group solidarity having evolved in the context suggested here and the rivalries between brothers being a manifestation of the almost universal competitive drive in males, developed for excellent biological reasons proposed in earlier chapters.

Still other affectional ties must have been formed among the members of small protohuman groups, both individual attachments and group ties. One remarkable type is that of fellowship among adult males. In Chapter 5 it was mentioned that successful hunting of large game required the formation of teams of hunters and sustained cooperation among them. Now it can be added that the prolonged sharing of hardships and dangers, failures and triumphs, must have engendered a sense of fellowship, loyalty, and mutual aid among members of hunting teams. Such feelings and relationships would have grown up among early hunters through a combination of learning and inborn dispositions. Men who possessed the genetic potentiality would have had an advantage in hunting, and would have left more well-nourished descendants than congenital loners did. In the 1960s the anthropologist Lionel Tiger published an extended argument buttressing the thesis that genetically-determined 'male bonding' tendencies were developed in early hunters and that the same tendencies underlie various familiar types of male associations in our own Western culture – medieval guilds, masonic orders, the College of Cardinals, men's clubs, men's sports, men's professions such as politics and war, college fraternities, and men's bars. Although some women of today, resolute and redoubtable, are establishing material for an important addendum, the thesis remains basically valid if due allowance is made for the contributions of cultural evolution. (Male bonding has nothing to do with homosexuality; on the contrary it seems to be a tendency of thoroughly average, thoroughly heterosexual males. Homosexual men, for their part, also show a tendency to cluster together, forming gay associations.)

More broadly, while higher primates in general are group-living animals, protohumans must have been among the most social of all primates. It was proposed in Chapter 6 that our early ancestors were under selective pressure to develop a demographic pattern consisting of many small separate breeding populations; these would have been isolated groups large enough to be able to avoid the deadly hazards of incestuous matings but small enough so that new genetic traits and new cultural patterns could be established in relatively short periods of time, resulting in rapid evolutionary differentiation and diversification and thus a fair chance of survival in at least a few cases. This was proposed as the primary reason for the unmistakable segregationist tendency in the surviving lines of humans today. In the present context the emphasis is not on the negative aspects of that tendency – the racism, nationalism, or tribalism found in practically all societies – but rather on the positive aspects, namely the sentiments of solidarity and loyalty among the members of a particular social group, the consciousness of shared interests and shared values, the sense of personal identification with the group, often a desire to help others or a willingness to accept obligations for the good of others in the group, often a tendency to look for help from others. Biological evolution (working partly through kin selection) must have been producing sentiments somewhat like those which have united the members of extended families or clans in certain modern or recent societies; it must have been developing a genetic predisposition for forming multiple ties of affection and loyalty among members of social groups. And all this must have been reinforced and rapidly extended by cultural evolution, and afterwards preserved, because of the great value of such ties in social groups.

## Feelings of solidarity within larger social groups

Today, in spite of all the dark lessons of recent history, a latent love of one's own race, one's own country or tribe, one's own linguistic or religious community (in addition to one's own extended family), as opposed to other races, countries, or communities, is very widespread indeed, and in times of crisis it wells up to the surface and finds expression, often in violence but also at times in noble acts of generosity and self-sacrifice.

It may well be, as I speculated in Chapter 6, that at some intermediate stage of Plio–Pleistocene evolution, after many diversified gene pools had been established and after survival had become less precarious, an integrationist tendency developed. In any case the original small social groups did, sooner or later, coalesce to form larger and larger groups – tribes, chiefdoms, nations, empires, federations. It is perhaps by virtue of these developments that today there exists a potential human capacity for emotional engagement in groups of all sizes, including an impersonal or abstract kind of fellowship uniting the members of very large groups, indeed in some individuals all humanity. It is even sometimes possible to experience a kind of love for all living things, or an access of gladness to be part of nature as a whole; J. Z. Young has given warm testimony of this in his recent book *Programs of the Brain*.

Most of the time, in most people, such far-reaching forms of affection are not expressed or consciously felt. Nevertheless, subconscious emotional potentials of our social nature can at times show up in situations of an evocative character. When a mass of people burst into spontaneous applause – for a well-loved leader or public hero, for example, or for a good performance of well-loved music – a rolling wave of shared emotion is generated which can carry many among us far towards the point of tears. Political leaders know this well, and make use of it; they are also apt to be strongly responsive to it themselves, sometimes showing hunger for the acclaim of masses of people. Military parades have by now lost much of their emotional appeal in mature societies, but more peaceable group activities can still open the hearts of most people, for example group singing – traditional songs, Christmas carols, even a national anthem in some cases, youthful innovations.

Individuals vary enormously in the intensity of their social impulses, ranging from those who require a large measure of solitude to those who are so dependent on contact with others that they dread being left alone for a few hours. And to some extent emotional responses such as those mentioned above can be merely learned from experience and the association of events. Yet most of us seem to be peculiarly susceptible to the sharing of emotional responses with masses of others of our kind. It can be seen also in some very ugly mob reactions. It is this feature, this automatic enhancement or intensification of emotional experiences when they are shared with a mass of others, which suggests a genetic component, developed in the course of our evolution as extremely social primates, protohumans, and humans.

## The love of God

There are genetic elements in religious experiences too. One such element, a curious one, is indoctrinability. The acquisition of knowledge about the world has been extremely useful for the survival of protohumans and humans; consequently natural selection has placed in most of us a propensity for inquiring, exploring, searching for causes, and thinking about them. But at the same time there has also been some positive adaptive value in a readiness to take things on faith, in a willingness in many individuals to accept and believe whatever their leaders and their social groups taught them to believe – especially if it happened to be true, but even, within limits, if it was false. The adaptive value of indoctrinability has been noted by several biologists, including particularly E. O. Wilson.

Given the extraordinary plasticity of human behavior, and given the fact that extremely little accurate knowledge of the world existed in the Plio–Pleistocene, it is reasonable to speculate that small groups of protohumans living in environments full of surprises and shocks needed widely-shared beliefs of some kind, accompanied by rituals promoting stability and group solidarity. Supernatural explanations of events were the easiest to imagine and the hardest to refute. Protohuman groups completely lacking shared beliefs and rituals probably fell apart from time to time, and in the end left relatively few survivors to perpetuate their free-thinking genes, while other groups, tending to preserve traditional beliefs and rituals, maintained more social coherence and fared better in the end, even if the beliefs accepted in common were sometimes far from true and the rituals incomprehensible.

We today may be living through a demonstration of something like that: the current widespread loss of traditional faiths and traditional values may well have contributed, as many people say, to the nihilistic tendencies of the moment in our shaken societies – the alienation, the violence, the terrorism, the disintegration of the arts. All these nihilistic tendencies, by the way, illustrate well the snowballing characteristic of cultural evolution. Violence in particular, perhaps first learned by soldiers in modern wars or by oppressed or disadvantaged groups of people in various stages of revolt, has been disseminated through all the vivid modern media of communication and entertainment and commercialized even in children's toys, becoming accepted as commonplace, and has then been imitated, added to, and improved upon until it has reached nightmare dimensions in several parts of the world.

But the main suggestion offered here is that our ancestors became believers in the Plio–Pleistocene and continued by and large to be believers thereafter. Even now, as a matter of fact, there is some bizarre evidence that we are born with a readiness to believe things whether or not they make sense: today, after two or three centuries of enlightenment and scientific advance, but with traditional faiths lost, many people in our educated societies are evidently drawn to wonders such as astrology, parapsychology, and witchcraft, not to mention various impassioned ideological beliefs. (Perhaps some undeviating skeptic will place in the same category my own faith in the ability of science to penetrate further and further into the unknown, correcting its errors as it goes.) This, it seems, is one of the reasons why many religions have been able to attract and hold believers even though their doctrinal content was largely emancipated from objective reality.

Many other and more visible factors have also been at work. Nearly all of the world's successful religious movements have been promoted by charismatic leaders. Islam, with perhaps the largest numbers of practicing followers, was originally carried far by military conquest. Most religions with mass appeal have thrived on popular ignorance and want. Most of them have promised personal immortality, with rewards for the good and punishment for the bad. Several of the great religions have given rise to lofty philosophical ideas. Different forms and functions of religion have evolved in different human circumstances.

Christianity is of particular interest for this book. Its spread has not as a rule depended on military conquest, even though long and terrible wars have been fought between adherents of different Christian confessions. Nor has Christianity been confined to societies with low levels of education or material welfare; on the contrary, during more than half of its long history it has been the dominant religion of societies with relatively high levels of culture, popular education, and material accomplishments. Several major religions preach charity and pity for human suffering, but Christianity added good works in unequaled measure, actually doing something about it. Other factors which contributed to its spread and extraordinary influence in the world included the scholarship of monastic orders in an age when scholarship was rare, the elevation of the status of women, and a great flowering of the arts that was associated with the Christian Church. Changing social and political environments were also powerful factors, including the support of various temporal authorities from the time of Constantine onwards.

But inherent in many of the factors mentioned, and inspiring some of them, there was in addition an internal dynamic of great potency. In the view of this book, that dynamic was human love, the capacity for love and the need for love which had evolved in protohuman and human primates without their understanding why.

A strong current of love had been flowing through the Judaic religion which fed into Christianity, but it broadened out and gathered strength in Christianity. A new stream rose in the life and teachings of Jesus himself – compassion for the sick, comfort for the meek, the poor, and the heavy-laden, open arms welcoming all children, a call for childlike trust in God and for brotherhood among all believers. In merely human terms, Jesus can be seen as a compassionate young prophet and faith-healer, followed from place to place by a growing throng of faithful, a messiah who felt tempted to establish a kingdom of the Jews on earth but renounced it, who identified himself with God and was finally crucified by a mob of unbelievers. And when a little later some devoted followers carried the teachings abroad, adorning them with simple legends, a response of faith sprang up quickly, faith in the God of love and the brotherhood of man. Many men and women of that time were very ready for such a message; in some cases when it reached human communities it awakened them almost as a decennial rain causes grass to spring up overnight on an Andean desert. It must have been partly that same message which later, in the Roman and medieval worlds, enabled the Christian faith to continue spreading for many centuries, providing a central inspiration for all of Western civilization.

These things are so familiar that one forgets their importance. A major part of their meaning is overlooked: that most human beings have a capacity and a need for widely diffused and shared affection which most of the time exist unrecognized, which are pushed aside by rougher impulses, overridden by more urgent desires. Also that the love inherent in the Christian faith had its origins in biological evolution just as surely as other varieties of human love. In fact it was the same thing. The sublime love which was evoked by Jesus and his early followers, and which illuminated the Western world for so many centuries, was essentially a summation or apotheosis of several different varieties of earthly human love – the trusting love which children have, the protectiveness which women and men feel for children in general, compassion for those who suffer, ties of affection and fellowship uniting the members of small and large human groups, love between a mother and her son, between a man and a woman, devotion to a sacrificed leader, adoration of a tender young mother, veneration for a powerful and protecting father.

It is more easily remembered that the early innocence was often lost in later centuries, as Christian churches acquired political and economic ambitions, lending themselves to alliances with very temporal powers. The really remarkable fact is that in spite of all its corrupting or deadening transformations Christianity as a religion somehow continued to survive, to spread, and to exercise a major influence in the world. To account for such extraordinary vitality one must invoke many diverse factors, including all of those mentioned above and particularly, I submit, the capacity and need for love which had evolved in the human species.

In the end, of course, in the last two or three centuries, science has progressively dispersed the Judeo–Christian theology, until today for many people in our societies there is not very much of it left. The simple cosmology went first, though that was not fatal; it could always be regarded as allegorical or as non-essential. Much more serious was the growing recognition that events in the universe were not likely to be altered by the intervention of a God acting in response to human prayers. More recently, another fatal loss has been that of the crucial principle of personal immortality: by now, far too much is known about the physical determinants underlying human personality, the individual mind or soul, and what must inevitably happen to it when those determinants decompose. These harsh realities, by now apprehended consciously or unconsciously by most educated people no matter what ritual declarations they may recite, have undermined the Christian faith for great numbers of people.

Consequently, although there are still, after 2000 years, devoted men and women who give their lives to works of Christlike charity, and a remarkable number of other faithful Christians who genuinely believe and try to live the message of Jesus, yet the religious faith evoked by it, and the accompanying rituals affording solace, reassurance, and steadying influences, have been lost by great numbers of people in the transitional generations of our time. Most fundamentally, an emotional void is left which has not been filled yet. The underlying human capacity and need for widely shared love still exist.

# 13

## *Highlights and Reflections*

*Summary*

Here is a quick summary of some of the main conclusions reported or proposed in the preceeding chapters, many of them provisionally until more complete information becomes available:

* The beginnings of human evolution can be seen as early as 65,000,000 years ago, when the placental mammals were starting to branch out in many directions. Their great legacy to us is the emotional bond uniting mothers and their young, and this may conceivably be the nucleus of emotion in general, as a primary activating and directing force in mammals at all levels.

* After 35,000,000 BP, when the monkeys and apes were spreading over much of the world, many new physical and behavioral adaptations were added, prefiguring human advances.

* Before 3,000,000 BP, homonids existed which stood and walked erect. This book takes that date, somewhat arbitrarily, as the beginning of the stage of evolution in which the other distinctively human adaptations evolved, first in the challenging environments of the eastern African savannas and much later in northern regions.

* The most fundamental of those adaptations were a tripling of the size of the brain and an increased and lengthened dependency of the young; together they opened up the vast potentialities of language and culture.

∗ Cultural evolution then became a major adjunct to biological evolution, interacting with it in complex ways, proceeding much more rapidly, following fundamentally different rules and exerting a great influence in protohuman and human affairs.

∗ Our ancestors began adding significant quantities of meat to their diets at some very early date, probably by scavenging at first and later by hunting. By around 2,000,000 BP our male ancestors had probably begun to hunt large animals.

∗ Starting then or even earlier, protohumans established home bases which small groups probably used for extended periods, doubtless intermittently. This was part of an inferred complex of behavioral patterns in which the sharing of food was central. The food-sharing complex included also the making and use of tools and other equipment, and a division of labor between the sexes, the males scavenging or hunting and providing physical protection for the females and young, and the females caring for the young and gathering plant foods. These activities must have been accompanied by some improvement in communication.

∗ Protohumans came to depend in a significant measure on meat for their nourishment, particularly because of its concentrated protein content. Natural selection must have called forth in male hunters a number of behavioral adaptations of great value, including intelligence, varied skills, courage, self-discipline, and cooperation.

∗ Both biological evolution and cultural evolution favored the retention and development in protohuman males of a set of traits enabling some of them to establish dominance or leadership over other males in their groups. A restless, propulsive trait of striving for leadership became nearly universal in protohuman males, and powerful in some.

∗ Meanwhile the physical evolution of protohuman females was oriented primarily towards childbearing and care of the young; with this came a generalized predisposition for nurturance and tenderness in most females.

* The inferred role of the females was arduous and of vital importance to family groups. It must have required the development of an intelligence equal or superior to that of the males, of an intelligence equal or superior to that of the males characterized by quick and sensitive perception and by skill in handling social relationships, together with constant attention to the needs of their children. The females may have made an important contribution to the development of language.

* During the 3,000,000 years of protohuman and human evolution, up to the end of the Pleistocene Epoch at about 10,000 BP, the overall average rate of population growth was approximately zero. Birth-rates were undoubtedly very high, but infant and child mortality rates must have been perilously high, often approaching and sometimes exceeding extinction levels.

* With survival in the protohuman line very precarious during the first million years and also during long periods afterwards, natural selection must have favored genetic tendencies to segregate into small separate breeding populations, facilitating rapid evolutionary differentiation and diversification – both biological and cultural – and enabling the members of some of the populations to survive. This, it is suggested, is why a variety of baneful segregationists tendencies exist today in practically all surviving human populations; they are partially offset by integrationist tendencies which may have evolved later.

* It is proposed that by 2,000,000 BP, perhaps earlier, the sexual interaction of protohuman males and females had evolved towards durable attachments of an emotional character, the beginnings of love. This protohuman adaptation was strongly favored by natural selection because it increased the

chances that the exceptionally vulnerable and long-dependent young would survive until reproductive age. Meanwhile the protective tendencies of the males were gradually expanding to include paternal affection for individual children.

\* Alongside the strong primary tendency being developed generally in males and females to form enduring emotional bonds, it is suggested that in a good many of them a secondary tendency to take an interest in a new partner after a time was preserved. Jealousy must have made its appearance at a very early stage.

\* As an illustration of the far-reaching influence which unsuspected genetic factors can have on human tendencies and human cultures, there is persuasive evidence that incest-avoidance tendencies and incest taboos were developed, in the evolutionary past, mainly because of a dangerous load of harmful recessive genes in our heritage.

\* The stark physiological discrepancy between the sexes in potential rates of reproduction gave rise to divergent reproductive tendencies in protohuman males and females: it is suggested that although some polygamous leanings were preserved in both sexes they persisted with somewhat greater strength and higher frequency in males, and that distinctly promiscuous leanings were preserved in significant numbers of males, especially during adolescence, while in females a predisposition for lasting emotional attachments developed more commonly.

\* A few clues and some ethnographic and other evidence indicate that polygyny, unequal polygyny, was predominant among varied mating patterns of males and females in the Plio–Pleistocene, This pattern would have resulted from several factors, including the physiological discrepancy just mentioned, and it would have left both genetic and cultural traces in human societies.

* The divergent reproductive tendencies which developed in the two sexes in the Plio–Pleistocene as indicated above are found in men and women today, along with many other differences. The psychosexual differences, in some major part genetic, include in most men a more powerful spontaneous sexual impulse, a more intense and assured response to sexual stimulation, and a leaning towards promiscuity (especially in youth), all accompanied usually by some real emotional need for women's love; in most women they show themselves in a greater dependence on slow and lasting emotional bonding.

* While there is great individual variation in all these characteristics, resulting in large areas of overlap between the two sexes, and while external influences and personal experiences can have a predominant effect in individual cases, the differing characteristics are basic to the physical and emotional needs of most men and women today in their relationships with each other.

* Protohuman evolution produced another important physiological difference between the sexes: in males the curve of reproductive activity rises precipitously during puberty and then declines very gradually, in most cases lasting until old age, whereas in females it rises very slowly to a plateau lasting until middle age, when childbearing drops to zero.

* It is suggested that the menopause, having arisen as one of the many early female adaptatations associated with the long dependency of protohuman children, led to the evolution of a pertinacious tendency in most men to turn their reproductive attentions away from aging women and towards young ones, accompanied by an intense interest in women's physical appearance, an interest to which most women readily respond.

* It appears that in general women tend to be less obsessed with youth and beauty in their prospective partners, because even in the Plio–Pleistocene the males were reproductively serviceable until much older and because it was advantageous

for females to pay greater attention to indications that their partners would be dependable protectors and providers. Natural selection may have favored a hesitant amenability in women.

\* The prevalence of monogamy in advanced human cultures, and especially the associated ideal of lifetime fidelity, appear to be comparatively recent developments, strongest in Western cultures and in large part attributable to Christian teaching. In most modern societies the monogamy actually practiced is rather shallow; given the conditions prevailing at present in the United States, more than half of the marriages of people starting out in adult life can be expected to end in divorce or separation.

\* The biological paradox of homosexuality in an appreciable percentage of human males (considerably higher than the percentage of females) now appears to have a substantial measure of genetic causation, though there must be experiential factors that are also of substantial importance. It is proposed that genetic factors (some which can be visualized) may have arisen during relatively sheltered stages of protohuman or human prehistory, as incidental and non-adaptive by-products of selection for a highly adaptive new type of heterosexual male, this adaptive type having been distinguished by reduced aggressiveness, strengthened emotional bonding tendencies, enhanced sensitivity and flexibility, and improved capacities for communicating and learning. Thus male homosexuality can be seen as partly a by-product of evolutionary events which made vital contributions to the development of human culture.

\* In the evolution of the genus *Homo* as one of the most social of primates, emotional tendencies to form other attachments have been developed also, notably enduring affection among members of extended families, fellowship among male companions, and solidarity among members of larger social groups, from tribes to nations. Most of us today seem to have a latent emotional affinity with members of our groups, in some cases very large groups, our own kind collectively; such feelings show up in times of crisis or in evocative situations.

    \* A multiplicity of factors made possible the spread, duration, and extraordinary influence of the Christian religion and the response of a large part of the world to the life and teachings of Jesus, but one of the more potent factors seems to have been an extremely widespread human capacity and need for love. Today, with the Christian religion weakened and undermined, and with no adequate replacement yet found, great numbers of people have lost an ultimate emotional haven. The capacity and need for widely shared affection still exist.

    But where do such judgements as these lead? What significant human truth, if any, do they reveal or confirm? What practical value have they? Can anything be done to make use of them, and if so what?

## A plea for new psychological research

I will attempt to answer those questions, but first I will venture to underline once more a recurrent message of this book: that much better information is needed about the experiences of love, reliable quantitative information about the emotional attachments that people commonly form. It goes without saying that a great deal of other information is needed too, in many different scientific disciplines, but those needs are in general well recognized, and large numbers of specialists are working hard at them. It is in the domain of people's emotional experiences, particularly the experiences of love, that the deficiency of information is most serious and unrelieved. Our understanding of normal human emotional experiences should not continue to be so dependent on extrapolation from clinical data concerning small numbers of individuals undergoing psychiatric treatment, on merely anecdotal information about other individuals, on the implications of literature and films, on personal impressions, or on roundabout inferences, speculations, or guesses like those made in this book. Psychologists and psychiatrists should not be expected to work miracles with the merely qualitative information now available to them.

Essentially, what is needed is representative and quantitative information concerning the frequencies, the durations, the inferred or comparative intensities, and the correlations, of the various emotional attachments and needs that ordinary men and women commonly experience at different stages of their lives from childhood onwards. Obtaining such information will be a major undertaking and an expensive one. But it is perfectly possible – just as possible as Kinsey's monumental research on sexual behavior was, a generation or so ago. Human emotional tendencies are not beyond the reach of modern scientific research, and it is by now high time for them to be reached.

In this context as in Kinsey's, appropriate use should be made of scientific sampling techniques: very large and representative samples of contemporary men and women should be secured, and they should all be given detailed structured interviews by professional psychologists or psychiatrists. In the Kinsey interviews, answers to between 300 and over 500 different prepared questions were obtained from each of the thousands of men and women selected for study, under careful assurances of non-disclosure. Today, thanks to computers, data so obtained can be rapidly subjected to advanced statistical manipulation.

Chapters 9 and 11 have given other examples of research already carried out on human behavior, subject to important limitations of one kind or another. For a study of emotional tendencies, novel and untried techniques will surely be called for. The Cameron–Fleming study reported on pages 178–80 is one suggestive example of what can be accomplished by indirect methods of investigation.

Work in this area deserves to be encouraged and adequately financed. It can well be hoped that progressive foundations, universities, and governmental agencies will before long provide the needed support. The work should be conducted not in isolation from the biological sciences but in continuous interchange with them, taking cognizance of the background of human evolution. Comprehensive cross-cultural studies would be a vast undertaking, but it is highly desirable to have, as at least a start, a partial sampling of a few representative contrasting cultures.

In order to explore properly all of the most important experiences, capacities, and needs in the domain of the emotions, questions would have to be designed and used in even larger total numbers than in the Kinsey studies of sexual behavior. It would be impossible and indeed undesirable to have work of that kind undertaken all at once in one gigantic program. It would be much better to have a number of separate and independent research projects carried out over a period of years; in order to avoid useless duplication it would be advisable to have all such projects notified, in advance and on completion, to one or more central recording agencies.

## Provisional significance

As the needed information became available, the judgements of this book and others would have to be progresssively reviewed and revised. One could then begin to give definite answers to questions about the significance and the practical application of the judgements. For the present, the remarks which follow are offered as provisional and illustrative.

The first question is whether any important human truth is revealed or confirmed. Here is one, I submit. In the discussion of cultural evolution in Chapter 2, examples were offered of some familiar but truly remarkable human behaviors in which, under strong cultural influences, individuals act for the real or supposed good of others and at great cost to themselves in biological terms, that is, in terms of reproductive success or even personal survival. The examples were those of religious devotees who take vows of celibacy, of kamikaze pilots and suicide squads who willingly die for their countries, and of millions of young men who risk their lives as soldiers in wartime. There can now be added to these the cases where, even if there are no coinciding cultural influences, a person is moved by such an intense desire to save the life of another that he or she does so without any concern for his or her own safety, and in fact at very substantial risk – a parent for a child, a person of any age for a brother or sister, or for an unrelated close friend or loved-one. Essentially, these are cases where in a crisis the desire to save the other person's life takes ascendancy over the self-preservation drive: the person acting incurs a risk of death, and in a few extraordinary cases death may even be inevitable and foreseen, but in all cases the ruling impulse is an intense desire to save the other person.

Such cases are rare, but in the human world as a whole they occur many times every day, and probably in a rather substantial proportion of all the situations where the person acting is confronted with a critical test; they are rare primarily because the situations are rare.

Now mathematical equations of kin selection and systems of reciprocal altruism, which work admirably well when applied to the types of altruistic behavior which occur in certain social insects or other nonhuman animals, can sometimes account for these human acts of the last type (to be specific, in some of the cases in which the person acting saves the lives of two or more close relatives at the same time, or in which the biological cost of the act to that person is less than the benefit to the person saved). But I would predict that, among all the cases where human lives are at stake, those which can be fully accounted for by kin selection or systems of reciprocal altruism represent in total only a minority. If so, it follows that some additional explanation is needed, a more powerful one.

Underlying *all* the human behaviors referred to above, there must be some inborn tendency of sufficient force to overcome, sometimes with the aid of strong cultural influences, the powerful and almost universal drives of self-preservation or reproduction. The additional explanation that recommends itself in this book is the simplest possible one: that the evolution of our species has produced in most of us an assortment of inborn tendencies to form emotional attachments with others, in some contexts a concentrated and intense attachment with one or two others or a very few, in other contexts a very diffuse attachment with many.

In this additional explanation it is no longer necessary to demonstrate that a particular self-sacrificing act is likely to have results biologically advantageous to the person acting or to his or her genes; nor is there any need to assume, as in standard sociobiological reasoning (pages 19–20), that the only possible genetic cause of altruistic behavior is 'a gene for altruism.' In the view of this book, what is biologically advantageous is the complex of tendencies to form emotional attachments with others. And this has been highly advantageous in protohuman and human evolution, primarily and mainly at the individual level and secondarily at the group level. The greatest advantage, though by no means the only one, has been that in the Plio–Pleistocene some of those tendencies, especially the mother–infant bonding tendencies, the male–female bonding tendencies, and the paternal tendencies, helped substantially to keep the rate of infant and child mortality below some critical extinction level – for example, perhaps 68 per cent, at which slightly more than two-thirds of all live-born children would have been dying before they reached the age of 14 or 15. This advantage was then important enough so that without it the line of evolution leading to humans would probably have ended in extinction.

And tendencies to form emotional attachments with others can bring about altruistic behavior as a by-product, not merely behavior that *looks* altruistic but also behavior that can be considered genuinely altruistic. Such tendencies become fatally costly to an individual if and when they actually cause complete self-sacrifice. But that is a rare event. Of a thousand mothers who today are compellingly and continuously actuated by love to give their children the care they need for survival, perhaps only one will ever find herself in a situation where she must elect to risk her life if she is to save one of them (though in the Plio–Pleistocene such situations probably occurred much more often), and even then the mother may in some cases not lose her own life. Of a thousand modern lovers who are passionately devoted to each other, probably only one will ever have to elect to risk death to save the other (an event probably rarer still in the Plio–Pleistocene).

This subject is broader than altruism. Emotional attachments generate a great variety of behaviors in addition to those cited in the standard discussions of altruism. In the primary area of child care, they produce an infinity of particular actions of biological value, and as a rule these involve little or no biological cost to anybody. The same is true of a very wide range of interactions between pairs of adults and between individuals and their social groups. On the other hand, in some grievous circumstances very strong emotional attachments can result in nervous breakdown, illness, or even suicide, without any biological benefit to anybody. Emotional attachments can produce benefits without costs, and costs without benefits; altruistic behavior is only part of the subject.

If all this is essentially correct, it can contribute to a considerably more complete explanation of many human behaviors, including those of extreme self-sacrifice. In the context of modern evolutionary science, the point can be stated thus: the average human being of today inherits tendencies to love others – in various ways, in various degrees, and in various numbers – because in the evolutionary past such tendencies were as a general rule highly advantageous to individual protohumans possessing them and to their children, and incidentally to their groups. And the general advantage to those individuals, in terms of reproductive success, was on average so great that it outweighed the costs to them, even though a few of them were lost through rare acts of self-sacrifice.

Putting it very crudely, what I suggest is not a gene for altruism but a gene for love, or, slightly less crudely, a complex of many genes for various kinds and degrees of human affection. This complex of genes has been highly advantageous in human evolution, and it sometimes results in altruistic behavior.

Apart from Darwin and a few other exceptions, self-respecting evolutionists have tended to shy away from love as a subject for study. Some may have been repelled by the quavering lyricism sometimes associated with it; some may have preferred to leave it to poets and others specialists. But I hope this will change. I hope it will be agreed that evolutionary studies should give much more attention to emotional factors as primary motivating forces in human behavior.

I turn now to more specific applications of the judgements reached in this book. Taking men and women first, everybody agrees, without help from evolutionary biology, that the majority of us have an inborn need, often an intense need, for physical and emotional union with a person of the opposite sex.

The evolutionary perspective merely provides an explanation for what we already know: that when there is an all-encompassing love between a woman and man – combining strong emotional and erotic elements and in addition companionship, security, and harmony of tastes and temperaments – that relationship surpasses all other human experiences.

But the evolutionary perspective can make useful contributions of its own. On the negative side, it should help particular couples to appreciate and understand the risks of a disturbance of their union in the future, depending upon individual personalities and circumstances. In this sense, the counsel of biology is in accord with the present trend among our young people, to refuse to accept it as the normal and inevitable pattern of life to marry and have children. Other patterns, including the practice of living together openly without being married, will probably spread. Many firmly united couples will refrain from marrying until they have some good pragmatic reason for it, such as a decision to have a child together.

And it is to be hoped that couples will reflect carefully before taking the decision to have a child. In the Plio–Pleistocene human survival depended on very high birth-rates, but today human welfare depends on reaching very much lower average birth-rates. Adequate nourishment and living standards are only the beginning of the matter. In our favored societies, considering the unquestionable need of infants and small children for continuous interaction with a mother-figure, and the probable need of older children for a father-figure too, it would seem that ideally a couple should not bring a child into the world unless they are satisfied, from their knowledge of themselves and each other, with the aid of the biological perspective, that they have a good chance of living together harmoniously until the child is at least eight or ten years old. In other situations it may often be more merciful towards a possible child to prevent it from reaching conscious life, so far as possible by contraception and failing that by abortion.

When couples do marry, they will take increasing account of the chances of a break-up in the future. It would seem to be valuable arrangement for *both* partners to have a major outside interest – a professional career, a working occupation as congenial as possible, a major avocation in the arts or sciences, welfare work on a serious scale. Thus the biological perspective provides added justification for the belief that two-career marriages are a desirable pattern for men and women in the professional classes. That arrangement should in no way restrain or compromise the ardors of love; probably it can often help to preserve or enhance them. For most men in our world, competitive work is almost a necessity, psychologically speaking, and for a woman a professional career can provide, in addition to its immediate benefits to her and to others, a safety net in case something goes wrong in her marriage.

A problem will often arise for a two-career marriage when there is also a baby or a small child. The mother can normally withstand the strain of daily separations from her child, if only because she understands and controls what is happening, but for the baby or small child such separations can be dangerous. To solve the problem, it would seem that the mother must either curtail her career quite drastically during the two or three years when the child is very small, or else ensure that the child is provided continuously during those years with another loving and acceptable mother-figure.

Solutions will have to be found too for the particularly distressing problem of the small children who have lost their parents altogether. As mentioned in Chapter 7, it will always be very difficult for large institutions to provide the continuous mother-figure interaction that infants and small children need. The ultimate solutions for this problem may lie in the direction of regarding the institutions more and more as a temporary haven for infants and small children until they can be adopted individually. To this end, it may be advisable to introduce a variety of measures to facilitate and encourage private adoptions, subject only to reasonable evidence that the intending adoptive parents are responsible and genuinely anxious to have a child to care for.

It is tempting to speculate about changes in marriage patterns that might be promoted by the evolutionary perspective. One safe prediction is that the present trend towards easier divorce will be continued and reinforced; the problem of ensuring proper care for young children will always impose limits, but it may be alleviated a little by a parallel trend towards increased restraint in having children.

For many men and women, so it would appear, the pattern best suited to their needs is one of marriage, divorce, and re-marriage, perhaps repeated more than once in the course of a long and well-supplied life. No one knows at present how many men and women are born or made for that pattern, and it is desirable to find out. The first question is whether and to what extent there is a difference between the sexes in this respect. The second is how any such difference can most tolerably be accommodated. Meanwhile the successive-marriage pattern is likely to continue to spread. (The simplistic idea of fixed-term marriages, however, can hardly be taken seriously, since it is much too calculated and chilling for an emotional relationship and almost anybody would prefer liberalized procedures for divorce if and when needed.)

From time to time in the past few generations a learned voice has been raised – always a male voice – suggesting that polygamous arrangements of some kind might be a rational response to human needs. Havelock Ellis and Bertrand Russell were heard to this effect, and more recently the Austrian ethologist Irenäus Eibl–Eibesfeldt has pointed out delicately that parents have no difficulty in loving two or more children at the same time, while children normally love both their parents, the implication being that love need not be exclusive. Meanwhile, some recent sociological inquiries in the United States have found that possibly around five percent of American married couples are currently experimenting more or less conscientiously with various forms of 'consensual adultery' or 'co-marital sex' – with the initiative being taken significantly more often by the husbands than by the wives. No reliable evaluation of the results of these experiments has yet appeared, but a significant correlation has been established between participation in the experiments and 'pre-marital permissive-ness,' so that an increase may be in store. A few young people seem to be experimenting earnestly with group-marriage arrangements, proclaiming that possessiveness in love is wrong.

In a majority of adults of both sexes, however, there is an unmistakable predisposition to passions of jealousy which far surpass the possible effects of any cultural influence. In the view of this book it is an ancient human tendency, extremely difficult and sometimes impossible to suppress. This seems to argue that there is an important element of exclusivity in the emotional bonds which most men and women form. No comparable reactions are seen in children, except occasionally during a short period after the arrival of a new baby. This may be one of the differences which have developed between parent–child love and the love between a man and a women. Moreover it seems to be a confusion to equate exclusivity with possessiveness. A relationship can be exclusive from choice and preference, without either partner possessing the other in the sense of having property rights or a right to lifelong fidelity.

However, it does seem that substantial majorities of adult men and women do want and need emotional attachments which are exclusive while they last. If this is correct, most adults will continue to refrain from promiscuity, consensual adultery, and group marriage, not to speak of the unspeakable sport of wife-swapping or group sex known as 'swinging.'

Polygyny as a particular form of polygamy may warrant separate mention because of its suggested importance in the human past. Although polygyny would cope with certain problems which still exist – the difference between men and women in sexual appetite, the desirability of prolonged care of children by both parents, the less monogamous disposition of most men, and an aging man's fancy for younger women – it is impractical as a solution in contemporary Western societies: some men would enjoy it, but it would be unacceptable to the men left out, and most modern women would prefer divorce.

But a precise view of the future of marriage is an unnecessary as it is impossible. When men and women come to see more clearly their genetically-established tendencies, and the extent to which they can be successfully modified by experience and learning (this book is meant to help in that process), the institution of marriage will inevitably be affected. Broadly, marriage customs of the future are sure to provide greater freedom for accommodating the great variety of human needs, and greater ease of change. Since that should permit more harmonious lives, men and women of goodwill can reasonably want to accelerate the process. The goal should be to establish the facts about our genetic heritage and about the potentialities and limits of our plasticity. Then things can work themselves out in rough conformity, first in actions, later in prevailing social norms and attitudes, and finally in laws and institutions; then, in other words, the course of cultural evolution in this domain can be influenced by enlightened human intelligence.

It is to be hoped that the legislative and institutional lag will not be too long. Even the illustrative changes suggested above would call for further changes in divorce laws, abortion laws, adoption requirements and facilities, tax laws, inheritance laws, and of course laws and regulations of all kinds affecting the opportunities and scales of compensation for women. Some of these further changes are already badly overdue.

## *The position of women*

Concerning particularly the status and rights of women in modern societies, the Plio–Pleistocene perspective can perhaps contribute something to an understanding of the real nature of that rankling problem, and suggest a new approach. It is evident that solutions are badly needed.

Earlier chapters have indicated that throughout the 3,000,000 years of protohuman and human prehistory natural selection was promoting (among other things) the development of two contrasting sets of behavioral tendencies in males and in females, with sexual selection sometimes assisting and with cultural evolution also participating – in some males the multiple traits of dominance or leadership, and in nearly all males the insistent competitive drive, but in females a complex of nurturing tendencies.

These diverging tendencies fared very differently as proto-human and human cultures evolved. At the hunting–gathering stage, which lasted some 2,000,000 years, the dominance or leadership traits of the males provided protection and leadership for the members of small groups. The functions were vitally necessary for their survival, but were provided on a very limited scale, originally only for the members of small home-base groups and considerably later for the members of tribes, and they were relatively simple in character. After the end of the Pleistocene, however, as social groups rapidly grew larger and more complex, forming agricultural communities and later expanding from tribes to peoples to nations to empires or confederations, there came to be vastly greater scope for the traits of leadership, indeed vastly greater and more diverse needs for them. Naturally and inevitably, men moved into the pursuit of power and success, through politics, war, and economic activity. Moreover, leadership could be exercised not only at the summit of political and economic life but at intermediate and even lower levels in an endless variety of activities. Thus, the capacities for leadership which had evolved in males came to be far more widely put to use than in the beginning and far more elaborately rewarded; there were unlimited opportunites for the nearly universal competitive drive.

The case was entirely different for the nurturing propensities of females, with an even longer evolutionary history. In hunting–gathering times, the females' roles were just as vital as the males', just as critical to survival of the children and adults in small protohuman groups. And their roles were extremely demanding. The bearing, feeding, carrying, and care of the young fulfilled their deepest emotional urges but also amounted to an exhausting labor. In addition, it is inferred that females were responsible for the work of gathering plant foods for their groups, and that if they survived to old age they assumed a task of mothering or caring for all those who needed it. The homemaking function was exacting in certain environments. Later, when the agricultural level was reached, women were often charged with heavy physical work. Above all, and in all early cultures, the females educated the children and prepared them for life. It seems quite possible that in their intimate interaction with their small children they played an important part in the evolution of spoken language. For nearly all of our 3,000,000 years, females were the custodians and bearers of the greater part of protohuman and human culture.

To be sure, the females were critically dependent on males' protection and support. In all probability many of them suffered physically under rough handling by the more muscular and agressive sex, and many must have suffered emotionally under polygynous arrangements which they were constrained to accept. On the other hand, the females themselves were of such enormous and unchallengeable importance in protohuman affairs that they must have been held in respect. When young they must have been pursued and courted assiduously, if often aggressively, by males of all ages; once mated, they were probably guarded jealously; and if they lived to old age they probably continued to perform important and honored functions in their groups.

But later on, when cultural development reached the stages of settled agricultural communities, quasi-political organization, and wars, the roles of women could not in the nature of things develop and expand on a scale with those of men. Nurture was essentially, and continued to be, a function relating to only a small number of individuals in a family circle. The roles of women necessarily became less prominent, less visible, than those of men. The course of cultural evolution suggested here finds support in a recent paper by Eleanor Leacock, based on evidence from some hunting–gathering societies of today.

It seems possible that on the whole the social status of women reached its lowest point in some of the last centuries before the Christian era. It was low in classical Greece. In the Roman era some improvement took place. The Christian religion, as it spread, certainly was increasingly concerned about the welfare of women in this world and the next. In the Western world improvement took place irregularly and fitfully over a period of many centuries; obviously it started later in most Asian, Arab, and African societies.

Nevertheless, despite the advances of civilization, the fact remained that the functions for which females had been bred for millions of years did not expand. On the contrary, in our Western societies of today some of the most vital and honored of those functions have been largely taken away from women: the care and teaching of small children has been partly assumed by kindergartens and nurseries; education of older children has been assumed by schools; care of the sick and injured has been largely taken over by hospitals and nursing homes. It is true that the various institutions mentioned are staffed largely by women, but this accounts for only a very small minority of all women. Furthermore, those who are involved are not devoting themselves to their own loved ones; they are merely workers or salaried employees in institutions organized and directed mainly by men.

In short, the suggestion offered here – to be added to the many valid judgements which others have reached concerning the status of women – is that most women of very recent times can be seen as victims of a kind of technological underemployment, having lost some of the highly important functions for which they were prepared by evolution throughout the Plio–Pleistocene; in addition most women lack the predisposition for dominance and are not propelled willy-nilly by the restless competitive drive which plagues the great majority of men. It should therefore not be surprising that they have today both status and rights markedly lower than men's. In our societies, leaving out of consideration the tiny number of women whose very exceptional abilities and powers enable them to succeed, regardless of all handicaps, in careers generally reserved for men, and those women who make careers in certain fields for which they are recognized to be at least as gifted as men, the majority of contemporary women are left with very restricted roles: taking care of any children they may have until the children are big enough for school, home-making, talking, sleeping with their husbands or lovers and otherwise ministering to their needs, at modest economic levels engaging in ill-paid manual work or unpaid housework, and at high economic levels being pampered, beautified, and entertained.

All this represents a grievous under-utilization of most women's great resources of intelligence and emotion. No wonder they are resentful or angry. If they were men they would not be limiting themselves to complaints or participating in women's movements; many of them might be carrying on guerrilla warfare against the establishment; more than a handful of them would have joined the terrorist fringe of our societies.

But unacceptable as the situation of modern women is, it is an error to blame it all on men. To a very large extent it does not result from deliberate oppression by men and was not planned or wanted by men any more than by women. Possibly it is because most men and women know this intuitively that the militant protest movement has not succeeded in enlisting general support. Fundamentally, the situation of women came about as a result of complex processes of biological and cultural evolution, in ways which have not been understood.

At this moment the winds of change are blowing favorably. The situation of women is being improved; it has already improved enough so that women can and do protest openly instead of hiding their resentment. But there is still far to go before women's abilities will be fully utilized and equitably rewarded. To reach that goal, what is needed is not polemics but thoughtful and creative cooperation between enlightened men and women.

There are unquestionably substantial differences between the sexes. Comparatively few women want to wrestle or box, to shoot or throw bombs; probably not many of them would consecrate their working lives to a remote chance of becoming the head of a powerful nation or the chief executive of a multi-national company, even if they had fully equal opportunities with men in competing for those jobs. Yet today in many fields of professional work women who have had both an opportunity for advanced study and enough conviction to pursue it are proving equal or superior to the men engaged in the same work; this can be illustrated by more than 30 books or papers listed in my Bibliography. The task is to bring about through the spread of knowledge and through political action a state of affairs in which women can compete fairly and equally in whatever fields they want to enter.

It is in everybody's interest to bring this about. The change, however, will not be easy to accomplish, especially if it is to take place rapidly. It must be accomplished in a world where unemployment is already a disturbing economic and social problem. It must be accomplished under conditions which ensure that infants and small children will have a fair chance of receiving the kind of care and attention they need. Men's talents in planning, organization, and politics will be required as well as women's.

The foregoing has to do mainly with the social or public position of women. If it is found that there is too often an inequality of position also in the private relationships between particular men and particular women, if it is too often the man who, in the vulgar metaphor, wears the trousers, it may be necessary to look further. Some of the factors already mentioned may be operative, especially men's traits of dominance-seeking developed in the context of relations with other men; and normative social pressures tending to confine women pointlessly to traditional roles certainly play a major part also; at very primitive levels of behavior, men's superior physical strength may sometimes be felt. But there may be a significant additional factor, in the form of differences between men and women in their ways and degrees of loving each other. I revert again to the fact that most men have a considerably stronger sexual appetite than most women, and are somewhat less monogamous, and to the inference that for most women the emotional element in a relationship is the more important one. With all due allowance for great individual variations and for a wide range of patterns worked out between particular men and women, it seems possible that in more than half of the cases it is the women whose emotional attachment is the more deep and enduring. If this should be so – and it is a disgrace that reliable information is not yet available on a question of such crucial importance in the lives of ordinary normal people – it would tend to place the woman in such cases in the weaker position in the relationship: it would inevitably make her the more vulnerable, the more solicitous partner; and the statistics of the matter would be reflected in social norms and social attitudes.

This problem would be considerably more delicate and more difficult to solve that that of women's inferior status and rights in society. It would require not only searching analysis of the facts but great understanding and wisdom on the part of both women and men; there would have to be cultural evolution drawing as heavily as possible on men's resources of protectiveness, responsibility, and love.

Turning then to homosexual love, or more precisely the enigmatic phenomenon of consistent homosexuality in an appreciable percentage of men, a further change in prevailing attitudes is plainly called for. The homosexual men who have been so disdained in our society should rather be accorded our deep and grateful appreciation: quite apart from the environmental factors which have helped to form them, they are, I suggest, incidental by-products, and at the same time sacrificial victims, of an evolutionary development which has contributed greatly to the rise of civilization. Moreover, as individuals today they are likely to possess non-sexual characteristics of substantial value in our society. At the same time, men whose erotic and emotional tendencies are consistently homosexual in adult life should be spared the vexation of useless attempts at re-orientation. And assuming confirmation that in most cases the genetic factor is no more than a susceptibility and would not find expression in a definite homosexual orientation without the aid of coinciding personal experiences and outside influences, it may be hoped that systematic research will soon identify reliably the most important of those environmental factors, so that they can be avoided in the future, since in an inevitably heterosexual world the homosexual orientation will always be at best an inconvenience and at the worst a cause of real suffering. For that same reason, there should be careful examination of the possibility suggested by Dörner, however remote it may be, that hormonal irregularities in unborn babies might be detected and counteracted medically.

## Closing thoughts

There is also something to say about the more diffused or generalized affectional feelings which humans commonly experience. One can reasonably hope that improved understanding will in time open the way to creative new uses of our genetic endowment in this area – as, for example, women's nurturing tendencies have been used in schools and hospitals, or as men's protecting tendencies have been used to shelter women and children from dangers far different from the saber-toothed tiger of the Pliocene, and indeed are being used these days, in a most pleasing irony of cultural evolution, to save endangered species of tigers and other animals from extinction.

Above all, we may hope that our latent feelings of identification with our own kind, and our capacity and need for widely shared affection, can be awakened and made fully effective. Today, this hope must be based squarely on mortal human capacities and aspirations, illuminated by scientific knowlege as it exists and as it will be extended in the future.

Biologically speaking, the potentiality is there. It exists in some very large proportion of humans – in just how large a proportion, and within just what limits, are vital questions awaiting a practical test. What is needed is the emergence of a new awakening influence capable of bringing the potentiality to realization. Human affairs are so marvelously unpredictable that no one can foresee whether or exactly when or where such an influence may emerge.

Possibly one will arise among the protesting young, who were the first to sense, as swallows sense an approaching storm, that our civilization was heading towards ruin. Some of them seem to be drawn towards the life and teachings of Jesus, and doubtless what attracts them is not a church or a religion but simply the man Jesus as an embodiment of love, charity, and compassion. Perhaps they can salvage that human treasure from amid the ecclesiastical decay. Or, conceivably, a new awakening influence might emerge in the form of a charismatic leader, one animated by a genuine and powerful love of humanity.

Or perhaps the best chance is that it will be generated by a human community: not by a desert commune sitting amid squalor and drug-induced phantasms, not by an ancient settlement on a remote mountaintop, and certainly not by a group held in bondage to a money-making charlatan, but by an educated modern community where people find a way to live together in a state of active human fellowship, with understanding, affection, and tolerance. Obviously such a community will require the utmost use of human intelligence – for making the conditions of life favorable, for minimizing injustices and material causes of conflict, for coping creatively with the aggressive tendencies which most evidently exist in human primates. (And admittedly the ultimate fate of any human community will depend upon future success in working out rational and supportable arrangements for collective security against military aggression, combined with effective arrangements for the peaceful settlement of disputes.) But intelligence is not enough. Another fundamental need is that human fellowship and affection should be brought to the fore and given full expression, as they were, for example, in some early Christian communities.

In recent times a great many small communities and a few larger ones – some youthful farming communes in Vermont, some Israeli kibbutzim, some Swiss cantons, to give examples of three types – have experimented with modes of community life in which the highest values have been assigned to enlightened cooperation and tolerant human fellowship. So far all such communities have fallen short of success in one way or another and for diverse reasons. But many of them are continuing to try, and the present predicament of our civilization will surely press others to try. Someday, in one or more of all those communities, enough success may be achieved so that others will learn and follow.

We can reasonably hope that some such event will take place in a current lifetime, before it is too late, and that when it does take place it will start to turn the cultural evolution of our societies in a new direction – that learned behaviors charged with hostility, violence, and irrationality will not continue to develop and spread as they have in the recent past, and that instead cultural evolution will gather strength in the direction of a full expression of human fellowship and enlightened human reason.

# Bibliography

1. ACOSTA, F. X. (1975). Etiology and treatment of homosexuality: A review. *Archives of Sexual Behavior* **4** (1), 9–29.
2. ACSÁDI, GY. and NEMESKÉRI, J. (1970). *History of Human Life Span and Mortality*. Akadémiai Kiadó, Budapest (translated from Hungarian).
3. ADAMS, M. and NEEL, J. V. (1967). Children of incest. *Pediatrics* **40**, 55–61.
4. AINSWORTH, M. D. et al. (1962). *Deprivation of Maternal Care, A Reassessment of its Effects*. World Health Organization, Geneva.
5. ALEXANDER, R. D. (1974). The evolution of social behavior. *Annual Review of Ecology and Systematics* **5**, 325–83.
6. ALTMANN, S. A. (1979). Baboon progressions: Order or chaos? A study of one-dimensional group geometry. *Animal Behavior* **27**, 46–80.
7. ANDREWS, P. and TEKKAYA, I. (1976). *Ramapithecus* in Kenya and Turkey. In *Colloque VI, Les Plus Anciens Hominidés, IXᵉ Congrès de l'Union Internationale des Sciences Préhistoriques et Protohistoriques, Nice, septembre 1976*. Centre National de la Recherche Scientifique, Paris.
8. BANCROFT, J. H. J. (1970). Homosexuality in the male. *British Journal of Hospital Medicine* **3**, 168–81.
9. ———— (1978). The relationship between hormones and sexual behaviour in humans. In *Biological Determinants of Sexual Behaviour* (ed. J. B. Hutchison). Wiley, Chichester and New York.
10. BARASH, D. P. (1977). *Sociobiology and Behavior*. Elsevier, New York.
11. BARKOW, J. H. (1978). Social norms, the self, and sociobiology: Building on the ideas of A. I. Hallowell. Also related Comments. *Current Anthropology* **19** (1), 99–118.
12. ———— (1978). Culture and sociobiology. *American Anthropologist* **80** (1), 5–20.
13. BATESON, P. P. G. and HINDE, R. A. (eds.) (1976). *Growing Points in Ethology*. Cambridge University Press.
14. BELL, A. P. and WEISBERG, M. S. (1978). *Homosexualities*. Simon & Schuster, New York.
15. BENGIS, I. (1974). *Combat in the Erogenous Zone*. Quartet Books, Lóndon.
16. BERNARD, J. (1972). *The Future of Marriage*. World, Chicago.
17. BIEBER, J. et al. (1962). *Homosexuality*. Basic Books, New York.
18. BLACK, P. (1970). *Physiological Correlates of Emotion*. Academic Press, New York and London.
19. BODMER, W. F. and CAVALLI–SFORZA, L. L. (1976). *Genetics, Evolution, and Man*. Freeman, San Francisco.

20. BOEHM, C. (1978). Rational preselection from hamadryas to *Homo sapiens*: The place of decisions in the adaptive process. *American Anthropologist* **80** (2), 265–96.

21. BOWEN, B. E. and VONDRA, C. F. (1973). Stratigraphical relationships of the Plio–Pleistocene deposits, East Rudolf, Kenya. *Nature* **242**, 391–3.

22. BROCK, A. and ISAAC, G. LL. (1974). Paleomagnetic stratigraphy and chronology of hominid-bearing sediments east of Lake Rudolf, Kenya. *Nature* **247**, 344–8.

23. BUREAU OF THE CENSUS, US (1976). *Population Profile in the United States, 1975*. Current Population Reports, Series P–20, No. 292.

24. BURTON, J. (1972). *Animals of the African Year: The Ecology of East Africa*. Eurobook, London.

25. BUTZER, K. W. (1971). *Environment and Archaeology: An Ecological Approach to Prehistory*, 2nd edn. Aldine, Chicago.

26. —— (1974). Paleoecology of South African australopithecines: Taung revisited. *Current Anthropology* **15** (4), 367–82.

27. —— and ISAAC, G. LL. (eds.) (1975). *After the Australopithecines*. Mouton, The Hague.

28. CAMERON, P. and FLEMING, P. (1975). *Self-Reported Degree of Pleasure Associated with Sexual Activity across the Adult Life-Span*. Mimeographed report, Division of Human Development, St Mary's College of Maryland.

29. CAMPBELL, B. G. (1974). *Human Evolution: An Introduction*, 2nd edn. Aldine, Chicago.

30. CAMPBELL, D. T. (1975). On the conflicts between biological and social evolution and between psychology and moral tradition. *American Psychologist* **30**, 1103–26.

31. CHAGNON, N. A. and IRONS, W. (eds) (1979). *Evolutionary Biology and Human Social Behavior: An Anthropological Perspective*. Duxbury, North Scituate, Mass.

32. CIBA FOUNDATION (1979). *Sex, Hormones and Behaviour*. Symposium No. 62. Excerpta Medica, Amsterdam and London.

33. CLARK, C. (1967). *Population Growth and Land Use*. Macmillan, London.

34. CLARK, J. D. (1970). *The Prehistory of Africa*. Praeger, New York.

35. —— and KURASHINA, H. (1979). Hominid occupation of the east–central highlands of Ethiopia in the Plio–Pleistocene. *Nature* **282**, 33–9.

36. CLUTTON-BROCK, T. H. and HARVEY, P. H. (1976). Evolutionary rules and primate societies. In *Growing Points in Ethology* (eds. P. P. G. Bateson and R. A. Hinde). Cambridge University Press.

37. —— —— (eds.) (1978). *Readings in Sociobiology*. Freeman, Reading and San Francisco.

38. COCKBURN, T. A. (1971). Infectious diseases in ancient populations. Also related comments. *Current Anthropology* **12** (1), 45–62.

39. COMMISSION OF THE EUROPEAN COMMUNITIES, THE (1975). *European Men and Women*. The Commission, Brussels.

40. COPPENS, Y. (1975). Evolution des hominidés et de leur environnement au cour du Plio–Pleistocène dans la basse vallée de l'Omo en Ethiopie.

*Comptes rendus des séances de l'Académie des Sciences*, Tome 281, Série D, 1693–6.

41. —— et al. (eds.) (1976). *Earliest Man and Environments in the Lake Rudolf Basin: Stratigraphy, Paleoecology, and Evolution.* University of Chicago Press.

42. —— et al. (1976). *Origines de l'Homme.* Musée de l'Homme, Paris.

43. COULT, A. D. (1965). *Cross Tabulation of Murdoch's World Ethnographic Sample.* University of Missouri Press.

44. COX, A. (1969). Geomagnetic reversals. *Science* **163**, 237–46.

45. CURRENT ANTHROPOLOGY (1965). Symposium, *The Origin of Man.* Vol. 6 (4), 343–431.

46. —— (1974). Review Symposium on *History of Human Life Span and Mortality* by Gy. Acsádi and J. Nemeskéri. Vol. 15 (4), 495–507.

47. CURTIS, G. H. et al. (1975). Age of KBS Tuff in Koobi Fora Formation, East Rudolf, Kenya. *Nature* **258**, 395–8.

48. DALRYMPLE, G. B. and LANPHERE, M. A. (1969). *Potassium–Argon Dating.* Freeman, San Francisco.

49. DALY, M. and WILSON, M. (1978). *Sex, Evolution & Behavior.* Duxbury Press, North Scituate, Mass.

50. DARWIN, C. (1874). *The Descent of Man and Selection in Relation to Sex*, 2nd edn. Murray, London.

51. DAVIS, K. B. (1922). *Factors in the Sex Life of Twenty-two Hundred Women.* Harper, New York.

52. DAWKINS, R. (1976). *The Selfish Gene.* Oxford University Press.

53. —— (In press 1979). Good strategy or evolutionarily stable strategy? In *Sociobiology: Beyond Nature/Nurture?* (eds. G. W. Barlow and J. Silverberg). Westview Press, Boulder, Colorado.

54. —— and CARLISLE, R. T. (1976). Parental investment, mate desertion and a fallacy. *Nature* **262**, 131–2.

55. DEEVEY, E. S. (1960). The human population. *Scientific American* **203** (3), 194–204.

56. DEVORE, I. (ed.) (1965). *Primate Behavior: Field Studies of Monkeys and Apes.* Holt, Rinehart and Winston, New York.

57. DIAMOND, M. (1965). A critical evaluation of the ontogeny of human sexual behavior. *Quarterly Review of Biology* **40**, 147–75.

58. DOBZHANSKY, T. (1970). *Genetics of the Evolutionary Process.* Columbia University Press.

59. DOERNER, G. et al. (1975). A neuroendocrine predisposition for homosexuality in men. *Archives of Sexual Behavior* **4** (1), 1–8.

60. DOUGLAS-HAMILTON, I. (1972). *On the Ecology and Behaviour of the African Elephant: The Elephants of Lake Manyara.* Ph.D. thesis, Oriel College, Oxford.

61. EHRHARDT, A. A. (1973). Maternalism and fetal hormonal and related syndromes. In *Contemporary Sexual Behavior: Critical Issues in the 1970s* (eds. J. Zubin and J. Money). Johns Hopkins University Press.

62. EIBL-EIBESFELDT, I. (1971). *Ethology: The Biology of Behavior.* Holt, Rinehart and Winston, New York (translated from German).

63. ———— (1973). *Love and Hate*. Methuen, London (translated from German).

64. EISENBERG, J. F. (1967). A comparative study in rodent ethology with emphasis on evolution of social behavior. *Proceedings of the US National Museum*, Smithsonian Institution, Washington.

65. ————, MUCKENHIRN, N. A., and RUDRAU, R. (1972). The relation between ecology and social structure in primates. *Science* **176**, 863–74.

66. EMBER, M. (1975). On the origin and extension of the incest taboo. *Behavior Science Research* **10**, 249–81.

67. FISHER, S. H. (1965). A note on male homosexuality and the role of women in ancient Greece. In *Sexual Inversion: The Multiple Roots of Homosexuality* (ed. J. Marmor). Basic Books, New York.

68. FITCH, F. J. and MILLER, J. A. (1970). Radio-isotopic age determinations of Lake Rudolf artefact site. *Nature* **226**, 226–8.

69. ————, HOOKER, P. J., and MILLER, J. A. (1976). $^{40}Ar/^{39}Ar$ dating of the KBS Tuff in Koobi Fora Formation, East Rudolf, Kenya. *Nature* **263**, 740–2.

70. FORD, C. S. and BEACH, F. A. (1951). *Patterns of Sexual Behavior*. Harper & Row, New York.

71. FOX, R. (1972). Alliance and constraint: Sexual selection in the evolution of human kinship systems. In *Sexual Selection and the Descent of Man* (ed. B. Campbell). Aldine, Chicago.

72. FRIEDMAN, R. C., RICHART, R. M., and VANDE, R. L. (eds.) (1974). *Sex Differences in Behavior*. Wiley, New York.

73. FUJII, H. (1975). A psychological study of the social structure of a free-ranging group of Japanese monkeys in Katsumaya. In *Contemporary Primatology* (eds. S. Kondo, M. Kawai, and A. Ehara), proceedings of the Fifth International Congress of Primatology, Nagoya, Japan, August 1974. Karger, Basel.

74. GARDNER, B. T. and GARDNER, R. A. (1971). Two-way communication with a chimpanzee. In *Behavior of Non-Human Primates* (eds. A. M. Schrier and F. Stollnitz). Academic Press, New York.

75. ———— ———— (1975). Early signs of language in child and chimpanzee. *Science* **187**, 752–3.

76. GEER, J. H. (1965). The development of a scale to measure fear. *Behaviour Research and Therapy* **3**, 45–53.

77. GEHRING, U. and TOMKINS, G. M. (1974). Characterization of a hormone receptor defect in the androgen insensitivity syndrome. *Cell* **3**, 59–64.

78. GERMAN, J. et al. (1978). Genetically determined sex-reversal in 46 XY humans. *Science* **202**, 53–6.

79. GHISELIN, M. T. (1974). *The Economy of Nature and the Evolution of Sex*. University of California Press.

80. Glick, P. C. (1975). *The Changing American Family Structure. Statement before the House of Representatives Committee on Census and Population, 12 November 1975*. US Department of Commerce, Washington.

81. GOLDMAN, B. D. (1978). Developmental influences of hormones on neuro-endocrine mechanisms of sexual behaviour. In *Biological Determinants of*

*Sexual Behaviour* (ed. J. B. Hutchison). Wiley, Chichester and New York.

82. GOLDSCHMIDT, W. (1976). Comment. *American Psychologist* **31**, 355–7.

83. GOODALL, J. and HAMBURG, D. A. (1975). Chimpanzee behavior as a model for the behavior of early man. In *New Psychiatric Frontiers, Volume 6 of American Handbook of Psychiatry*, 2nd edn. Basic Books, New York.

84. GOODMAN, M. and TASHIAN, R. E. (eds.) (1976). *Molecular Anthropology: Genes and Proteins in the Evolutionary Ascent of the Primates*. Plenum, New York.

85. GOULD, S. J. (1978). *Ever Since Darwin*. Burnett Books, London.

86. ———— (in press 1979). Sociobiology and the Theory of Natural Selection. In *Sociobiology: Beyond Nature/Nurture?* (eds. G. W. Barlow and J. Silverberg). Westview Press, Boulder, Colorado.

87. GOY, R. W. (1968). Organizing effects of androgen on the behaviour of rhesus monkeys. In *Endocrinology and Human Behaviour* (ed. R. P. Michael). Oxford University Press.

88. GRAY, J. A. (1972). The structure of the emotions and the limbic system. In *Ciba Foundation Symposium No. 8 (New Series), Physiology, Emotion and Psychosomatic Illness*. Excerpta Medica, Amsterdam and London.

89. GRUMBACH, M. M. and WYCK, J. J. VAN (1974). Disorders of sex differentiation. In *Textbook of Endrocrinology* (ed. R. H. Williams), 5th edn. Saunders, Philadelphia.

90. GUINNESS BOOK OF RECORDS (1975). Guinness Superlatives, Enfield.

91. HAMBURG, D. A. (1963). Emotions in the perspective of human evolution. In *Expression of the Emotions in Man* (ed. P. H. Knapp). International Universities Press. Reprinted 1968 in *Perspectives on Human Evolution* (eds. S. L. Washburn and P. C. Jay). Holt, Rinehart and Winston, New York.

92. HAMILTON, W. D. (1964). The genetical evolution of social behaviour. *Journal of Theoretical Biology* **7**, 1–52.

93. HAMPSON, J. L. and HAMPSON, J. G. (1961). The ontogenesis of sexual behavior in man. In *Sex and Internal Secretions* (ed. W. C. Young), 3rd edn. Williams and Wilkins, Baltimore.

94. HAQ, B. U., BERGREN, W. A., and COUVERING, J. A. VAN (1977). Corrected age of the Plio–Pleistocene boundary. *Nature* **269**, 483–8. Criticisms and reply (1978). *Nature* **272**, 287–8.

95. HARCOURT, A. (1979). Sexual behavior of gorillas in the wild. In *Reproductive Biology of the Great Apes*. Academic Press, New York.

96. HARLOW, H. F. (1958). The nature of love. *American Psychologist* **13**, 673–85.

97. ———— and HARLOW, M. K. (1965). The affectional systems. In *Behavior of Non-Human Primates* (eds. A. M. Schrier, H. F. Harlow, and F. Stollnitz). Academic Press, New York.

98. HARPENDING, H. (1976). Regional variation in !Kung populations. In *Kalahari Hunter–Gatherers* (eds. R. B. Lee and I. DeVore). Harvard University Press.

99. HARRIS, J. M. (1977). Paleomagnetic stratigraphy of the Koobi Fora Formation, east of Lake Turkana. *Nature* **268**, 669–70.

100. HARRISON, G. A. et al. (1977). *Human Biology*, 2nd edn. Oxford University Press.
101. HESTON, L. L. and SHIELDS, J. (1968). Homosexuality in twins. *Archives of General Psychiatry* **18**, 149–60.
102. HILL, J. H. (1972). On the evolutionary foundations of language. *American Anthropologist* **74** (3), 308–17.
103. HILL, J. L. (1974). *Peromyscus*: effect of early pairing on reproduction. *Science* **186**, 1042–4.
104. HINDE, R. A. (1974). *Biological Bases of Human Social Behavior*. McGraw–Hill, New York.
105. HOLLOWAY, R. L. (1973). New endocranial values for the East African early hominids. *Nature* **243**, 97–9.
106. HOOKER, E. (1968). Sexual behavior: Homosexuality. In *International Encyclopedia of the Social Sciences*, Vol. 14 (ed. D. L. Sills). Macmillan, New York.
107. HOWELL, F. C. (1969). Remains of Hominidae from Plio–Pleistocene formations in the lower Omo basin. *Nature* **223**, 1234–9.
108. —— (1978). Hominidae. In *Evolution of African Mammals* (eds. V. J. Maglio and H. B. S. Cooke). Harvard University Press.
109. —— and BOURLIÈRE, F. (eds.) (1963). *African Ecology and Human Evolution*. Viking, New York.
110. HOWELL, N. (1976). The population of the Dobe !Kung. In *Kalahari Hunter–Gatherers* (eds. R. B. Lee and I. DeVore). Harvard University Press.
111. —— (1979). *Demography of the Dobe !Kung*. Academic Press, New York.
112. HURFORD, A. J., GLEADOW, A. J. W., and NAESER, C. W. (1976). Fission-track dating of pumice from the KBS Tuff, East Rudolf, Kenya. *Nature* **263**, 738–40.
113. HURLEY. P. M. (1968). The confirmation of continental drift. *Scientific American* **218** (4), 52–64.
114. HUTT, C. (1972). *Males and Females*. Penguin, Harmondsworth.
115. IMANISHI, K. (1965). The origin of the human family. A primatological approach. In *Japanese Monkeys* (ed. and publisher S. A. Altmann). Alberta, Canada.
116. IMPERATO-MCGINLEY, J. et al. (1974). Steroid 5α-reductase deficiency in man: An inherited form of male pseudohermaphroditism. *Science* **186**, 1213–15.
117. ISAAC, G. Ll. (1971). The diet of early man: Aspects of archaeological evidence from Lower and Middle Pleistocene sites in Africa. *World Archaeology* **2** (3), 278–98.
118. —— (1976). Traces of early hominid activities from the lower member of the Koobi Fora Formation, Kenya. In *Acte du V Colloque, Les Plus Anciennes Industries en Afrique, IX<sup>e</sup> Congrès de l'Union Internationale des Sciences Préhistoriques et Protohistoriques, Nice, septembre 1976*. Centre National de la Recherche Scientifique, Paris.
119. —— (1977). *Olorgesailie: Archeological Studies of a Middle Pleistocene Lake Basin in Kenya*. University of Chicago Press.

120. ———— (1978). The food-sharing behavior of protohuman hominids. *Scientific American* **238** (4), 90–108.

121. ———— (1978). Food sharing and human evolution: Archaeological evidence from the Plio–Pleistocene of East Africa. *Journal of Anthropological Research* **34** (3), 311–25.

122. ———— (In press 1979). Casting the net wide: A review of archaeological evidence for early hominid land-use and ecological relations. In Nobel Symposium, *Current Argument on Early Man.* Pergamon, Oxford.

123. ———— and CRADER, D. C. (In press 1979). Can we determine the degree to which early hominids were carnivorous? A critical review of potential archaeological evidence from the Pliocene and Lower Pleistocene periods. In *Omnivorous Primates: Gathering and Hunting in Human Evolution* (eds. R. S. O. Harding and G. P. Teleki). Columbia University Press.

124. ———— and McCOWN, E. R. (eds.) (1976). *Human Origins: Louis Leakey and the East African Evidence.* Benjamin, Menlo Park, California.

125. ITANI, J. (1963). The social construction of national troops of Japanese monkeys in Takasakiyama. *Primates* **4** (3), 1–43.

126. IZARD, C. E. (1977). *Human Emotions.* Plenum, New York and London.

127. JACOB, F. and MONOD, J. (1961). On the regulation of gene activity. *Cold Spring Harbor Symposia on Quantitative Biology* **26**, 193–209.

128. JACOB, T. (1972). The absolute date of the Djetis Beds at Modjokerto. *Antiquity XLVI* 182, 148.

129. ———— (1973). *Morphology and Paleoecology of Early Man in Java.* Paper prepared for IXth Congress of Anthropological and Ethnological Sciences, Chicago.

130. JELÍNEK, J. (1969). Neanderthal Man and *Homo sapiens* in Central and Eastern Europe, together with critical comments. *Current Anthropology* **10** (5), 475–503.

131. JERISON, H. J. (1973). *Evolution of the Brain and Intelligence.* Academic Press, New York.

132. JOHANSON, D. C. and TAIEB, M. (1976). Plio–Pleistocene hominid discoveries in Hadar, Ethiopia. *Nature* **260**, 293–7.

133. JOHANSON, D. C. and WHITE, T. D. (1979). A systematic assessment of early African hominids. *Science* **203**, 321–30.

134. JOLLY, A. (1972). *The Evolution of Primate Behavior.* Macmillan, New York.

135. JOLLY, C. J. (1970). The seed eaters: A new model of hominid differentiation based on a baboon analogy. *Man* **5** (1), 5–26.

136. JOST, A. et al. (1973). Studies on sex differentiation in mammals. *Recent Progress in Hormonal Research* **29**, 1–41.

137. KALLMANN, F. J. (1952). Comparative twin study on the genetic aspects of male homosexuality. *Journal of Nervous and Mental Diseases* **115**, 283–98.

138. ———— (1960). Remarks in a discussion of homosexuality and heterosexuality in identical twins (J. D. Ranier and others). *Psychosomatic Medicine* **XXII** (4), 251–9.

139. KANIN, E. J., DAVIDSON, K. R., and SCHECK, S. R. (1970). A research

note on male–female differentials in the experience of heterosexual love. *Journal of Sex Research* **6** (1), 64–72.

140. KAWAI, M. (1965). Newly-acquired pre-cultural behavior of the national troop of Japanese monkeys on Koshima Islet. *Primates* **6** (1), 1–30.

141. KENYON, F. E. (1970). Homosexuality in the female. *British Journal of Hospital Medicine* **3**, 183–206.

142. KINSEY, A. C., POMEROY, W. B., and MARTIN, C. E. (1948). *Sexual Behavior in the Human Male*. Saunders, Philadelphia.

143. ———————— and GEBHARD, P. H. (1953). *Sexual Behavior in the Human Female*. Saunders, Philadelphia.

144. KIRKPATRICK, C. (1959). Chapter in *Premarital Dating Behavior* (ed. W. Ehrmann). Holt, New York.

145. KLEIMAN, D. G. (1977). Monogamy in mammals. *Quarterly Review of Biology* **52**, 39–69.

146. KLEIN, R. G. (1977). The ecology of early man in southern Africa. *Science* **197**, 115–26.

147. KLITGORD, K. D. et al. (1974). The geomagnetic time scale, 0 to 5 m.y. BP. *Eos* **55**, 237ff.

148. KOLATA, G. B. (1976). Primate behavior: Sex and the dominant male. *Science* **191**, 55–6.

149. ———————— (1979). Sex hormones and brain development. *Science* **205**, 985–7.

150. KOLODNY, R. C. et al. (1971). Plasma testosterone and semen analysis in male homosexuals. *New England Journal of Medicine* **285** (21), 1170–4.

151. KORTLANDT, A. (1976). The ecosystem in which the incipient hominines could have evolved. In *Colloque VI, Les Plus anciens Hominidés, IXᵉ Congrès de l'Union Internationale des Sciences Préhistoriques et Protohistoriques, Nice, septembre 1976*. Centre National de la Recherche Scientifique, Paris.

152. KREZOI, M. (1975). New ramapithecines and *Pliopithecus* from the Lower Pliocene of Rudabánya in northeastern Hungary. *Nature* **257**, 578–81.

153. LAMBERT, H. L. (1978). Biology and equality: A perspective on sex differences. *Signs* **4** (1), 97–117.

154. LANCASTER, J. B. (1975). *Primate Behavior and the Emergence of Human Culture*. Holt, Rinehart and Winston, New York.

155. LAWICK–GOODALL, J. VAN (1968). The behavior of free-living chimpanzees in the Gombe Stream Reserve. *Animal Behaviour Monographs* **1**, 165–311.

156. ———————— (1971). *In the Shadow of Man*. Houghton Mifflin, Boston.

157. LAWS, R. M. et al. (1970). Elephants and habitats in North Bunyoro, Uganda. *East African Wildlife Journal* **8**, 163–80.

158. LEACOCK, E. (1978). Women's status in egalitarian society: Implications for social evolution. And related comments. *Current Anthropology* **19** (2), 247–75.

159. LEAKEY, M. D. (1970). Early artefacts from the Koobi Fora area. *Nature* 226, 228–30.

160. ———————— (1971). *Olduvai Gorge, Volume III, Excavations in Beds I and II, 1960–1963*. Cambridge University Press.

161. ——— (1976). The early hominids of Olduvai Gorge and the Laetolil Beds. In *Colloque VI, Les Plus Anciens Hominidés, IX<sup>e</sup> Congrès de l'Union Internationale des Sciences Préhistoriques et Protohistoriques, Nice, septembre 1976*. Centre National de la Recherche Scientifique, Paris.

162. ——— (1979). Footprints in the ashes of time. *National Geographic* **155** (4), 446–57.

163. ——— et al. (1976). Fossil hominids from the Laetolil Beds. *Nature* **262**, 460–6.

164. ——— and HAY, R. L. (1979). Pliocene footprints in the Laetolil Beds at Laetoli, northern Tanzania. *Nature* **278**, 317–23.

165. LEAKEY, R. E. F. (1973). Evidence for an advanced Plio–Pleistocene hominid from East Rudolf, Kenya. *Nature* **242**, 447–50.

166. ——— (1974). Further evidence of Lower Pleistocene hominids from East Rudolf, North Kenya, 1973. *Nature* **248**, 653–6.

167. ——— (1976). New hominid fossils from northern Kenya. *Nature* **261**, 574–6.

168. ——— and WALKER, A. C. (1976). *Australopithecus, Homo erectus*, and the single species hypothesis. *Nature* **261**, 572–4.

169. LEE, R. B. and DeVORE, I. (eds.) (1968). *Man the Hunter*. Aldine, Chicago.

170. ——— (eds.) (1976). *Kalahari Hunter–Gatherers*. Harvard University Press.

171. LEGROS CLARK, W. E. (1966). *History of the Primates: An Introduction to the Study of Man*, 5th edn. University of Chicago Press.

172. LERNER, I. M. and LIBBY, W. J. (1976). *Heredity, Evolution and Society*. Freeman, San Francisco.

173. LESSIOS, H. A. (1979). Use of Panamanian sea urchins to test the molecular clock. *Nature* **280**, 599–601.

174. LEVINE, S. (1971). Sexual differentiation: The development of maleness and femaleness. *California Medicine* **114** (1), 12–17.

175. LEWIS, R. A. and BURR, W. R. (1975). Premarital coitus and commitment among college students. *Archives of Sexual Behavior* **4** (1).

176. LICHT, H. (1932). *Sexual Life in Ancient Greece*. Routledge & Kegan Paul, London (translated from German).

177. LIEBERMAN, P. (1977). More on hominid evolution, speech, and language. *Current Anthropology* **18** (3), 550–1.

178. LLOYD, B. and ARCHER, J. (eds.) (1976). *Exploring Sex Differences*. Academic Press, London and New York.

179. LOVEJOY, C. O. (in press 1979). The origin of Man. *Science*.

180. LUMLEY, H. DE (1969). A paleolithic camp at Nice. *Scientific American* **220** (5), 42–50.

181. LYON, M. F. and HAWKS, S. G. (1970). X-linked gene for testicular feminization in the mouse. *Nature* **227**, 1217–19.

182. MACLEAN, P. D. (1949). Psychosomatic disease and the 'visceral brain': Recent developments bearing on the Papez theory of emotion. *Psychosomatic Medicine* **11**, 338–53.

183. ——— (1970). The limbic brain in relation to the psychoses. In *Physio-*

*logical Correlates of Emotion* (ed. P. Black). Academic Press, New York and London.

184. MACCOBY, E. E. and JACKLIN, C. N. (1974). *The Psychology of Sex Differences.* Stanford University Press.

185. MALINOWSKI, B. (1929). *The Sexual Life of Savages in North-Western Melanesia.* Harcourt Brace and World, New York.

186. MARGOLESE, M. S. and JANIGER, O. (1973). Androsterone/etiocholanone ratios in male homosexuals. *British Medical Journal* **3**, 207–10.

187. MARKS, I. M. (1969). *Fears and Phobias.* Heinemann, London.

188. MASTERS, W. H. and JOHNSON, V. E. (1979). *Homosexuality in Perspective.* Little, Brown, Boston.

189. MAY, R. M. (1976). Sociobiology: A new synthesis and an old quarrel. *Nature* **260**, 390–2.

190. —— (1979). When to be incestuous. *Nature* **279**, 192–4.

191. MAYNARD SMITH, J. (1978). *The Evolution of Sex.* Cambridge University Press.

192. —— (1978). Parental investment – a prospective analysis. And Evolution and the theory of games. In *Readings in Sociobiology* (eds. T. H. Clutton-Brock and P. H. Harvey). Freeman, Reading and San Francisco.

193. MAYR, E. (1978). Evolution. *Scientific American* **239** (3), 39–47.

194. McBRIDE, A. F. and HEBB, H. O. (1948). Behavior of the captive bottlenose dolphin. *Journal of Comparative and Physiological Psychology* **41** (2), 111–123.

195. McEWEN, B. S. (1976). Interactions between hormones and nerve tissue. *Scientific American* **235** (1), 48–58.

196. McGUINNESS, D. (1976). Sex differences in the organization of perception and cognition. In *Exploring Sex Differences* (eds.) B. Lloyd and J. Archer). Academic Press, London and New York.

197. MEYER, W. J. III, MIGEON, B. R., and MIGEON, C. J. (1975). Locus on human X chromosome for dihydrotestosterone receptor and androgen insensitivity. *Proceedings of the National Academy of Sciences, USA* **72** (4), 1469–72.

198. MISSAKIAN, E. A. (1973). Genealogical mating activity in free-ranging groups of rhesus monkeys (*Macaca mulatta*) on Cayo Santiago. *Behaviour* **45**, 225–41.

199. MIZUHARA, H. (1964). Social changes of Japanese monkey troops in Takasakiyama. *Primates* **4** (3), 27–52.

200. MONEY, J. and EHRHARDT, A. A. (1972). *Man and Woman, Boy and Girl.* Johns Hopkins University Press.

201. MONEY, J. and SCHWARTZ, M. (1978). Biosocial determinants of gender identity differentiation and development. In *Biological Determinants of Sexual Behaviour* (ed. J. B. Hutchison). Wiley, Chichester and New York.

202. MONTAGNA, W. and SADLER, A. (eds.) (1974). *Reproductive Behavior.* Plenum, New York.

203. MURDOCK, G. P. (1961). *World Ethnographic Sample.* Human Relations Area Files, Yale University.

204. NAGEL, U. (1970). Social organization in a baboon hybrid zone. In *Proceedings of the Second International Congress on Primatology, Zurich* **3**, 48–57.

205. NATIONAL COMMISSION ON THE CAUSES AND PREVENTION OF VIOLENCE (Chairman, M. S. Eisenhower) (1969). *Commission Statement on Violent Crime: Homicide, Assault, Rape, Robbery.* Government Printing Office, Washington.

206. NEW YORK ACADEMY OF SCIENCES (1976). *Conference documents, Origins and Evolution of Language and Speech.* Annals of the Academy, New York.

207. OAKLEY, K. P. (1964). *Man the Tool-Maker*, 3rd edn. University of Chicago Press.

208. OETZEL, R. (1966). Annotated bibliography: Classified summary of research in sex differences. In *The Development of Sex Differences* (ed. E. E. Maccoby). Stanford University Press.

209. O'MALLEY, B. W. and BIRNBAUMER, L. (eds.) (1978). *Receptors and Hormone Action.* Academic Press, New York and London.

210. OUNSTED, C. and TAYLOR, D. C. (eds.) (1972). *Gender Differences: Their Ontogeny and Significance.* Churchill, London.

211. PADDAYA, K. (1976). Excavation of an Acheulean site at Hunsgi, South India. *Current Anthropology* **17** (4), 760–1.

212. PARKER, G. A. (1978). Selfish genes, evolutionary games, and the adaptiveness of behaviour. *Nature*, **274**, 849–55.

213. PARKER, S. (1976). The precultural basis of the incest taboo: Toward a biosocial view. *American Anthropologist* **78** (2), 285–305.

214. PETERSEN, W. (1975). A demographer's view of prehistoric demography. And related comments. *Current Anthropology* **16** (2), 227–46.

215. PIETROPINTO, A. and SIMENAUER, J. (1979). *Husbands and Wives: A Nationwide Survey of Marriage.* Times Books, New York.

216. PILBEAM, D. (1972). *The Ascent of Man: An Introduction to Human Evolution.* Macmillan, New York.

217. ———— (1976). Neogene hominids of South Asia and the origins of the Hominidae. In *Colloque VI, Les Plus Anciens Hominidés, IXᵉ Congrès de l'Union Internationale des Sciences Préhistoriques et Protohistoriques, Nice, septembre 1976.* Centre National de la Recherche Scientifique, Paris.

218. ———— et al. (1977). New hominoid primates from the Siwaliks of Pakistan and their bearing on hominoid evolution. *Nature* **270**, 689–95.

219. PLAPINGER, L. and McEWEN, B. S. (1978). Gonadal steroid–brain interactions in sexual differentiation. In *Biological Determinants of Sexual Behaviour* (ed. J. B. Hutchison). Wiley, Chichester and New York.

220. PREMACK, D. (1976). *Intelligence in Ape and Man.* Erlbaum, Hillsdale, N.J.

221. QUAREZ, J. (1975). *Allo, oui, ou les Mémoires de Madame Claude.* Stock, Paris.

222. QUIATT, D. (1979). Aunts and mothers: Adaptive implications of allomaternal behavior of nonhuman primates. *American Anthropologist* **81** (2), 310–19.

223. RAFFLER-ENGEL, W. VON and LEBRUN, Y. VAN (eds.) (1976). *Baby Talk*

*and Infant Speech.* Swets and Zeitlinger, Amsterdam.
224. RAPHAEL, D. (1972). Comments. *Current Anthropology* **13** (2), 253–4.
225. RENSCH, B. (1972). *Homo Sapiens, from Man to Demigod.* Methuen, London (translated from German).
226. REYNOLDS, V. (1980). *The Biology of Human Action.* 2nd edn. Freeman, Oxford and San Francisco.
227. ROCHEBLAVE–SPENLÉ, A.–M. (1964). *Les Rôles Masculins et Féminins.* Centre National de la Recherche Scientifique, Presses Universitaires de France, Paris.
228. RUMBAUGH, D. M. (ed.) (1977). *Language Learning by a Chimpanzee: The Lana Project.* Academic Press, New York.
229. RUSE, M. (1979). *Sociobiology: Sense or Nonsense?* Reidel, Dordrecht, Boston, and London.
230. RUTTER, M. (1972). *Maternal Deprivation Reassessed.* Penguin, Harmondsworth.
231. SADE, D. (1968). Inhibition of son–mother mating among free-ranging rhesus monkeys. *Scientific Psychoanalysis* **12**, 18–37.
232. SAGHIR, M. T. and ROBINS, E. (1973). *Male and Female Homosexuality: A Comprehensive Investigation.* Williams and Wilkins, Baltimore.
233. SAHLINS, M. D. (1976). *The Use and Abuse of Biology.* University of Michigan Press.
234. SARICH, V. (1971). A molecular approach to the question of human origins. In *Background for Man: Readings in Physical Anthropology.* (eds. P. Dolhinow and V. Sarich). Little, Brown, Boston.
235. ——— and WILSON, A. C. (1967). Immunological time-scale for hominid evolution. *Science* **158**, 1200–1203.
236. SAUCIER, J.–F. (1972). Correlates of the long postpartum taboo: A cross-cultural study. Also comments (D. Raphael and others). *Current Anthropology* **13** (2), 238–67.
237. SAVAGE–RUMBAUGH, E. S., RUMBAUGH, D. M., and BOYSEN, S. (1978). Symbolic communication between two chimpanzees *(Pan troglodytes).* *Science* **201**, 641–4.
238. SCHALLER, G. B. (1963). *The Mountain Gorilla: Ecology and Behavior.* University of Chicago Press.
239. SCHATZBERG, A. F. et al. (1975). Effeminacy. I. A quantitative rating scale. *Archives of Sexual Behavior* **4** (1), 31–41.
240. SCHOFIELD, M. et al. (1965). *The Sexual Behaviour of Young People.* Longmans, London.
241. SCHULL, W. J. and NEEL, J. V. (1965). *The Effects of Inbreeding in Japanese Children.* Harper & Row, New York.
242. SCHULTZ, A. H. (1961). Some factors influencing the social life of primates. In *Social Life of Early Man* (ed. S. L. Washburn). Aldine, Chicago.
243. *SCIENCE* (1976). Letters: The implications of sociobiology. **192**, 424–8.
244. SCLATER, J. G. and TAPSCOTT, C. (1979). The history of the Atlantic. *Scientific American* **240** (6), 120–32.
245. SCOTT, J. P. (1964). The effects of early experience on social behavior

and organization. In *Social Behavior and Organization among Vertebrates* (ed. W. Etkin). University of Chicago Press.

246. SEEMANOVÁ, E. (1971). A study of children of incestuous matings. *Human Heredity* **21**, 108–28.

247. SHEPHER, J. (1971). Mate selection among second generation kibbutz adolescents and adults: Incest avoidance and negative imprinting. *Archives of Sexual Behavior* **1** (4), 293–307.

248. SHIELDS, J. (1962). *Monozygotic Twins Brought up Apart and Brought up Together*. Oxford University Press.

249. SIMONDS, P. E. (1974). *The Social Primates*. Harper & Row, New York.

250. SIMONS, E. L. (1972). *Primate Evolution*. Macmillan, New York.

251. ——— (1976). Relationships between *Dryopithecus*, *Sivapithecus* and *Ramapithecus* and their bearing on hominid origins. In *Colloque VI, Les Plus Anciens Hominidés, IXᵉ Congrès de l'Union Internationale des Sciences Préhistoriques et Protohistoriques, Nice, septembre 1976*. Centre National de la Recherche Scientifique, Paris.

252. ——— (1977). *Ramapithecus*. *Scientific American* **236** (5), 28–35.

253. ——— and PILBEAM, D. (1978). *Ramapithecus* (Hominidae, Hominoidea). In *Evolution of African Mammals* (eds. V. J. Maglio and H. B. S. Cooke). Harvard University Press.

254. SMITH, L. G. and SMITH, J. R. (1973). Co-marital sex: The incorporation of extramarital sex into the marriage relationship. In *Contemporary Sexual Behavior: Critical Issues in the 1970s* (eds. J. Zubin and J. Money). Johns Hopkins University Press.

255. SPIRO, M. E. (1958). *Children of the Kibbutz*. Harvard University Press.

256. STEPHENS, W. N. (1963). *The Family in Cross-Cultural Perspective*. Holt, New York.

257. STERN, C. (1973). *Principles of Human Genetics*, 3rd edn. Freeman, San Francisco.

258. SYMONS, D. (1979). *The Evolution of Human Sexuality*. Oxford University Press, New York.

259. TAUXE, L. (1979). A new date for *Ramapithecus*. *Nature* **282**, 399–401.

260. TAVRIS, C. and OFFIR, C. (1977). *The Longest War: Sex Differences in Perspective*. Harcourt Brace Jovanovich, New York.

261. TERMAN, L. M. (1938). *Psychological Factors in Marital Happiness*. McGraw–Hill, New York.

262. TERRACE, H. S. et al. (1979). Can an ape create a sentence? *Science* **206**, 891–902.

263. THOMAS, P. J. (1974). A receptor mediating sexual differentiation. *Nature* **252**, 259–60.

264. TIGER, L. (1969). *Men in Groups*. Nelson, London, and Random House, New York.

265. TOBIAS, P. V. (1965). Early man in East Africa: Recent excavations in Olduvai Gorge. *Science* **149**, 22–5.

266. ——— (1973). New developments in hominid paleontology in South and East Africa. In *Annual Review of Anthropology*, Vol. 2. Annual Reviews, Palo Alto, California.

267. TOKUDA, K. (1961–2). A study of sexual behavior in the Japanese monkey troop. *Primates* **3**, 1–40.
268. TRINKAUS, E. and HOWELLS, W. W. (1979). The Neanderthals. *Scientific American* **241** (6), 94–105.
269. TRIVERS, R. L. (1971). The evolution of reciprocal altruism. *Quarterly Review of Biology* **46**, 35–57.
270. —— (1972). Parental investment and sexual selection. In *Sexual Selection and the Descent of Man, 1871–1971* (ed. B. Campbell). Aldine, Chicago.
271. —— and HARE, H. (1976). Haplodiploidy and the evolution of the social insects. *Science* **191**, 249–63.
272. TUTIN, C. E. G. (1974). Exceptions to promiscuity in a feral chimpanzee community. In *Contemporary Primatology* (eds. S. Kondo, M. Kawai, and A. Ehara), proceedings of the Fifth International Congress of Primatology, Nagoya, Japan, August 1974. Karger, Basel.
273. —— (in press 1979). Mating patterns and reproductive strategies in a community of wild chimpanzees. *Behavioral Ecology and Sociobiology*.
274. WADE, M. J. (1978). A critical review of the models of group selection. *Quarterly Review of Biology* **53** (2), 101–14.
275. WAGNER, G. A. (1977). Fission-track dating of pumice from the KBS Tuff, East Rudolf, Kenya. *Nature* **267**, 649.
276. WALES, E. and BREWER, B. (1976). Graffiti in the 1970s. *Journal of Social Psychology* **99**, 115–23.
277. WALKER, A. (1972). The dissemination and segregation of early primates in relation to continental configuration. In *Calibration of Hominoid Evolution* (eds. W. W. Bishop and J. A. Miller). Scottish Academic Press, for the Wenner–Gren Foundation, New York.
278. —— and ANDREWS, P. (1973). Reconstruction of the dental arcades of *Ramapithecus wickeri*. *Nature* **244**, 313–14.
279. —— and LEAKEY, R. E. F. (1978). The hominids of East Turkana. *Scientific American* **239** (2), 44–56.
280. WASHBURN, S. L. (ed.) (1961). *Social Life of Early Man*. Aldine, Chicago.
281. —— (1968). *The Study of Human Evolution*. University of Oregon Press.
282. —— and CIOCHON, R. L. (1974). Canine teeth: Notes on controversies in the study of human evolution. *American Anthropologist* **76** (4), 765–84.
283. WEIDENREICH, F. (1943). The skull of *Sinanthropus Pekinensis*. *Palaeontologica Sinica* **10**.
284. WENDT, H. (1965). *The Sex Life of the Animals*. Simon & Schuster, New York (translated from German).
285. WEST, D. J. (1968). *Homosexuality*, 3rd edn. Duckworth, London.
286. WEST-EBERHARD, M. J. (1975). The evolution of social behavior by kin selection. *Quarterly Review of Biology* **50** (1), 1–33.
287. WESTERMARCK, E. (1922). *The History of Human Marriage*, 5th edn. Allerton, New York.
288. WHITE, T. D. and HARRIS, J. M. (1977). Suid evolution and correlation of African hominid localities. *Science* **198**, 13–21.

289. WHYTE, M. K. (1978). *The Status of Women in Preindustrial Societies.* Princeton University Press.

290. WILLIAMS, B. J. (in press 1979). Kin selection, fitness, and cultural evolution. In *Sociobiology: Beyond Nature/Nurture?* (eds. G. W. Barlow and J. Silverberg). Westview Press, Boulder, Colorado.

291. WILLIAMS, G. C. (1966). *Adaptation and Natural Selection.* Princeton University Press.

292. WILSON, E. O. (1975). *Sociobiology: The New Synthesis.* Belknap, Harvard University Press.

293. ——— (1978). *On Human Nature.* Harvard University Press.

294. WINDLEY, B. F. (1977). *The Evolving Continents.* Wiley, New York.

295. WINOKUR, G. et al. (1958–9). Developmental and sexual factors in women: A comparison between control, neurotic, and psychotic groups. *American Journal of Psychiatry* **115**, 1097ff.

296. WINTER, J. S. D. and FAIMAN, C. (1972). Pituitary–gonadal relations in male children and adolescents. *Pediatric Research* **6**, 126–35.

297. WITTIG, M. A. and PETERSEN, A. C. (eds) (1979). *Sex-Related Differences in Cognitive Functioning.* Academic Press, New York.

298. WOOD, B. (1977). *The Evolution of Early Man.* Lowe, London.

299. WRESCHNER, E. E. (1976). The red hunters: Further thoughts on the evolution of speech. *Current Anthropology* **17** (4), 717–19.

300. WRIGHT, S. (1977 and 1978). *Evolution and the Genetics of Populations.* Vols. 3 and 4. University of Chicago Press.

301. YERKES, R. M. and YERKES, A. W. (1935). *Social Behavior in Infrahuman Primates.* Clark University Press.

302. YOUNG, J. Z. (1971). *An Introduction to the Study of Man.* Oxford University Press.

303. ——— (1978). *Programs of the Brain.* Oxford University Press.

304. YOUNG, W. C., GOY, R. W., and PHOENIX, C. H. (1964). Hormones and sexual behavior. *Science* **143**, 212–18.

305. ZIHLMAN, A. L. (1978). Women in evolution, Part II: Subsistence and social organization among early hominids. *Signs* **4** (1), 4–20.

# Index

This Index contains two sets of numbers: the first set refers to pages of the text, and the second (in parentheses) refers to numbered items in the Bibliography. With very few exceptions each book cited contains its own index, through which a given subject can be pursued.

ENDICOTT COLLEGE LIBRARY

3 1625 00100 1285

# DATE DUE

| | | | |
|---|---|---|---|
| DEC 1 2 2002 | | | |
| MAR 2 4 '03 | | | |
| | | | |
| | | | |
| | | | |
| | | | |
| | | | |
| | | | |
| | | | |
| | | | |
| | | | |
| | | | |
| | | | |
| | | | |
| | | | |
| | | | |
| | | | |

DEMCO 38-297

ENDICOTT COLLEGE

Beverly, Mass 01915